basic
concepts
of
ELEMENTARY
MATHEMATICS

New York
London
John Wiley & Sons, Inc.

WILLIAM L. SCHAAF

Professor of Education
Brooklyn College, Brooklyn, New York

basic
concepts
of
ELEMENTARY
MATHEMATICS

TO PETER AND BOB,
and the
"new generation"

Preface

The role of mathematics in contemporary society is unique. Our society is not only complex, it is apparently changing at an accelerated pace. One cannot therefore predict with assurance either the mathematical needs of today's learner, or the mathematical ideas required by tomorrow's society. Hence the most that one can reasonably expect education to contribute in this connection is an optimum concern with fundamental mathematical ideas and methods of mathematical thinking, together with a modicum of attention to mathematical information and specific mathematical skills and techniques. One of the chief tools for obtaining knowledge and arriving at conclusions is the deductive method, and, although much of mathematics is discovered or invented inductively, mathematics is still, *par excellence*, the science of deductive reasoning. It is clear, therefore, that we need to understand mathematical methods and the language of mathematics in order to apply them to the physical and social sciences.

Since instruction in secondary school mathematics rests squarely upon the foundations laid in elementary school arithmetic, it is obvious that the elementary school teacher should have an adequate understanding of elementary mathematics, including arithmetic, algebra, geometry, and related fields. It is an acknowledged truism that one cannot teach a subject effectively unless his knowledge and understanding go well beyond the scope of that which he is expected to teach. It is my purpose in this book, therefore, to supply some of the appropriate mathematical backgrounds so desperately needed by elementary school teachers of arithmetic. These basic backgrounds include, among other things, the nature of number and of systems of enumeration, the logical structure of arithmetic, the number system of arithmetic and algebra, informal and formal geometry, computation, measurement, trigonometry, functional relations, and certain concepts of statistics and probability. That this need is very real has been pointed out repeatedly. The effective teacher of any discipline should live intimately with that discipline. He should himself have far greater insight than he strives for in his students. Suppose one were to ask an elementary school teacher, "*Why* does $2 + 3 = 3 + 2$?" Is this equation a definition? Is it an undeniable fact? An arbitrary assumption? A remarkable coincidence? A fortunate accident? An eternal verity? How many readers, at this point, can answer correctly?

In short, teachers of arithmetic and junior high school mathematics require more than a conventional course in methods of teaching arithmetic. They need a *content* course in mathematics. Such a course should not be a simple review or refresher course in seventh and eighth year arithmetic, or a traditional course in algebra, geometry, trigonometry, and analytics. Nor should it be an experience designed to achieve desirable computational proficiency. On the contrary, this course should strive to give some insight into the nature and structure of mathematics, including not only arithmetic, but algebra and geometry as well.

As I write this preface imminent changes in mathematics curricula, from the college on down, suggest that sooner or later even the elementary school will feel the impact of the "new look" in mathematics. Although the extent of these changes on the secondary level is not yet altogether clear, the newer curricula will surely differ in approach and in emphasis. Somewhat greater stress will be laid upon the abstract point of view, with explicit attention to axiomatics and mathematical systems. Despite the criticisms and dire predictions in some quarters that this change cannot be made, it begins to appear that it is feasible, and is in fact *being* done. One can scarcely question the thesis that the teacher, at all events, should be reasonably familiar with the nature of modern mathematics and its implications for education. To be sure, the term "modern mathematics" will mean different things to different people. As the term is used here it refers essentially to mathematical ideas which were unknown (or not widely accepted) as recently as one hundred years ago. Notable among such ideas are the logical foundations of mathematics, abstract algebra, symbolic logic, and the contemporary theory of probability and statistical inference.

More specifically, this new approach will deal with the historical development of systems of numeration, the evolution of the number concept, the role of postulates and definitions in mathematics, generalization, abstraction, and formalism, the nature of mathematical proof, intuitive set theory, symbols, relations, and operations, the logical basis of the number system, measurement, approximations, variables and functions, statistical concepts.

It is my express purpose, in the following pages, to capture the spirit of contemporary mathematics and to integrate it with those aspects of "classical" mathematics which are pertinent to the elementary school. I sincerely hope that the day is not too far distant when the essence of mathematical thinking, the nature of mathematical relations, the significance of mathematical systems and models, and the relation of the rational numbers to the natural numbers, for example, will be as familiar to future elementary teachers as "concrete numbers," "borrowing in subtraction," and the "partition idea of division" have been to an earlier generation of teachers. In the interests of a more enlightened populace living in an increasingly complex culture predicated upon faith in science and technology, may that day soon arrive.

W. L. Schaaf

Flushing, New York
April 1959

Contents

In the French Revolution, when
called before the tribunal and asked
what useful thing he could do to de-
serve life, Lagrange answered:
"I will teach arithmetic."

CHAPTER 1

Modern Mathematics

The originality of mathematics consists
in the fact that in mathematical science
connections between things are exhibited which, apart from the agency of
human reason, are extremely unobvi-
ous.

—Alfred North Whitehead

THE AXIOMATIC POINT OF VIEW

historical retrospect

Popular opinion has it that mathematics is a precise science, that
its truths are absolute, and that the facts of mathematics are final
and unequivocal. How often do we hear the phrase "mathematically
certain," or the remark, "just as surely as two and two are four!"
Indeed, until comparatively recent times, this general attitude was
prevalent among mathematicians themselves. Yet nothing could be
more misleading concerning the nature of mathematical knowledge.
It should be said at once that we are speaking here about "pure"
mathematics rather than "applied" mathematics, although the distinction between the two is not always easily made.

1

Consider for a moment the older notions of the nature of mathematical knowledge. The word "mathematics" is derived from an ancient Greek word, *manthanein,* which meant "to learn." How did the mathematicians of an earlier day come by their knowledge? One of the oldest viewpoints was that of the classic Greek mathematicians and philosophers, who held that the truths of mathematics were independent of empirical data. Such truths did not require factual evidence such as observation, measurement, or other sensory experience. They were simply self-evident. Thus the axioms and postulates of Euclid and his successors were accepted as "obviously true." Who would deny that between two fixed points, one and only one straight line could be drawn? Or that if $a = b$, and $b = c$, then $a = c$?

Yet time decreed otherwise. After some twenty centuries, there came a revolution in mathematical thought, as surely as the transition from the Bronze Age to the Age of Iron, or the dramatic Industrial Revolution in Europe. When, about the middle of the nineteenth century, Lobachevsky and Bolyai hesitatingly announced the possibility of non-Euclidean geometry, the complacency of mathematicians was rudely shaken. In a sense, it has not yet recovered. What was this revolutionary change in viewpoint? In a word, the facts of mathematics were no longer regarded as self-evident or absolute truths; all mathematical assertions were henceforth regarded as relative or contingent truths.

Let us see why the idea of self-evident truths is untenable. In the first place, the decision as to which particular truths are self-evident is at best a subjective decision. Many students will feel that it is quite obvious, or self-evident, that two intersecting straight lines form two pairs of equal opposite angles, and that proof is unnecessary. On the other hand, most students would probably feel that it was necessary to prove that the diagonals of a parallelogram bisect each other, or that the sum of the angles of a triangle equals 180°; these relations are not so "obvious." In the second place, many apparently simple mathematical theorems are difficult to establish, even by professional mathematicians. As a case in point, consider the theorem that every algebraic equation has at least one root; or consider that between any two points on a line, however close together, there exists an infinite number of points. In the third place, many interesting theorems of abstract geometry and topology contradict the intuitive evidence of our senses. As examples, consider a curve without a tangent, or a continuous line which completely "fills" the plane, or a sheet of paper with only one side instead of two!

During the nineteenth century, there was a school of philosophy which maintained that mathematics, like physics, was an empirical science, only more general in character. But this view was also abandoned in due course. A classic example will show the futility of this approach to mathematics. Take the proposition that whenever $a = b$ and $b = c$, then $a = c$. We measure two rods, a and b, and find that they are equally long. We measure rod b and rod c, and find that they, too, are equally long, insofar as the precision of our instrument permits. But when we compare rod a with rod c, our measuring instrument detects a slight difference, and we see that the length of rod a does *not* equal that of rod c. Clearly, empirical evidence can be deceptive. The assertion that if $a = b$ and $b = c$ then $a = c$ can be accepted only on an *a priori* basis, and not on the basis of sensory experience.

If, then, the validity or acceptance of mathematics does not rest upon a supposed self-evident basis, or upon an empirical basis, upon what does it rest? As we shall soon see, it rests upon the power of the human mind to make stipulations. As Humpty Dumpty said: "When I use a word, it means just what I choose it to mean—neither more nor less." But we are getting ahead of our story.

mathematics is essentially deductive

We know that air exerts pressure; that sugar is more soluble in water than salt; that sound travels at the rate of about 1100 feet per second. How do we "know" these things? Clearly by observing, measuring, and testing under controlled conditions. We base our conclusions upon the evidence of our senses. This is the experimental method of science. It is essentially an inductive procedure. This does not always mean that we arrive at general statements from particular statements. What it does mean is that if a given phenomenon occurred five times under similar conditions, we might suspect that it would occur again under the same conditions. If we had observed its occurrence ten or twenty times, we would be reasonably certain that it would occur again. If we had observed it a hundred times, we would be even more certain. But—and this is the point—we can never be absolutely certain that it will occur the 101st time, or, for that matter, any "next" time.

A generalization based upon a limited number of observations or measurements, however large a number, is necessarily subject to some doubt, however slight. When a general statement covers more cases or objects than have actually been observed, it is based not on "fact," but on inference. Such reasoning is called generalizing by induction; the conclusion is an *inductive* inference.[1] We infer (or conclude) that what was true in the observed cases is true in all cases, *including those which have not been observed.* Thus we can never be completely certain about an inductive inference. An inductive generalization can only be *probable.* It may be highly probable, but it is always subject to possible revision in the light of new data. As Einstein once said: "No amount of experimentation can ever prove me right, but a single experiment might prove me wrong." The inductive method is a powerful tool in the hands of the scientist. From his experimental data he arrives at general statements of far-reaching significance. Just how probable these statements are depends upon the conditions under which he is working, upon the methods he is using, and upon the nature of the material with which he is dealing.

There is another way of arriving at a conclusion or making an inference. It differs from inductive thinking in that it does not depend upon experimental data or an appeal to sensory evidence. It is called *deductive* inference. This term does not always mean that we arrive at a particular statement from a more general statement; oftentimes it is just the reverse. Deductive inference does mean, however, that the element of certainty is present. Consider these two statements: (1) All residents of Detroit live in Michigan, and (2) John Harris lives in Detroit. We can infer at once, without any doubt, that (3) John Harris lives in Michigan. If statements 1 and 2 are "true," then statement 3 is also "true." Or, if we accept 1 and 2, we just have to accept 3. We accept 3 without question because of the nature of the logic we are unconsciously using. In deductive reasoning we accept a new statement derived from other supporting statements which have previously been accepted under mutually agreed upon conditions. There is no need for external evidence; the sole authority is orderly thinking. There is no question of probability—it is a matter of intellectual compulsion, of logical necessity. Deductive inference rests on confidence in the consistency of the human mind and on confidence in the system of logic employed. In other words, whereas the conclusions of inductive reasoning can only be probable at best, the conclusions of deductive reasoning are compelling, once the hypothesis is accepted.

Note that we used quotation marks about the word "true" in the

[1] This term is not to be confounded with *mathematical induction,* which is quite a different matter.

preceding paragraph. The reason for this distinction will become clear shortly. For the moment, let us not be concerned about the meaning of "actual truth," but think of "true" as a label of the "acceptability" of a statement. Whenever a conclusion follows of necessity from previous statements that are acceptable, the reasoning is valid. De-ductive reasoning is the process of arriving at valid conclusions from accepted hypotheses. Mathematical reasoning is essentially deductive reasoning.[2]

Any deductive system of discourse usually involves two kinds of content: (1) the things we are talking about, and (2) what we are saying about those things. We use words (or symbols) to designate the "things," and sentences (or statements) to say something about the things—their properties, their structure, the relationships between them, and so on. In rigorous discourse such as logic and mathematics we take pains to distinguish carefully between undefined words and defined words; we also distinguish between unprovable statements (assumptions) and provable statements (theorems).

undefined terms and definitions

It may seem strange that in mathematics some words are de-liberately left undefined. Yet a little reflection will show why, even outside the realm of mathematics, some few words must of necessity remain undefined. Consider the dictionary. Words are presumably defined in terms of other words whose meanings are already known. But clearly this leads either to circular reasoning, or to a point at which the meaning cannot be made any clearer by other known words. For example, to define "edge," we might say *sharp;* "sharp" might then be defined in terms of *knife-like;* this means *keen;* "keen" means having a fine *edge.* And so we are right back where we started. Or again, we might attempt to define a straight line segment as the shortest distance between two points; "shortest distance" means *taut;* "taut" means *in a straight line.* And so we have completed the circle once more.

It soon becomes clear that certain terms are so fundamental that they do not admit of definition. If we don't already understand the meaning of "straight," then no verbal definition will clarify our idea

---

[2] To be sure, mathematical discoveries and inventions, as well as the solution of original problems in mathematics, are not infrequently arrived at by a proc-ess akin to inductive reasoning. In any event, mathematical generalizations are not accepted unconditionally until subsequently "verified" by deductive processes.

of straightness. It is an idea associated with countless previous sensory experiences which have been indelibly registered in the nervous system since infancy. Some words often left undefined in mathematics include *point, line, plane, rotation, between, operation, relation, successor, number.* Mathematicians do not always select the same words as undefined terms, but are consistent in their subsequent use of terms. Since we have to make a beginning somewhere in a chain of definitions, these basic words are used freely, but no attempt is made to verbalize their meaning. At first, our intuitive experience helps us. Of course, everybody "knows" that a plane is "flat," and that to rotate means to "turn." And the imagery serves us well.[3] But as we make our mathematics more rigorous, we shake off the imagery, and let these primitive, undefined terms stand for anything—abstractions. Later we may interpret these abstractions as we will. The usefulness of such a procedure will be seen as we go on.

Having decided upon which terms to leave undefined, all other technical words in our deductive system are carefully defined in terms of these basic undefined terms, with the help, naturally, of ordinary non-technical English words. The characteristics of a good definition might be stated as follows:

1. A good definition of a new term should use only undefined terms, or other previously defined terms, and ordinary non-technical English words.

2. It should include all the possibilities and exclude all others.

3. It should be consistent.

4. It should not be redundant.

We should not, as the dictionary often does, confuse a logical or a mathematical definition with a brief description of the thing defined. A mathematical definition is essentially a verbal (or symbolic) expression which, by agreement, is equivalent to another verbal expression. For example: "Perpendicular lines are lines that meet at right angles" is a perfectly good definition of the term "perpendicular lines," provided that "right angle" has been previously defined as one-half of a straight angle. The expression "lines that meet at right angles" can then be substituted for the term "perpendicular lines," and vice versa. In short, a proper definition may replace the term defined without any change in meaning and without any inconsistency.

---

[3] At times, however, our intuitive experience is a hindrance rather than a help, as, for example, in non-Euclidean geometry, when we say there are no parallel lines.

propositions, assumptions, and theorems

In logic and mathematics a *proposition* is any statement which is meaningful enough to be regarded as being either "true" or "false." For example, these statements are propositions:

1. Lead is heavy.
2. If this is an acid, it will turn litmus red.
3. In the real number system, every number has two square roots.

But these are not propositions:

4. The sum of the three angles of a triangle is not very great.
5. Multiply the numerator and the denominator by the same number.

The words "true" and "false" as used in logic and in mathematics have a special meaning, quite different from their ordinary everyday connotations. In ordinary usage, truth is usually taken in an absolute sense. In mathematics, a proposition is true only in a relative sense; that is, if under certain conditions we are willing to accept it, we say it is true. So we shall try to forget the usual meanings of true and false, and think of true and false as relative, or contingent, designations of a proposition. The significance of the designations will be apparent later when we interpret a body of propositions.

In the matter of our definitions, since we had to start somewhere, we chose a few basic terms which remain undefined. Likewise with our propositions, we must again begin somewhere. We choose a very few propositions and arbitrarily designate them as "true." That is, we agree among ourselves that these few propositions are acceptable for purposes of our discourse. Such propositions are called *axioms*, *postulates*, or *assumptions*.[4] Their acceptability has nothing whatever to do with absolute truth, nor with being self-evident, nor with empirical facts, nor with intuition, observation, or common sense. A postulate is simply an initial proposition which is accepted by all concerned and is designated as true. Familiar examples of postulates in elementary mathematics are easily recognized:

1. Two distinct points determine one and only one line.
2. If $a = b$, then $b = a$.
3. If $x > y$, and $y > z$, then $x > z$.

[4] Originally the Greeks drew a distinction between an axiom and a postulate. In modern mathematics, however, the three terms are, to all intents and purposes, synonomous.

4. Any three non-collinear points determine a plane.
5. $a + b = b + a$.

It should be noted that, theoretically, any set of postulates may be used as a starting point for a deductive system. However, the mathematician usually bases his postulates or assumptions on some pattern of experience which suggests the form which the postulates take. For example, the familiar assumptions of Euclidean geometry are suggested by sensory experience and intuition concerning the form, size, and position of "real" objects. As we shall see later, the postulates underlying a number system are suggested in large part by experience with groups of discrete objects, or by the magnitude of an entity. The chief requisite of a usable set of postulates is that they be consistent. A system is free from inconsistency if there are no propositions in the system which can be proved both true and false.

In short, a deductive, abstract logical system, that is, a mathematical science, always consists of: (1) a few undefined words; (2) other words defined in terms of these basic words, together with ordinary English words; (3) some few initial propositions called postulates, of which we simply say, "these are true"; (4) many additional propositions called theorems, which are proved on the basis of the postulates and by using the conventional laws of logic. To "prove" a theorem means to show that if the assumptions are accepted as "true," then the given theorem must also be accepted as true in the same sense.

Perhaps you are wondering how we can reason or derive new propositions about undefined things! The answer is embodied in the following significant principles:

1. The characteristics of the undefined terms are exactly what we assume about them in our postulates.

2. Without postulates, there can be no proof or demonstration.

3. No demonstration proves more than is contained implicitly in the postulates.

Thus the theorems are simply logical consequences of the postulates and definitions. All that we can say of the theorems is that *if* the postulates are accepted, *if* the definitions are accepted, and *if* the reasoning methods are accepted, then the theorems must also be accepted. This is called *postulational thinking*. It is what was meant earlier when we characterized mathematical assertions as relative or contingent truths. Postulational thinking has been described by Bertrand Russell in a rather striking way:

Pure mathematics consists entirely of such asservations as that, if such and such a proposition is true of anything, then such and such another proposition is true of that thing. It is essential not to discuss whether the first proposition is really true, and not to mention what the anything is of which it is supposed to be true. . . . Thus mathematics may be defined as the subject in which we never know what we are talking about, nor whether what we are saying is true.

It is indeed a far cry from the classical Greek idea of mathematics as a body of truths having a separate existence apart from our own minds to the idea that mathematics is a completely man-made discipline, subject only to the laws of thought and the dictates of man's creative imagination.

EXERCISE 1–1

1. Explain the distinction between inductive and deductive inference.

2. How does validity differ from truth?

3. What is the difference between a postulate and an assumption? Between a postulate and a theorem?

4. By consulting a book on the history of mathematics, find what distinction the Greeks made between an *axiom* and a *postulate*.

5. The Oxford English Dictionary defines an axiom, in general (*circa* 1485), as "a proposition that commends itself to general acceptance; a well-established or universally-conceded principle." How is this definition related to the modern mathematical meaning of the term axiom?

6. The Oxford English Dictionary further defines axiom, as used in logic and mathematics (*circa* 1600), as "a self-evident proposition, not requiring demonstration, but assented to as soon as stated." What comment would you make here?

7. If you think it is easy to make an adequate definition, try to define:

(*a*) steamship   (*b*) ink   (*c*) garden   (*d*) book
(*e*) cat   (*f*) policeman (*g*) public carrier

8. To achieve satisfactory communication, or to carry on rigorous thinking, words must be adequately defined. In each of the following statements, indicate which words should be carefully defined in order to make the meaning precise:

(*a*) All public places of amusement must observe reasonable safety rules.

(*b*) All able-bodied men of middle age may be called upon in an emergency.

(*c*) In order to be eligible for a teaching certificate, the candidate must be in good health, his speech must be acceptable, and he must have a satisfactory scholastic standing.

9. Study each of the following definitions; indicate whether you think it is a good or a poor definition, and why:

(*a*) A straight angle is one-half a complete rotation.

(*b*) A gendarme is one who carries a gun.

(*c*) An isosceles triangle is a triangle with two equal sides and two equal angles.

(*d*) Similar triangles are triangles having the same shape.

(*e*) A diameter is a straight line passing through the center of a circle.

(*f*) The thread of a screw is a tapered, helical inclined plane.

10. Compare the mathematical meaning of the word proposition with its vernacular meaning, as in "I'll make you a proposition."

SETS AND RELATIONS

the idea of sets

Mathematicians use the term *set* to refer to any well-defined collection of discrete objects such as the books on that shelf, Johnny's toys, the pupils in the fifth grade, the grains of sand on Waikiki Beach, or the points on the line *AB*. The "objects" may be physical things, symbols, facts, or even ideas. A *set* may also be referred to as a *class*, an *assemblage*, an *aggregate*, a *space*, or a *manifold*. All these words convey the same idea—namely, a collection of things regarded as a whole. Note that we did not include the word "group." In mathematics, the word *group* refers not merely to a set as such, but to a set of things together with the specified rules of operating with those things.[5]

The individual objects included in a set are called the *elements* of the set. The elements are said to belong to the set, and are called members of the set. We speak of the set of lines passing through a given point, or the set of circles having a given center, or the set of all even numbers, or the set of all non-ending decimals, and so on. There are two common ways of designating a set, one of which is to make a list of all the members of the set. Examples are the list of names of the members of your class; the volumes of an encyclopedia, by number; the words in the English language, as given by the dictionary; or the set of all telephone subscribers in a given community

[5] Unfortunately it is the custom among arithmetic teachers to use the word "group" to mean the result of arranging and combining the objects of a set, as a "group of 5 and a group of 3 make a group of 8." The context, however, will generally obviate any ambiguity.

as listed in the local telephone directory. However, the elements of a set need not be listed explicitly in this way in order to designate the set precisely. Another way is to use some descriptive designation, as, for example, the set of all people with brown eyes, the set of all animals with six legs, the set of all the public libraries in Pennsylvania, the set of all polygons with equal sides and equal angles, the set of whole numbers divisible by five, and the set of all the angles inscribed in a given semicircle.

A set may contain no elements, only a few elements, or many elements. Johnny may have 8 toys; the fifth grade may have 120 pupils. The number of grains of sand on Waikiki Beach is obviously very large, but it is finite, even though it is difficult to determine. Some sets contain an infinite number of elements.[6] Thus the set of positive integers (1, 2, 3, 4 . . .) is an infinite set; so is the set of points on a line or the set of radii of a circle. On the other hand, a set may contain only three elements, as the medians of a given triangle, or only one element, as the set of all midpoints of a given line segment. It is even possible for a set to contain no elements at all; for example, the set of men more than ten feet tall; or the set of home runs in any inning of a scoreless game; or the set of real roots of $x^2 + x + 1 = 0$. A set containing no elements is called an *empty set*, or a *null set*, and is often denoted by the symbol $\emptyset$.

Today mathematicians and scientists think and talk in terms of sets. The idea is simple enough, yet it is a powerful mathematical tool. A set is the mental construct obtained by regarding several discrete things as constituting a single whole. Forming a set is thus a mental act; the human mind arbitrarily brings together certain things and regards the collection itself as a new kind of thing. This new thing is an artificial entity, in the sense that the unity lies entirely in the concept and not in the things themselves. The fact that the mind is capable of such conceptualization makes possible, among other things, the idea of number.

We shall regard the words *set* and *element* as undefined terms. The statement that "an element x belongs to the set A" shall also be regarded as an undefined relation. The fact that x is an element of set A, or that x is a member of the class A, is written symbolically: $x \epsilon A$. It is customary to use braces { } to denote the members of a set. For example, $\{p, q, r, s\}$ means the set whose elements are p, q, r and

---

[6] A set is said to be finite if the number of its elements is some positive integer or zero; otherwise it is said to be infinite. More illuminating definitions of finite and infinite will be given later.

s; $\{2, 4, 6, 8, \ldots\}$ means the set consisting of all even whole numbers.

Sometimes we are concerned with the objects comprising a large set, as for example, the set of all points in a given plane. Such a set is often called a *universal set*. Then if we single out all the points on a 5 inch-circle in this plane, we have a special set within the universal set. Or again, if the universal set is the set of all triangles, then special sets within this universe would be (1) the set of all right triangles, or (2) the set of all isosceles triangles, or (3) the set of all obtuse-angled triangles, and so on.

To help us understand the properties of sets, we often use Venn diagrams such as shown in Fig. 1–1. These, it must be understood, are strictly schematic representations.

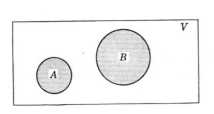

Fig. 1-1

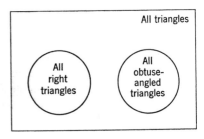

Fig. 1-2

Here the rectangle represents the universal set V; the elements of V are represented by the points in the rectangle. Particular sets of elements of V are represented by sets of points inside the rectangle, such as those within circles A and B, respectively. A specific example is shown in Fig. 1–2.

Suppose that two given sets, A and B, are so related that every

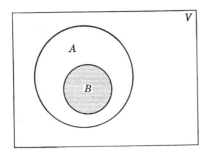

Fig. 1-3

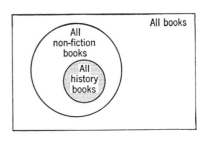

Fig. 1-4

object which belongs to set B also belongs to set A. (See Fig. 1–3.) Symbolically, for all x's, if $x \epsilon B$, then $x \epsilon A$. We may then say that set B is contained in set A, or that set A contains set B. We call set B a *subset* of set A. We write: $B \subset A$, or $A \supset B$. A specific example is shown in Fig. 1–4. By definition, then, a set S_k is a subset of a set S if every element of S_k is also an element of S.

Note that the relations ϵ and $\subset$ (or $\supset$) are *different kinds* of relations. To say that $A \epsilon B$ is not the same as saying that $A \subset B$. In Fig. 1–5, we can say that $F \subset E$, since the set of all Frenchman is a subset of the set of all Europeans; but we cannot say that $F \epsilon E$, since the set of all Frenchman *is not a* European.

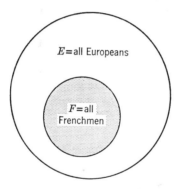

Fig. 1-5

In order to understand the meaning of a subset and of a null set more clearly, let us consider this question: from a given set S, which contains three elements a, b, c, how many possible subsets can be obtained?

$$S_1 : \{a, b, c\}$$
$$S_2 : \{a, b\}$$
$$S_3 : \{a, c\}$$
$$S_4 : \{b, c\}$$
$$S_5 : \{a\}$$
$$S_6 : \{b\}$$
$$S_7 : \{c\}$$
$$S_8 : \{ \ \}$$

To form a subset, we consider each of the elements in turn, and decide to include it in the subset or not—"take it or leave it." The result is that there are at most 8 possibilities. But now two questions arise. First, should $S_1 = \{a, b, c\}$ be regarded as a subset of S, when it contains *all* the elements of the original universal set? You might be inclined to say, no. But remember that the definition of a subset merely requires that every element of S_1 shall also be an element of S. Since $\{a, b, c\}$ satisfies this definition, we say that S_1 is a subset of S, or that any set may be regarded as a subset of itself. Clearly, in this connection, "sub" need not necessarily mean "smaller."

The second question is whether $S_8 = \{ \ \}$ should be regarded as a subset of S, when obviously it is a null set, containing none of the elements of S. Mathematicians have agreed to consider the null set as a subset. In our example, it represents the possibility in which we decided to exclude all the elements. Moreover, considering the null set as a subset does not violate the definition, which requires only that every element of the subset shall also be an element of the universal set.

To be consistent with the statement above, and to sharpen our concepts, we define S_p, a *proper subset of S*, as a subset which is not the entire set S (that is, at least one element of S is not an element of S_p). The concept of a null set may then be sharpened by saying that the null set, which has no elements, is a proper subset of every set except itself.

related sets

Two sets are said to be *identical* if every element of each set is an element of the other set—that is, if every member of A is a member of B, and every member of B is a number of A, or $A \subset B$ and $B \supset A$. We then write $A = B$. For example, the set consisting of Brown, Smith, Jones, and Porter is identical with the set consisting of Smith, Porter, Jones, and Brown, but it is not identical with the set consisting of Brown, Smith, Jones, and Greene.

Two sets that are not identical can nevertheless be such that their elements can be paired in a unique fashion. Consider, for example, the English and German alphabets, respectively, as two sets, P and Q:

$$(P) \ \{A, B, C, D, \ldots X, Y, Z.\}$$
$$(Q) \ \{\mathfrak{A}, \mathfrak{B}, \mathfrak{C}, \mathfrak{D}, \ldots \mathfrak{X}, \mathfrak{Y}, \mathfrak{Z}.\}$$

Obviously, a unique member of each set can be associated with a unique member of the other set. "Unique pairing" means that to each member of set P there corresponds *one and only one* member of Q, and to each member of Q there corresponds *one and only one* member of P. Such sets are said to be in "one-to-one correspondence," and are called *equivalent sets;* we write $P \leftrightarrow Q$.

These ideas may be summed up as follows:

1. Two identical sets are necessarily equivalent.

2. Two equivalent sets are not necessarily identical.

3. Any set is equivalent to itself: $A \leftrightarrow A$.

4. If $A \leftrightarrow B$, then $B \leftrightarrow A$.

5. If $A \leftrightarrow B$, and $B \leftrightarrow C$, then $A \leftrightarrow C$.

EXERCISE 1–2

1. Give three examples of sets in which the elements are: (*a*) animals, (*b*) trees, (*c*) numbers, (*d*) motor vehicles, (*e*) geometric figures, (*f*) rivers.

2. Make up some examples of universal sets and subsets for each of the following: (*a*) toys, (*b*) symbols, (*c*) tools, (*d*) children, (*e*) ideas.

3. Explain why the two subsets in Fig. 1–6 are represented by *overlapping* circles:

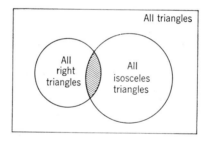

Fig. 1-6

4. Which of the following items do (does) *not* describe a *set?*

(*a*) the rational numbers
(*b*) the students who are studying this book
(*c*) the Babylonian papyri in the British Museum
(*d*) the contents of little boys' pockets
(*e*) ripe California oranges

5. Give two examples of sets that are adequately described by tabulating or listing all their elements; give two examples of sets that are adequately described by means of verbal or symbolic generalizations.

6. Give two examples of well-defined sets; two examples of ambiguous or not well-defined sets.

7. Give two examples of finite sets; two examples of infinite sets.

8. It can be shown that the total number of ways of forming sets by taking all, some, or none of a set of n objects is 2^n. How many non-empty subsets can be formed from a set of n elements? How many non-empty proper subsets can be formed from a set of n elements?

9. Show that there is a one-to-one correspondence between the letters of the alphabet and the set of symbols in the Morse telegraph code.

10. Show that the members of a string quartet and their instruments are equivalent sets.

11. Explain how it is possible to match, in more than one way, the set of letters of the alphabet and the set of numbers $\{1, 2, 3, 4, \ldots 26\}$ to show one-to-one correspondence.

12. Show that there are six possible different ways of matching the elements $\{a, b, c\}$ of set S_1 and the elements $\{x, y, z\}$ of set S_2.

13. Show that there is a one-to-one correspondence between the set of unit fractions (such as $\frac{1}{2}$, $\frac{1}{5}$, or $\frac{1}{8}$) and the set of positive integers $1, 2, 3, 4 \ldots$ (Consider $\frac{1}{1}$ as a fraction).

14. Give an example of two identical sets, such as the set of all right angles and the set of all 90° angles. Would you say that if two sets are identical, either set may be substituted for the other in our discourse? How is this related to a definition?

15. Draw Venn diagrams to show that: (a) all elements of P are elements of Q, and some elements of Q are not elements of P; (b) $A \supset B$; (c) $A \subset B$, and $B \subset C$; (d) all elements of R are elements of T, all elements of S are elements of T, R and S have no elements in common, and some elements of T are not elements of either R or S.

16. By means of a Venn diagram, show that if $A \subset B$ and $B \subset A$, then A and B are identical, that is, $A = B$.

17. Give an example of two equivalent sets that are not identical.

18. Give an example to show that if $A \leftrightarrow B$, then $B \leftrightarrow A$.

19. Give an example to show, by matching, that if $A \leftrightarrow B$, and $B \leftrightarrow C$, then $A \leftrightarrow C$.

20. Show that there is a one-to-one correspondence between the set of positive integers $\{1, 2, 3, 4, \ldots\}$ and the set of positive even integers $\{2, 4, 6, 8 \ldots\}$.

21. Show that there is a one-to-one correspondence between the set of points in the base of a triangle (AC) and the set of points in the segments RS terminating in the sides BA and BC, respectively (Fig. 1–7).

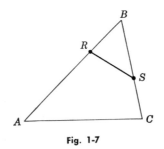

Fig. 1-7

constructing new sets from given sets

Although the elements of sets need not be numbers, or indeed, even mathematical symbols, the sets found most useful in mathematics are usually those which we construct deliberately. Among the many ways that new sets can be constructed from given sets, the following are important: (1) by forming their union, and (2) by forming their intersection.

If two given sets P and Q are combined in such a way as to form a new set whose elements are members of at least one of the given sets, the new set is called the *union* of the given sets; in symbols, we write $P \cup Q$. The shaded part in Fig. 1–8 represents $P \cup Q$. In other words, the union of two sets P and Q is the set of all those elements that belong either to P, or to Q, or to both P and Q.

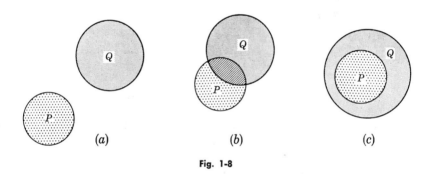

Fig. 1-8

A new set can also be derived from two initial sets P and Q by forming the *intersection* of the two sets, expressed as $P \cap Q$. The intersection of two sets P and Q, or $P \cap Q$, is the set of those elements which

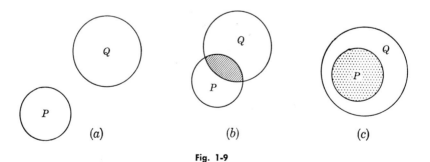

Fig. 1-9

belong to both P and Q. It is the shaded part in Fig. 1–9 which represents $P \cap Q$.

These relations are now recapitulated in a somewhat different arrangement to make their meaning clearer.

1. If sets P and Q have no elements in common:

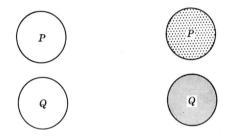

Fig. 1-10

The given sets P and Q.

$P \cup Q$ consists of all the elements of set P and all those of set Q.

$P \cap Q$ the null set ∅, since there are no elements common to P and Q.

2. If sets P and Q have some elements in common:

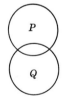

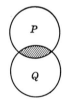

Fig. 1-11

The given sets P and Q.

$P \cup Q$ consists of all the elements in P which are not in Q, plus all the elements of Q which are not in P, plus all the elements which are in both P and Q.

$P \cap Q$ consists of all the elements which are in both P and in Q.

3. If set Q is a proper subset of P:

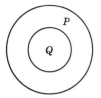
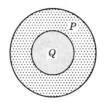
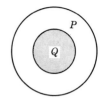

Fig. 1-12

The given sets P and Q. **P ∪ Q is set P.** **P ∩ Q is set Q.**

When three or more sets are involved, the situations are suggested by the four following diagrams. Given in Fig. 1-13 three sets P, Q, and R, all having some elements in common:

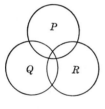

Fig. 1-13

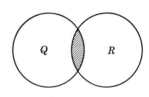

Fig. 1-14

Then $Q \cap R$ may be represented by the shaded area in Fig. 1-14.

Now, taking the union of P with the above intersection of Q and R, we get

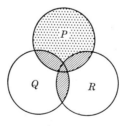

Fig. 1-15

where the shaded portion may be expressed in symbols as $P \cup (Q \cap R)$.

Similarly, the set $P \cap (Q \cup R)$ may be represented by the shaded area:

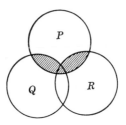

Fig. 1-16

In ordinary, everyday discourse, a "pair" simply means any two objects, usually distinct, although similar. In mathematics, an *ordered pair* is a set formed (*a*) by selecting one thing, and then selecting another, which need not be a different thing; and (*b*) by designating one of the two things selected as the "first" thing of the pair. These are examples of ordered pairs: (John, Mary), $(4, 3)$, (a, b). Note the symbolism; the two elements of an ordered pair are enclosed in parentheses, and the thing at the left of the comma is the first thing of the pair. Thus the ordered pair $(5, 8)$ is not the same as $(8, 5)$. Also note that the two things of an ordered pair may be identical, as in $(10, 10)$ or (b, b).

Since sets are mental constructs, there is an aspect of relativity about sets. Thus the number 3 is a member of the set of positive integers, but it is not a member of the set of all even numbers; it is a member of the set of all prime numbers, but it is not a member of the set of all numbers divisible by 5. In other words, whether something belongs to a set, or whether it is a set, is not solely a property of that something; it depends also upon how the set happens to have been defined. It is not strange, therefore, that a set may have properties that its elements do not have, and vice versa. A line segment (which is a set of points) has length, but none of the points (elements of this set) has length. Those citizens of a community who are eligible to vote constitute a set; every member of that set may vote, but that set (of citizens) cannot vote.

EXERCISES 1–3

1. Give an example of a familiar set that is the union of two familiar sets.

2. Give an example of a familiar set that is the intersection of two familiar sets.

3. If P is a set containing 4 elements and Q is a set containing 9 elements, what can be said about the number of elements in $P \cup Q$? In $P \cap Q$?

4. Explain why P is a subset of $P \cup Q$.

5. Explain why $P \cap Q$ is a subset of P.

6. Show that the set $\{1, 3, 5, 7, \ldots\}$ is a proper subset of the set $\{1, 2, 3, 4, 5, \ldots\}$.

7. If P is the set {Alice, Betty, Cora, Dot}, and Q is the set {Fred, Alice, Bill, Betty}, what are the elements of $P \cap Q$? Of $P \cup Q$?

8. Let $[p, q]$ represent the set of all points on a line segment, where p is the left end-point and q is the right end-point; let p and q also be members of this set:

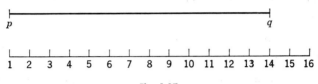

p q

1 2 3 4 5 6 7 8 9 10 11 12 13 14 15 16

Fig. 1-17

(a) Show that $[2, 4] \cup [4, 5]$ is $[2, 5]$.
(b) Find $[1, 5] \cup [3, 7]$.
(c) Find $[2, 8] \cup [3, 5]$.

9. Using the same notation as in number 8, find:

(a) $[2, 4] \cap [4, 5]$ (b) $[1, 5] \cap [3, 7]$ (c) $[2, 8] \cap [3, 5]$

10. Find $[2,4] \cup [12, 16]$; also, $[2, 4] \cap [12, 16]$.

11. If the null set is represented by ϕ, prove (a) that $\phi \cup P = P$; (b) $\phi \cap P = \phi$.

12. Suppose that R is the set of all points in the plane, and S is the set of all points *on* a given circle in the plane. Find $R \cap S$; $R \cup S$ (Fig.1-18).

13. If $P \subset Q$, prove that $P \cup Q = Q$; also, that $P \cap Q = P$.

14. Prove diagrammatically that in Fig. 1-19

$$A \cup (B \cup C) = (A \cup B) \cup C.$$

The parentheses indicate which operations are to be performed first.

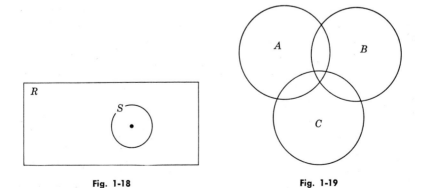

Fig. 1-18   **Fig. 1-19**

15. Prove that $A \cap (B \cap C) = (A \cap B) \cap C$.
16. Does $P \cup Q = Q \cup P$? Does $P \cap Q = Q \cap P$? Explain.

the idea of relations

Relations between sets of elements constitute another significant and penetrating tool of the mathematician. In ordinary discourse we often speak loosely about relations. Grammar and predication tend to confuse. Consider the two statements:

1. All equilateral triangles are plane figures.
2. All equilateral triangles are similar in shape.

The first statement merely tells us a property or quality of equilateral triangles, whereas the second tells us a relation between two or more equilateral triangles.

In elementary mathematics, examples of relations are: equal ($=$), greater than ($>$), less than ($<$), congruent ($\cong$), similar ($\sim$), parallel ($\|$), perpendicular ($\perp$), and functionality, written $f(x)$.

Relations can be expressed in terms of set notations. From this abstract point of view, a relation is a set of ordered pairs. Suppose that (x, y) represents an ordered pair of things, in which x is understood to precede y. The ordered pair (x, y) may or may not belong to the set R (that is, the relation R). To illustrate: consider all the ordered pairs of positive whole numbers such as $(5, 1)$, $(6, 4)$, $(3, 2)$, $(10, 4)$, $(9, 7)$, in which some number is subtracted from the first to give the second. In other words, consider all the ordered pairs of the form (a, b), where $a - k = b$, and k is a positive whole number. The relation defined by this set of ordered pairs (R) is the relation "greater than"; $a > b$. To be sure, it is simpler to write $5 > 1$, or $a > b$, than it is to write $(5, 1) \; \epsilon >$, or $(a, b) >_{\epsilon}$. Therefore instead of writing a relationship as $(x, y) \; \epsilon \, R$, we shall use the simpler form xRy, which is read "x has the relation R to y."

Among the important characteristics of relations is the property of reflexivity. A relation is said to be *reflexive* whenever xRx. For example, equality is a reflexive relation; a thing equals itself. So are the relations of congruence and similarity; a triangle is congruent to itself and also similar to itself. In a plane, a line may be said to be parallel to itself, but perpendicularity is obviously not a reflexive relation, nor are the relations "greater than" and "less than."

A relation is said to be *symmetric* if and only if xRy implies that yRx, and conversely, yRx implies that xRy. Equality is symmetric:

if $a = b$, then $b = a$. Parallelism and perpendicularity are also symmetric: if $l_1 \parallel l_2$, then $l_2 \parallel l_1$; if $l_3 \perp l_4$, then $l_4 \perp l_3$. Congruence and similarity are both symmetric relations. On the other hand, neither the relations $\subset$ and $\supset$, nor $>$ and $<$, are symmetric.

A *transitive* relation is one in which, if xRy and yRz are both true, then xRz. For example, equality and inequality are transitive: if $a = b$ and $b = c$, then $a = c$; also, if $m > p$, and $p > q$, then $m > q$. Other examples of transitive relations are congruence, similarity, parallelism, and the relations $\subset$ and $\supset$. But perpendicularity is not transitive; if $l_1 \perp l_2$, and $l_2 \perp l_3$, then l_1 is not $\perp l_3$.

A relation is said to be *asymmetric* when the truth of xRy implies the falsity of yRx. For example, "John is taller than Dick," "$x > y$," "x is to the right of y" are asymmetric relations. A relation that is not symmetric need not necessarily be asymmetric. Asymmetric relations suggest that reversing the order of a pair in R produces a new relation, R^{-1}, called the *inverse* of R. Thus a pair (a, b) is in R if and only if (b, a) is in R^{-1}. Or, in alternate notation, aRb if and only if $bR^{-1}a$. For example, if x is the father of y, then y is the son of x; or, if a is a descendant of b, then b is an ancestor of a; or again, if $p > q$, then $q < p$; etc.

Usually the most significant relations in mathematics are (1) those which are both transitive and symmetrical, and (2) those which are transitive but asymmetrical. We shall see later that cardinal number, which implies equivalence without order, is a relation of type 1, whereas ordinal number, implying sequence, is a relation of type 2.

EXERCISE 1–4

1. Give an example of a relation that is (a) *reflexive, symmetric* and *transitive;* (b) *reflexive, symmetric,* but not *transitive;* (c) *reflexive, transitive,* but not *symmetric;* (d) *transitive,* but neither *reflexive* nor *symmetric.*

2. Show by means of a Venn diagram that the relations $\supset$ and $\subset$ are transitive.

3. Which of the properties reflexive, symmetric, transitive applies to the relations below?

(a) "is greater than"
(b) "is the father of"
(c) "is heavier than"
(d) "is a descendant of"
(e) "is not equal to"
(f) "is a multiple of" (positive whole number)
(g) "is a neighbor of"

4. Give an example of a non-symmetric relation which is also not asymmetric.

5. Consider the relation of implication: P implies Q, that is, if P is true, than Q is true. Is this relation reflexive? Is it symmetric?

THE NATURE OF MATHEMATICS

distinguishing characteristics

If one were to ask "What are the distinguishing characteristics of mathematics?" the answer would have to include: (1) its abstract nature, (2) its generality, and (3) its concern for structure and pattern. We have already suggested the abstract entities with which mathematics deals—points, lines, numbers, ordered pairs, sets of elements, and the like. What these points or lines or numbers "actually" are cannot and need not be discussed in a mathematical science. What really matters, and what is roughly analogous to "verifiable" fact in empirical science, are structure and relationships—that two points determine a line, or that two lines determine a point, or that $a \times b = b \times a$, or that $\dfrac{a}{b} = \dfrac{c}{d}$ if and only if $a \times d = b \times c$, provided b and d are not zero. The spirit of mathematics lies in its viewpoint. We can think of a mathematical science as consisting of the deductive development of a body of theorems, derived from a set of undefined terms and a set of unproved assumptions by the use of logical principles. What interests the mathematician every bit as much as the "content" of the theorems is the pattern by which the theorems are interrelated and the manner in which they were derived from the undefined terms and the assumptions.

That the mathematician is constantly seeking broad generalizations is another characteristic of mathematics. If he is examining a quadratic equation, he wants to know what is true of a whole family of quadratics. If he is studying quadrilaterals, he wants to know the

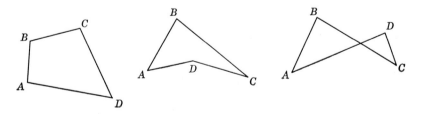

Fig. 1-20

properties of all quadrilaterals, convex, concave, and general quadrilaterals. If he is studying spaces of two and three dimensions, he doesn't stop there, or even with four dimensions; he explores n-dimensional spaces.

When we speak of the structure or the pattern of a mathematical system we are not limiting ourselves to geometry; we have in mind also algebra and arithmetic. In fact, every mathematical science has a unique pattern or structure. Geometry may be regarded as a study of invariance—that is, a study of the properties of figures that remain unchanged when subjected to various kinds of transformations; but there are other ways of structuring geometry. Algebra turns out to be a study of structure—the interrelations between symbols and operations performed on those symbols. In a certain sense, school arithmetic is a "special case" of a more general algebra. Arithmetic, too, has a unique logical structure.

abstract systems and concrete models

The primitives of a mathematical science are the undefined terms and the unproved postulates. Since the definitions are given in terms of the undefined ideas, and since the proofs of the theorems rest on the unproved postulates, one might be forgiven for asking "Of what value is the whole business?" The answer lies in the possibility of interpreting an abstract system in terms of a concrete model by assigning at will certain meanings to the primitives, which in turn give specific meanings to the theorems.

Let us look at a specific example of an abstract system. We shall deliberately create an abstract theory of order. Only two basic ideas are needed, and they are left undefined:

1. A set S whose elements are $\{a, b, c, \ldots\}$.
2. A relation called *between* which brings three elements of S together.

Note that nothing is said about the nature of the elements $a, b, c. \ldots .$ They might be a stack of books, a row of houses, or a string of pearls. Also, nothing is said about the meaning of "between" except that it involves three elements, and is expressed symbolically as (abc); it is read "b is between a and c," or "a, b, and c are in the order abc." In addition to these two primtives, we shall make the following assumptions:

A₁. If (abc), then a, b, and c are distinct (this simply means that $a \neq b$, $a \neq c$, and $b \neq c$).

A₂. If (abc), then (cba).

A₃. If (abc) and (bcd), then (abd) and (acd).

A₄. If (abc) and (acd), then (abd) and (bcd).

A₅. If a, b, and c are distinct, then at least one of the three relations (abc), (bca), or (cab) must hold.

From these five assumptions, a number of theorems may be derived by logical deduction. For example, it can be proved that: if (abc) and (abd), then (cad) is false. Or again: if (abd) and (acd), then (bdc) is false. These assumptions and any derived theorems are obviously abstractions. Yet they are easily translated into English. For example: A₂ states that if b is between a and c, then b is between c and a. In like fashion, A₃ states that if b is between a and c and c is between b and d, then b is between a and d and c is between a and d.

So far these statements are "meaningless" in the sense that they don't apply to anything specific nor describe anything concrete, unless, indeed, as you tried to understand them, you visualized points on a line. If you did, you were giving a concrete meaning to the primitives. You can, of course, interpret the elements a, b, c, . . . as points on a Euclidean line. The abstract symbol (abc) may then be interpreted

Fig. 1-21

as meaning that point b lies on line l and is between point a and point c, or, that in passing along the line from position a to position c, you have to "go through" position b. This is a physical, or concrete, interpretation of an abstract symbolism. It can be applied to all the

Fig. 1-22

assumptions and to all the theorems. For example, take A₃: if (abc) and (bcd), then (abd) and (acd). Clearly, b is between a and d, and also c is between a and d.

Another interpretation, of course, is also possible. Suppose we interpret the elements a, b, c, . . . as representing the ordinary whole numbers 1, 2, 3, 4, . . . n . . . ; and let us interpret (abc) to mean that the numbers which they represent satisfy one or the other of the following relations: (1) $a < b$ and $b < c$, or (2) $a > b$ and $b > c$, where the $<$ means "is less than" and $>$ means "is greater than." It is then easy enough to verify assumptions A_1–A_5. For example; A_4 states that if (abc) and (acd), then (abd) and (bcd); thus, if $a = 3$, $b = 5$, $c = 8$ and $d = 10$, we see that 5 is between 3 and 10 $(3 < 5 < 10)$, and that 8 is between 5 and 10 $(5 < 8 < 10)$.

Nor is it to be supposed that these are the only concrete interpretations possible. The elements a, b, c, d, . . . n might be thought of as people standing in line, or as the tones of a musical scale, or as the colors of the spectrum, and so on. The significant thing is that the abstract formulation admits of several interpretations, each of which is consistent within itself. Indeed, it is applicable to any "content" or concrete subject matter which may give appropriate meaning to the basic assumptions. Thus we see the true nature of modern mathematics: a collection of many axiomatic systems, each dealing with abstractions and embracing a body of relations which admit of various concrete interpretations.

You may well ask yourself, at this point, just how does the mathematician decide upon one set of postulates and primitives instead of another? In general, he prefers a set of postulates which seem to fit best the possible concrete interpretations, physical models, or practical applications in which he is interested. Frequently, but not always, the postulates and theorems are suggested by intuition or experience. Sometimes they are purely acts of creative imagination or intellectual adventure.

This characteristic of mathematics has been aptly described by Bourbaki in the following passage:[7]

From the axiomatic point of view, mathematics appears thus as a storehouse of abstract forms—the mathematical structures; and it so happens—without our knowing why—that certain aspects of empirical reality fit themselves into these forms, as if through a kind of preadaptation. Of course, it cannot be denied that most of these forms had originally a very definite intuitive content; but, it is exactly by deliberate throwing out of this content, that it has been possible to give these forms all the power which they were capable of displaying and to prepare them for new interpretations and for the development of their full power.

[7] N. Bourbaki, translated by A. Dresden, *American Mathematical Monthly*, vol. 57 (1950), pp. 222–232.

pure and applied mathematics

We conclude by pointing out the relation of pure mathematics to applied mathematics. We have seen how an abstract mathematical science may be created or built up. If concrete meanings or physical objects are associated with the undefined terms, then the postulates and theorems of the abstract system constitute a concrete interpretation of the abstract mathematical system. The abstract mathematical system is called a "mathematical model" of the physical or tangible interpretation. All abstract systems of mathematics considered together are called *pure mathematics;* all concrete interpretations are regarded as *applied mathematics.* This distinction applies with equal force to arithmetic, to algebra, and to geometry.

This modern point of view has been suggested by an eminent physicist as follows: [8]

The pure mathematician . . . will set up a branch of mathematics founded upon certain postulates having to do with quantities, letters, etc. that he chooses to be talking about. In this mathematical scheme, there will appear relationships between certain quantities which occur in the mathematics, and it will be his hope to invent a scheme of mathematics of this kind which shall form an analogue of the regularities of nature in the sense that there may be a one-to-one correspondence between certain things in the mathematics and the observable phenomena in nature. . . . When the correspondence has been set up, the postulates of his mathematics become the laws of nature in the physics.

If the reader has any doubts about the "utility" of such abstract systems, may we remind him of the central role played by complex numbers of the form $a + bi$ in the theory of alternating currents; or of Boolean algebra in relation to the theory of electronic computers; or perhaps even more dramatic, the role of non-Euclidean geometry in the development of relativity theory. Surely A. N. Whitehead was not exaggerating when he said: "It is no paradox that in our most theoretical moods we may be nearest to our most practical applications."

EXERCISE 1–5

1. Explain in your own words the meaning of (*a*) an abstraction, (*b*) a generalization.

2. What is the essential distinction between a proposition and a theorem?

3. Give a specific example to show that you know the meaning of *imply* and *infer.*

[8] W. F. G. Swann, "Reality in Physics," *Science* 75:113–114; 1932.

4. Explain what is meant by a mathematical model of an abstract system.

5. Discuss the meaning of the phrase, "if and only if," with particular reference to the nature of a definition.

6. Discuss the meaning of the phrase "necessary and sufficient condition." Give an example (1) of a condition which is necessary, but not sufficient for some other situation to hold; (2) a condition which is sufficient, but not necessary for another situation; (3) a condition which is both necessary and sufficient for another situation.

7. Explain the following statement: "Although the concept of number is an abstraction, man's earlier idea of number was closely related to reality and experience; that is, it was essentially concrete, not abstract."

8. Suggest another concrete interpretation for the theory of order given on page 26 and illustrate how each of the five postulates and the two theorems are "true" in this concrete interpretation.

9. Which (one or more) of the following words indicate substantially what is meant by the term "mathematical rigor," or "rigorous thinking": (*a*) *difficult,* (*b*) *complicated,* (*c*) *abstract,* (*d*) *elaborate,* (*e*) *precise,* (*f*) *erudite,* (*g*) *recondite.*

10. In the light of the present chapter, comment upon the following quotation from the late J. W. N. Sullivan, distinguished interpreter of science and mathematics:

By informing us of the nature of our own minds [mathematics] informs us of much that depends on our minds . . . it is even possible that we can experience nothing but what we have created, and that the greatest of our mathematical creations is the material universe itself.

FOR FURTHER READING AND STUDY

1. Bell, E. T. *Mathematics, Queen and Servant of Science.* New York: McGraw-Hill, 1951. Chapter 2.
2. Boehm, George A. W. *The New World of Math.* New York: The Dial Press, 1959.
3. Keyser, C. J. "The Meaning of Mathematics." In *Mathematics as a Culture Clue and Other Essays.* New York: Scripta Mathematica, Yeshiva University, 1947. Pp. 1–19.
4. Kline, Morris. *Mathematics in Western Culture.* New York: Oxford University Press, 1953. Chapter 28.
5. National Council of Teachers of Mathematics. Twenty-third Yearbook. *Insights into Modern Mathematics.* Washington, D. C.: The Council, 1957. Pp. 1–6; 36–46; 65–76.
6. Newsom, C. V. "An Introduction to Modern Mathematical Thought." In *Mathematics: Our Great Heritage,* by W. L. Schaaf (Editor). New York: Harper and Bros., 1948. Pp. 99–118.

CHAPTER 2

Elementary Logic

As an enterprise mathematics is characterized by its aim, and its aim is to think rigorously whatever is rigorously thinkable or whatever may become rigorously thinkable in the course of the upward striving and refining evolution of ideas.

—Cassius J. Keyser

PROPOSITIONS AND IMPLICATIONS

what is logical reasoning?

You have doubtless heard it said that one of the chief reasons for studying mathematics, and geometry in particular, is that it helps pupils learn to "think straight." This goal is variously referred to as that of "clear thinking," "critical thinking," or "rigorous thinking." What is meant, of course, is the discipline of logical reasoning. There is a vast difference between the traditional formal logic of classical times and modern mathematical logic, or symbolic logic. The latter is far more comprehensive and includes the former. Yet both have this in common, that they may be described, roughly, as the study of necessary inferences, or intellectually compelling conclusions.[1]

A statement is a sentence that is either true or false. Every statement is a sentence; but not every sentence is a statement. "How old are you?" "Hand me the key." "I wish the winter were over!" are sentences, but they are not statements; they are neither true nor false. Only declarative sentences can be statements. But not even all declarative sentences are statements. For example, sentences such as "I am hungry," "She is tired," "Los Angeles is far away," could be either true or false, depending upon the context or circumstances. Hence they are not statements, and cannot be said to have a "truth value"—that is, to be "true" or "false."

By the pattern or logical structure of a statement is meant the way in which ideas or relations are tied together by connecting words such as *and, or, not, if, then, but, some, all, every, any*, etc. For example, the following statements have the same logical structure:

(1) Every citizen is native born or naturalized.
(2) Every substance is organic or inorganic.
(3) Every student passed or failed the examination.

We say that a statement is *logically true* if it is true, or acceptable, solely because of its logical structure, that is, if all other statements having a similar structure are also true, regardless of their content or subject matter. Thus the three foregoing statements, 1, 2, and 3 are considered true. Furthermore, two statements are logically equivalent if they agree as to their truth or falsity again only because of their logical structure. For example, the statement: (4) If something is neither organic nor inorganic, it is not a substance, is logically equivalent to statement 2 above. The reader should realize that whether a statement is true or false, whether one statement is equivalent to another or not, and whether one statement implies another or not, are questions not always as obvious or readily answerable as these few illustrations might suggest. The techniques of logic, however, furnish effective tools for answering such questions.

We are now in a position to characterize what is meant by a logical, or deductive, inference. If we accept as true a statement based

---

[1] We are referring here essentially to deductive logic, or deductive inference, to the exclusion of inductive inference. The field of inductive logic, the basis of scientific method, involves both experimental and statistical inference. The distinction between deductive and inductive thinking has already been discussed (see page 4).

on one or more other statements that have previously been accepted as true, and if this acceptance is made solely because of the form or structure of the original statement(s), regardless of content or meaning, we are making a *deductive inference*.

propositions

Statements which are either "true" or "false" but not both at the same time, in the sense indicated above, are known as *propositions*. The terms true and false are left undefined; it is assumed that their meaning is intuitively understood. Propositions which make use of such terms as "all," "every," "some," "any," are called *general propositions;* propositions which do not contain these terms are called *particular propositions*. When simple component propositions are combined by the use of such words as "and," "or," "not," the resulting propositions are called composite propositions. It is customary to represent simple component propositions by such symbols as p, q, r, etc. Thus the letter p might represent the proposition "the lines are parallel"; q might represent the proposition "the lines intersect." It is understood that when we say "p," we mean that p is true.

connectives

It so happens that both in logical discourse as well as in mathematics, certain words or phrases occur over and over again, and are indispensable for purposes of analysis. We have already alluded to these connectives; the following ones are among the most common, whereas the symbols here suggested are in common but not universal use:

Connective Word	Symbol	Name
1. "not"	$\sim$	*negation* or *denial*
2. "and"	$\wedge$	*conjunction*
3. "or"	$\vee$	*disjunction,* or *alternation*
4. "if . . . then"	$\rightarrow$	*implication,* or *conditional*
5. "if and only if"	$\leftrightarrow$	*biconditional*

These words serve to give a logical structure or pattern to any statement or to any inferences deduced therefrom. All but the first of these ("not") serve to connect two component statements to form a third, composite statement.

The *negation* or denial of a given proposition p is the proposition *not-p*, which is expressed symbolically as $\sim p$ (read "curl p"). It means "p is false"; or, "it is not true that p"; or, "p is not the case." For example:

p	$\sim p$
1. John is a Republican.	1'. John is *not* a Republican.
2. The base angles are equal.	2'. The base angles are *unequal*.
3. a is greater than b.	3'. a is *not* greater than b.
4. All polygons are regular.	4'. *Not* all polygons are regular.

By the conjunction of two propositions p and q is meant the proposition "p and q," or, "both p and q." Expressed in symbols, we write: $p \wedge q$. It is understood to be true whenever both of the propositions p and q are true; otherwise the propositions $p \wedge q$ is false.

Examples.

1. p: A quadrilateral is a polygon.
   q: A hexagon is a polygon.
   $p \wedge q$: A quadrilateral is a polygon and a hexagon is a polygon.
2. p: $l_1 \parallel l_2$.
   q: $l_2 \parallel l_3$.
   $p \wedge q$: $l_1 \parallel l_2$ and $l_2 \parallel l_3$.
3. p: The midjoin of a triangle is parallel to the base.
   q: The midjoin of a triangle is equal to half the base.
   $p \wedge q$: The midjoin of a triangle is parallel to the base and equal to half of it.

By the *disjunction* of two propositions p and q is meant the composite proposition "p or q," symbolized as $p \vee q$. The disjunction of two propositions p and q is understood to be true when at least one of the propositions p, q is true; otherwise $p \vee q$ is false. Note carefully that the connective *or* when used in a disjunction is used in the *inclusive* sense; that is, "or" means p or q, or both.[2] Hereafter, the word *or* will always be used in the inclusive sense unless otherwise specified.

Examples.

1. p: *Angle x =* angle y.
   q: *Angle a =* angle b.
   $p \vee q$: Angle x = angle y, or angle a = angle b (or both).
2. p: It is cold.
   q: The wind is blowing.
   $p \vee q$: It is cold or the wind is blowing (or both).

[2] The exclusive sense of "or" would mean p or q, but *not* both.

By convention, the proposition $p \lor q$ is true whenever either or both p and q are true; otherwise it is false.

One of the most fruitful concepts in mathematics is the *"if-then"* idea, or the notion of *implication*. It is very common in everyday thinking as well. For the beginner, it is helpful to think of "if" as meaning "whenever."

Examples.

1. *If* the criminal is caught, *then* he will be punished.

2. *If* I meet the qualifications, *then* I will be accepted.

3. *If* two straight lines intersect, *then* the opposite angles are equal (in pairs).

4. *If* two lines are perpendicular, *then* they will form right angles.

Symbolically, we write $p \to q$, which means "p implies q," and is a short way of saying "if p is true, then q is true."

The last of our connectives, "if and only if," symbolized by $p \leftrightarrow q$, is important in connection with definitions. As we shall have occasion to point out later, this connective, although often omitted in a definition, is always understood. For example:

1. Two lines are perpendicular *if and only if* they intersect (or meet) at right angles.

2. A closed curve is a circle *if and only if* every point on the curve is equidistant from a given point within the curve.

3. A triangle is equilateral *if and only if* all three sides are equal.

fundamental principles of logic

When a composite proposition is always true regardless of its particular content, we call such a proposition a *principle of a particular system of logic*. Two such important principles are the following:

A. Law of the Excluded Middle. For every proposition p, either p is true or p is false; that is, $p \lor (\sim p)$. Note that here we are using "or" in the exclusive sense: "either, but not both."

Examples.

1. Angle $x =$ angle y, or angle $x \neq$ angle y.

2. The lines l_1 and l_2 are parallel or they are not parallel.

3. The number n is even or it is not even.

4. Triangle ABC is similar to triangle $A'B'C'$ or it is not similar to triangle $A'B'C'$.

B. Law of Contradiction. For every proposition p, it is false that both p is true and p is false; or, $\sim[p \wedge (\sim p)]$. In other words, a proposition cannot be both true and false at the same time.

Examples.

1. A line cannot be both parallel and not parallel to another line.
2. A number cannot both be a root of an equation and not a root of the same equation.
3. An angle cannot be both congruent and not congruent to another angle.

logical implication

When discussing propositions in the *if-then* form, the *if* clause indicates the set of things about which something is said; it is called the *hypothesis* of the proposition or theorem. The *then* clause, which indicates what is being said about the set of things in question, is called the *conclusion*.

Examples.

1. If a person lives in Dallas, then he lives in Texas.
2. If a person is a male citizen over 21, then he may vote.
3. If two angles are right angles, then they are equal.

The word "then" is not essential; it could be omitted, and the meaning would still be the same. The word "then" helps us to distinguish between the hypothesis and the conclusion. This is very important, as we shall soon see.

Hypothesis	*Conclusion*
1. If a person lives in Dallas,	he lives in Texas.
2. If a person is a male citizen over 21,	he may vote.
3. If two angles are right angles,	they are equal.

The *if*-clause does not have to come at the beginning of the sentence; it may come last, but it is still the hypothesis. Thus,

1. A person lives in Texas if he lives in Dallas.
2. A person may vote if he is a male citizen over 21.
3. Two angles are equal if they are right angles.

The word "if" could be replaced by "whenever" or "suppose that"; this substitution would not change the meaning of the statements. It is in this sense that we say "hypothesis." You may not know whether Tom Brown lives in Dallas or not, but *if* he does, then you *know* he lives in Texas. You may not know whether Mr. Smith is a citizen over 21, but *if* he is, then you *know* he may vote. And so on. That is what we mean by p implies q.

General statements do not always have a subordinate clause beginning with "if." For example:

1. Good citizens obey the laws.
2. Diamonds are hard.
3. Spiders are not insects.

In such cases the statement can easily be changed to use the word *if*, and yet still express the same thought:

1. If he is a good citizen, then he obeys the laws.
2. If this substance is a diamond, then it is hard.
3. If this is a spider, then it is not an insect.

Even more complicated statements can be put into the if-then form: "Seniors who have an average above 90 per cent and have not been absent more than three times are excused from final examinations." This sentence can be restated: "If he is a senior with an average above 90 per cent, and if he has not been absent more than three times, then he is excused from final examinations." Here the hypothesis is the subject of the sentence together with all its modifiers; the conclusion consists of the verb and the predicate of the sentence.

EXERCISE 2–1

In each of the following propositions, tell which is the hypothesis and which is the conclusion.

1. You will not be admitted if you are under fourteen years of age.

2. If this farm land is well drained and has rich soil, then it will yield a good crop.

3. He is a bad insurance risk if he has heart trouble.

4. He will be able to buy this house if he has enough for a down payment and can afford to pay the monthly carrying charges.

5. Owning one's own home is economical if one has a large family and is handy about the house.

6. I would be happier if I had more friends and could play more games.

7. If she were prettier and dressed more becomingly she would be more popular.

8. If the machine is put together properly it will run without noise, provided it is oiled sufficiently.

9. If two sides of a triangle are equal, the angles opposite those sides are equal.

10. Vertical angles are equal.

11. Corresponding sides of congruent triangles are equal.

12. A point is equally distant from the ends of a line segment if the point lies on the perpendicular bisector of the segment.

13. If a figure is a parallelogram, its diagonals bisect each other.

14. A line is tangent to a circle if it is perpendicular to a radius at the outer extremity of the radius.

15. A student who does not study may expect to fail.

16. Those who eat proper food will be healthy.

17. He is thrifty who plans his expenditures.

18. The base angles of an isosceles triangle are equal.

19. The diagonals of a rhombus are perpendicular.

20. "Corresponding angles of parallel lines are equal."

DEDUCTIVE REASONING

deductive inference

An *implication* by itself is not very fruitful. Consider the implication: (*a*) If the train is late, then I will miss my appointment. Also, with (*a*), consider this proposition: (*b*) The train is late. Taking (*a*) and (*b*) together, we conclude that: (*c*) I will miss my appointment. Clearly, if we accept both (*a*) and (*b*) as true propositions, we can *infer* or deduce that proposition (*c*) is true. This is more than we could say just by considering (*a*) alone.

Notice that insofar as the pattern of the reasoning is concerned, it doesn't matter what the contents of the propositions are; it is the *form* or structure that counts. Thus, in general:

$$1.\ p \rightarrow q$$
$$\underline{2.\ p}$$
$$3.\ \therefore\ q$$

In words we may say: since the implication $p \rightarrow q$ is true, and since p is also true, therefore q must be accepted as true. The symbol ($\therefore$) means "therefore." This is known as the *Fundamental Rule of Inference*. It asserts: Whenever an implication, $p \rightarrow q$, is accepted as true, and the hypothesis p is also accepted as true, we must accept the conclusion q as true. The distinction between a deductive inference (such as the three-step procedure above) and a simple implication is this: the truth of the implication $p \rightarrow q$ does not necessarily mean that either p or q is true; but the truth of both p and $p \to q$ necessarily means that q is also true.

syllogisms

The three-step arrangement is called a *syllogism;* steps 1 and 2 are called the *premises,* and step 3 is called the inference or *conclusion.*[3] Of course, the order of steps 1 and 2 is of no consequence; the same syllogism could also have been written:

$$1.\ p$$
$$2.\ p \to q$$
$$3.\ \therefore\ q$$

Examples.

1. (*a*) If it has rained, the ground is wet.
    (*b*) It has rained.
    (*c*) $\therefore$ The ground is wet.
2. (*a*) If a figure is a rhombus, its diagonals are perpendicular.
    (*b*) This is a rhombus.
    (*c*) $\therefore$ Its diagonals are perpendicular.

An extension of the fundamental rule of inference leads to the so-called *chain rule,* which asserts:

$$1.\ p \to q$$
$$2.\ q \to r$$
$$3.\ \therefore\ p \to r$$

That this principle is fundamental can readily be seen by assuming p as a hypothesis; combining this with $p \to q$ yields q; this in turn may be combined with $q \to r$ to yield r. Thus we get $p \to r$. In the same way, this rule may be generalized: $p \to q,\ q \to r,\ r \to s;\ \therefore\ p \to s$; etc.

In order to help the reader, we shall from time to time introduce simple diagrams known as *Euler's circles.* Thus the proposition $p \to q$ can be interpreted as "All p's are q's," that is, every element of set p is also an element of set q, but not every element of set q is an element of p (Fig. 2-1). Then, from the diagram, the syllogism follows at once:

1. $p \to q$	1. Every element of set p is an element of q.
2. p	2. This is an element of p.
3. $\therefore\ q$	3. $\therefore$ It is an element of q.

---

[3] This use of the term "conclusion" is not to be confused with the conclusion of an implication; the context will avoid any ambiguity.

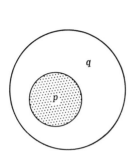

Fig. 2-1

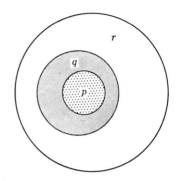

Fig. 2-2

Similarly for the chain rule (Fig. 2-2):

1. $p \rightarrow q$	1. Every element of p is an element of q.
2. $q \rightarrow r$	2. Every element of q is an element of r.
3. $\therefore p \rightarrow r$	3. $\therefore$ Every element of p is an element of r.

EXERCISE 2–2

Fill in the blanks in each of the following sets of propositions, following the fundamental rule of inference; do not be concerned with the truth or falsity of any of the propositions involved, but simply assume the first two propositions as premises in every case:

1.   (a) If a man lives in Indiana, he is a Hoosier.
     (b) John Harris lives in Indiana.

     (c) $\therefore$ ——————————————

2.   (a) If Albany is north of New York, then Troy is north of Albany.
     (b) Albany is north of New York.

     (c) $\therefore$ ——————————————

3.   (a) If Albany is north of New York, then Troy is south of Albany.
     (b) Albany is north of New York.

     (c) $\therefore$ ——————————————

4.   (a) Polygon P is similar to polygon P'.
     (b) If polygon P is similar to polygon P', their corresponding angles are equal.

     (c) $\therefore$ ——————————————

5.   (a) ——————————————
     (b) Unemployment has increased.

     (c) $\therefore$ Taxes will be reduced.

Change each of the following syllogisms to the *if-then* form, express it in symbols, and draw an appropriate diagram (Euler circles):

6. (a) All A's are B's.
    (b) All C's are A's.
    (c) ∴ All C's are B's.

7. (a) All C's are A's.
    (b) All A's are B's.
    (c) ∴ All C's are B's.

8. (a) All fractions are numbers.
    (b) All decimals are fractions.
    (c) All decimals are numbers.

Complete each syllogism and draw a diagram:

9. (a) All triangles are polygons.
    (b) All polygons are plane figures.
    (c) ∴ —————————————————

10. (a) All squares are regular polygons.
     (b) All regular polygons have equal angles.
     (c) ∴ —————————————————

11. (a) All *prali* are *soli*.
     (b) All *umpi* are *prali*.
     (c) ∴ —————————————————

Using the chain rule, complete each of the following:

12. (a) If $a < b$, then $m > n$.
     (b) If $m > n$, then $r < s$.
     (c) ∴ —————————————————

13. (a) If $ABCD$ is a rhombus, its diagonals are perpendicular.
     (b) If the diagonals of a rhombus are perpendicular, the diagonals
          bisect the angles of the rhombus.
     (c) ∴ —————————————————

14. Explain by means of the fundamental rule of inference and with the
aid of a diagram, why, if q is known to be false, we must conclude that
either the premise p or the premise $p \rightarrow q$ must be false.

15. Express each of the following symbolic statements in words:

(a) $p \lor (\sim p)$
(b) $p \land (q \lor r)$
(c) $(p \land q) \lor r$
(d) $\sim[p \land (\sim p)]$
(e) $(\sim p) \lor q$
(f) $(\sim p) \rightarrow (\sim q)$
(g) $\sim[(p \rightarrow q) \land (q \rightarrow p)]$
(h) $(p \rightarrow q) \leftrightarrow (\sim q \rightarrow \sim p)$

validity of reasoning

The truth or falsity of propositions, whether they be premises or
conclusions, depends upon their content. The validity of the method
of reasoning depends upon the structure of the argument, regardless

of the actual truth or falsity of the premises or conclusions. We shall see that valid reasoning may lead to both true and false conclusions; also, unfortunately, non-valid reasoning may lead to true conclusions as well as false conclusions. You have seen how the fundamental rule of inference can be used to derive a new proposition, q, from the given premises, $p \rightarrow q$, and p, irrespective of the truth or falsity of the premises. In other words, the fundamental rule, of itself, gives no assurance that the deduced proposition is true. If either premise is false, the conclusion is false; but if both premises are true, the conclusion must be true. Hence if q is known to be false, we know that either the premise p or the premise $p \rightarrow q$ must have been false. To help understand invalid forms of reasoning, we introduce the ideas of converse and opposite.

You will doubtless recall the "converse of a theorem" from your high school geometry. The converse of the implication "if p, then q" is the implication "if q, then p." In other words, the *converse* of a given proposition is the proposition obtained by interchanging the hypothesis and conclusion of the given proposition.

Examples.

Proposition	*Converse*
1. If two lines are perpendicular, they meet at right angles.	1′. If two lines meet at right angles, they are perpendicular.
2. If a line is tangent to a circle, it touches the circle in one and only one point.	2′. If a line touches a circle in one and only one point, it is tangent to the circle.
3. If two sides of a triangle are equal, the opposite angles are equal.	3′. If two angles of a triangle are equal, the opposite sides are equal.
4. $p \rightarrow q$.	4′. $q \rightarrow p$.

Sometimes a statement looks like a converse, but isn't. For example:

(a) If there is no wind, a yacht cannot sail.
(b) A yacht cannot sail if there is no wind.

These are not converses. It seems that statement (b) is the converse of (a) because the "if clause" now comes at the end of the sentence, whereas in (a) it came at the beginning of the sentence. The position of the "if clause" in the statement is unimportant. An "if clause" is a logical hypothesis wherever it appears in the sentence; merely reversing the order of the clauses in a statement does not form the converse.

A little reflection will show that the truth of a proposition does not assure the truth of its converse. For example:

Proposition	*Converse*
1. If two angles are right angles, they are equal.	1′. If two angles are equal, they are right angles.
2. If it is raining, the ground is wet.	2′. If the ground is wet, it is raining.
3. If two triangles are congruent, they are similar.	3′. If two triangles are similar, they are congruent.
4. If he is a thief, he is a lawbreaker.	4′. If he is a lawbreaker, he is a thief.

The opposite of a given proposition is the proposition obtained by negating both the hypothesis and the conclusion of the given proposition. Thus the opposite of the implication "if p, then q," is "if *not-p*, then *not-q*." For example:

Proposition	*Converse*
1. If two lines are perpendicular they meet at right angles.	1′. If two lines are *not* perpendicular, they do *not* meet at right angles.
2. If two sides of a triangle are equal, the opposite angles are equal.	2′. If two sides of a triangle are *not* equal, the opposite angles are *not* equal.
3. $p \rightarrow q$.	3′. $(\sim p) \rightarrow (\sim q)$.

As in the case of a converse, the truth of a proposition does not assure the truth of its opposite. The following opposites are obviously not necessarily true.

Proposition	*Opposite*
1. If two angles are right angles, they are equal.	1. If two angles are not right angles, they are not equal.
2. If it is raining, the ground is wet.	2. If it is not raining, the ground is not wet.
3. If two triangles are congruent, they are similar.	3. If two triangles are not congruent, they are not similar.

We now proceed to show two common invalid forms of reasoning.

(I) 1. $p \rightarrow q$ (II) 1. $p \rightarrow q$

    2. q _____   2. $\sim p$ _____

    3. $\therefore p$ 3. $\therefore \sim q$

It will be seen that I is tantamount to assuming that the converse of a true proposition is necessarily true, which it is not. Diagramatically this may be shown as in Fig. 2-3; the invalidity is clear at once. Every element of p is an element of q, but not every element of q is an element of p. Hence we cannot conclude that because something is an element of set q that it is necessarily an element of set p.

Examples.

1. (a) All roses are flowers.
   (b) This is a flower.
   (c) ∴ This is a rose.
2. (a) A triangle is a polygon.
   (b) This is a polygon.
   (c) ∴ This is a triangle.

In II the invalid argument is tantamount to assuming that the opposite of a true proposition is necessarily true. Figure 2-4 suggests

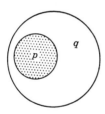

Fig. 2-3

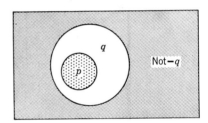

Fig. 2-4

why this is invalid. Every element of p is an element of q; but some elements of q are not elements of p, that is, something which is not an element of p could be an element of q. Hence we cannot conclude that because something is not an element of p it cannot be an element of q.

Examples.

1. (a) All soldiers have uniforms.
   (b) This man is not a soldier.
   (c) ∴ This man does not have a uniform.
2. (a) A quadrilateral is a polygon.
   (b) This figure is not a quadrilateral.
   (c) ∴ This figure is not a polygon.

In short, arguing from a proposition to assert the converse, or the opposite, is completely invalid reasoning; neither

$$\frac{p \to q}{\therefore \; q \to p}, \quad \text{nor} \quad \frac{p \to q}{\therefore \; (\sim p) \to (\sim q)},$$

are ever valid arguments. Yet people often thoughtlessly or unwittingly assume that the converse of a statement is true simply because the original statement is true. For example:

Statement: (*a*) If the pen is an Omega pen, it writes smoothly.
Converse: (*b*) If a pen writes smoothly, it is an Omega pen.

Even if the original statement *a* is true (and it may well be), does it follow necessarily that the converse statement *b* is true? Not at all, for this would imply that the only pen which wrote smoothly was the Omega pen, which is probably not true at all. Yet the makers

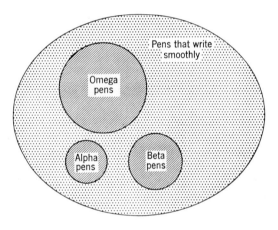

Fig. 2-5

of the Omega pen might wish us to believe that *b* is true. Is it safe, therefore, to reason from the converse and decide to buy an Omega pen? This sort of situation—leading people to think that the converse of a true statement is necessarily true—is often used by demagogues, politicians, propagandists, advertisers, and so on.

The same pitfall may arise in the misuse of the opposite of a statement. For the sake of dramatic effect, an advertiser asserts: "If it isn't an Alpha cigarette, it isn't a cool smoke!" (If $\sim$ Alpha, then $\sim$ cool.) He hopes you will regard the opposite of this statement to be true also (If Alpha, then cool). So, beware of converses and opposites. You may meet them anywhere—in editorials, over the radio or on television, in advertisements, or in debates and arguments.

EXERCISE 2–3

1. First give the converse of each of the following statements; then give its opposite:

(a) If a man is hungry, he will steal.
(b) If two lines are perpendicular, they meet at right angles.
(c) If John is Henry's father, Henry is John's son.
(d) If Helen likes Mary, Mary likes Helen.
(e) If it is windy, the flag is unfurled.
(f) If two sides of a triangle are equal, the base angles are equal.

2. Change each of these statements to the *if-then* form and then state both the converse and the opposite:

(a) All musicians are temperamental.
(b) Half a straight angle is a right angle.
(c) All hexagons are regular polygons.
(d) The diagonals of a rectangle intersect at right angles.
(e) The base angles of an isosceles triangle are equal.
(f) In a Perfecto razor, the blade never gets dull.

3. Make up a pair of statements that look like converses, but are not.

4. Make up a pair of converse statements in which both statements are true.

5. Make up a pair of converse statements in which one of the statements is true and the other is not true.

6. Explain why the following are examples of poor reasoning:

(a) Helen was late for her music lesson. Her teacher concluded that she had not left her home on time.

(b) If a man is a good businessman, he will make a good mayor. Jones is a good mayor. So he must be a good businessman.

(c) Beautiful women use *Wunder Kream*. Alice switched to *Wunder Kream*, because she wishes to be a beautiful woman.

7. "The best always costs more. So—be sure to buy ABC toothpaste!" (Even though it costs more than other toothpastes.) Explain how a converse is misleading in this advertisement.

8. Examine each of the following arguments and tell whether it is valid or not, giving your reason; disregard the truth or falsity of the premises and conclusions.

(a) (1) If Mexico is colder than Iceland, then the North Pole is warmer than Florida.
(2) Mexico is colder than Iceland.
(3) ∴ The North Pole is warmer than Florida.

(*b*) (1) If this is April, three months hence will be July.
        (2) This is not April.
        (3) ∴ Three months hence will not be July.
(*c*) (1) If John is on time, he will be admitted.
        (2) John will be admitted.
        (3) ∴ John will be on time.
(*d*) (1) If aluminum is heavier than lead, then copper is heavier than iron.
        (2) Aluminum is heavier than lead.
        (3) ∴ Copper is heavier than iron.
(*e*) (1) If side a = side b, then angle A = angle B.
        (2) But we know that angle A = angle B.
        (3) ∴ Side a = side b.

RELATED PROPOSITIONS

logical equivalence

We turn now to the idea of equivalent implications. As we have just seen, the converse of a true implication does not *have* to be true, but of course it *may* be true. If, then, two propositions mutually imply each other, they are said to be *logically equivalent*. Thus if $p \to q$ and $q \to p$, we say that the propositions p and q are equivalent, and we write $p \leftrightarrow q$.

Another almost obvious equivalence is the double negation; a double negative proposition is equivalent to the corresponding positive proposition. Thus, for every proposition p, we have

$$[\sim(\sim p)] \leftrightarrow p.$$

For example, if p means "water is wet," then

$$[\sim(\sim p)] \leftrightarrow p$$

means: "it is false that water is not wet" is equivalent to saying that "water is wet."

One of the most useful logical equivalences is the equivalence of a proposition and its contrapositive. The contrapositive of a proposition is the converse of its opposite, or the opposite of its converse. Thus:

I. *Proposition:* $p \to q$ (If p, then q.)
II. *Converse:* $q \to p$ (If q, then p.)

III. *Opposite:* $(\sim p) \rightarrow (\sim q)$ (If *not–p*, then *not–q*.)
IV. *Contrapositive:* $(\sim q) \rightarrow (\sim p)$ (If *not–q*, then *not–p*.)

Examples.

Proposition	*Contrapositive*
1. If it is a horse, it has four legs.	1′. If it does *not* have four legs, it is *not* a horse.
2. If he is a native Frenchman, he is a European.	2′. If he is *not* a European, he is *not* a native Frenchman.
3. If two lines are perpendicular, they meet at right angles.	3′. If two lines do *not* meet at right angles, they are *not* perpendicular.

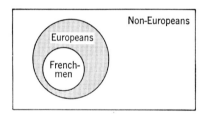

Fig. 2-6

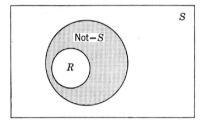

Fig. 2-7

Study the above examples; do you see that in each case, the contrapositive is the opposite (denial) of the converse, as well as the converse of the opposite (denial)? The same relation holds between the following pairs of contrapositives:

4. If he is a citizen, he is not an alien.	4′. If he is an alien, he is not a citizen.
5. If two (coplanar) lines are parallel, they do not intersect.	5′. If two (coplanar) lines intersect, they are not parallel.
6. If R, then *not–S*.	6′. If S, then *not–R*.
7. If *not–P*, then Q.	7′. If *not–Q*, then P.

Now study these illustrative examples thoughtfully. Can you see that they are actually equivalent statements—that if you accept either one of a pair of contrapositives as true you must accept the other also? The diagrams should help you to see this equivalence.

The equivalence of a proposition and its contrapositive can also be shown as follows. Let us first recall the fundamental rule of infer-ence:

$$1. \ p \rightarrow q$$
$$\underline{2. \ p}$$
$$3. \ \therefore \ q$$

If 1 and 2 are given both true, then 3 must be true.

Now assume, in the following syllogism, that 1 and 2 are both true:

$$1. \ p \rightarrow q$$
$$\underline{2. \ \sim q}$$
$$3. \ \therefore \ (?)$$

At what possible conclusions about p can we arrive in 3? Obviously, only that either p or $(\sim p)$. Suppose we conclude that p is true; then, by the fundamental rule of inference above, $(\sim q)$ would be a false premise. But this contradicts the original hypothesis, namely, that $(\sim q)$ is a true premise. Therefore we cannot conclude that p is true, and we are left with $(\sim p)$ as the only true conclusion. Thus:

$$1. \ p \rightarrow q$$
$$\underline{2. \ \sim q}$$
$$3. \ \therefore \ \sim p$$

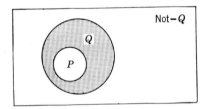

Fig. 2-8

In other words, from the given premise $(p \rightarrow q)$, we have derived the further implication $\sim q \rightarrow \sim p$. This last implication is the contraposi-tive of the given implication; we have shown that they are logically equivalent, or that

$$(p \rightarrow q) \leftrightarrow (\sim q \rightarrow \sim p)$$

We can now see clearly how the four implications are related to one another:

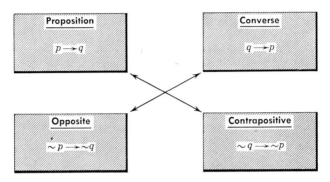

Fig. 2-9

In summarizing, we can say:

1. A proposition and its contrapositive are logically equivalent. If either is true, the other is true; if either is false, the other is false. If either has been proved as a theorem, the other is "automatically" established as a theorem, and does not require separate proof.

2. In like manner, the opposite and the converse of the same proposition are also logically equivalent. If either is true, the other is true; if either is false, the other is false. If either has been proved as a theorem, the other is "automatically" established as a theorem, and does not require separate proof.

3. Proving a proposition obviates the need for proving its contrapositive, and vice versa.

4. Proving the converse of a proposition obviates the need for proving the opposite of that proposition, and vice versa.

5. Because a proposition and its contrapositive are both true, it does *not* follow that the converse and opposite are both true; they may both be false or both true.

6. Because the converse and the opposite of a proposition are both true, it does *not* follow that the proposition and its contrapositive are both true; they may both be false or both true.

7. Proving a proposition does not establish either its converse or its opposite; if, however, either the converse or the opposite is also proved, independently, then all four propositions are established as theorems.

These relations between propositions and their validity are of importance in developing a logical system of geometry, especially when establishing the validity of locus theorems (pages 84–85).

necessary and sufficient conditions

Mathematicians frequently refer to relationships as being either necessary or sufficient, or both. Specifically, they speak of "a necessary condition that p be true is that q be true"; or, "a sufficient condition that p be true is that q be true." These ideas are not nearly as difficult as they might seem.

When we say that q is a *necessary* condition for p, we mean that p implies q; or, $p \rightarrow q$. In other words, for an object to be an element of p it is necessary that it be an element of q, although this is not sufficient, since the object might be an element of r (all p's are q's, but not all q's are p's). See Fig. 2-10.

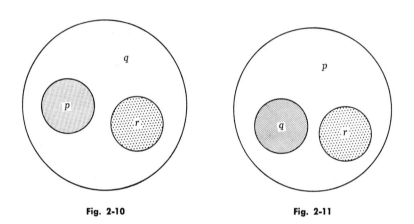

Fig. 2-10   Fig. 2-11

When we say that q is a *sufficient* condition for p, we mean that q implies p; or, $q \rightarrow p$. In other words, for an object to be an element of p it is sufficient for it to be an element of q, although this is not necessary, since an object could be an element of p without being an element of q (all q's are p's, but not all p's have to be q's). See Fig. 2-11.

When we say that q is both a *necessary and a sufficient* condition for p, we mean that p and q are logically equivalent, that is, each implies the other ($p \leftrightarrow q$).

Example 1.

For an animal to be a rodent it is *necessary* for it to be a quadruped. This is not a sufficient condition, however, since it could be a quadruped without being a rodent (for example, a dog or a horse). For an animal to be a rodent it is *sufficient* for it to be a mouse. This is not a necessary condition, however, since it could be a rodent without being a mouse (for example, rat or a squirrel).

Example 2.

A *necessary* condition that a quadrilateral shall have equal diagonals is that it be a parallelogram. This is not sufficient condition, however, since the diagonals of an oblique parallelogram are not equal.

A *sufficient* condition that a quadrilateral shall have equal diagonals is that it be a square. This is not a necessary condition, however, since the diagonals of a rectangle are also equal.

A *necessary and sufficient* condition that a quadrilateral shall have equal diagonals is that it be a right-angled parallelogram.

Example 3.

A *necessary* condition that a given whole number be exactly divisible by 4 is that it be divisible by 2. This is obviously not a sufficient condition, for 6, 18, and 22 are each divisible by 2, but not by 4.

A *sufficient* condition that a given whole number be exactly divisible by 4 is that it be divisible by 8. This is clearly not a necessary condition, since numbers such as 20, 28, and 36 are each divisible by 4, but not by 8.

A *necessary and sufficient* condition that a given whole number be divisible by 4 is that the number formed by the two right-hand digits of the given number is divisible by 4.

if and only if; definitions

Another phrase commonly used in mathematics is "if and only if." You already know what we mean by "if"; the significance of "only if" will be clear from the following considerations.

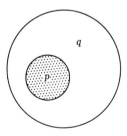

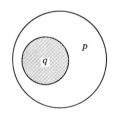

Fig. 2-12   Fig. 2-13

(I) p implies q, or $p \rightarrow q$. This means that p is true only if q is true; or, q is a *necessary* condition for p. In other words, the only time that p can be true is when q is also true.

(II) q implies p, or $q \to p$. This means that p is true if q is true; or, q is a *sufficient* condition for p. In other words, it is possible for p to be true even when q is not true. Since I and II are converses of each other, it is necessary to prove them separately. Hence to prove that "p is true if and only if q is true," the "if" part and the "only if" part of a theorem require separate proofs. This is exemplified rather nicely in the proofs of so-called "locus theorems," as we shall see in the next chapter.

It is also significant to note that every logically correct definition is "reversible," by which we mean that when changed to the "if-then" form, both the statement and its converse are true.

Examples.

1. If a triangle is isosceles, then it has (at least) two equal sides.

1'. If a triangle has (at least) two equal sides, then it is isosceles.

2. If an angle is a right angle, it is half a straight angle.

2'. If an angle is half a straight angle, it is a right angle.

3. If two polygons are regular, then they are both equiangular and equilateral.

3'. If two polygons are both equiangular and equilateral, then they are regular.

In short, a mathematical definition may be regarded as a necessary and sufficient condition. The ordinary phrasing of a definition is incomplete. Thus, when we define lines to be perpendicular if they meet at right angles, it is understood that we mean "if and only if" they

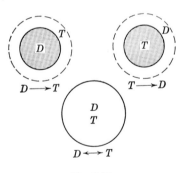

Fig. 2-14

meet at right angles. Similarly, a closed plane curve is a circle, by definition, if and only if every point on the curve is at the same distance from a fixed point within the curve. This "reversibility" of a correct, complete definition is no mystery when we stop to consider that *if and only if,* or *necessary and sufficient,* are tantamount to logical equivalence. And equivalence is exactly what a definition is; the name is a symbol which may replace the set of properties, or vice versa, without affecting the meaning. Thus a decagon is a ten-sided figure. If D represents the class of all decagons, and T the class of all ten-sided figures, both propositions are true:

1. If D, then T; (all D's are T's).
2. If T, then D; (all T's are D's).

fallacies and pitfalls

You have seen that a false premise will lead to a false conclusion, even though the syllogism is valid. Also, it is possible that a true conclusion can be obtained from an invalid syllogism. You have likewise learned that a false conclusion may be obtained by assuming the truth of the converse of a true proposition, or by assuming the truth of the opposite of a true proposition. We now add a few observations on other fallacies and dangers to be guarded against in logical reasoning.

One of the most common and subtle dangers lies in "hidden" assumptions; that is, tacit assumptions, or things that are not explicitly stated, but which are implicit in the situation. In our day-to-day activities we are likely to take such things for granted without realizing it. For example:

(*a*) We assume that people would rather be healthy than sick.

(*b*) We take it for granted that when we pay more for an article, it is superior or more desirable in one way or another.

(*c*) In a democratic government it is assumed that citizens can understand social and economic problems.

(*d*) The law assumes that a man is innocent until he has been proved guilty.

Some of the assumptions made in everyday life are true, and some are not. If our assumptions are false, our conclusions are false. We often make assumptions without being aware of it; advertisers and propagandists often take advantage of this.

Another frequent fallacy is that of "circular reasoning." It is a kind of double talk, like circular definitions.

1. "What is a straight line? Any line that isn't curved. What is a curved line? Any line that isn't straight."

2. "Since a degree is $\frac{1}{360}$ of a revolution, therefore a complete revolution must contain 360°."

In much the same way, people often "argue in a circle." They use the conclusion which they are trying to prove in the very proof itself. This practice amounts to assuming that the conclusion is true before you have proved that it is true. The mistake of reasoning in a circle is illustrated in geometry by either of the following inadmissible procedures:

1. If a theorem to be proved is used as a reason for some step in the proof of that theorem.
2. If in proving two theorems A and B, you use theorem B as a reason when proving theorem A, and you use theorem A as a reason when proving theorem B.

Other common pitfalls include: (1) *name-calling;* (2) *emotional appeal;* (3) *invoking great names;* (4) *bandwagon technique;* (5) *non-sequitur reasoning* (when the conclusion has nothing to do with the premises); (6) *post hoc ergo propter hoc* (in which it is naively assumed that if one event follows another, the first must be the cause of the second; (7) brashly *begging the question* (evading the issue); (8) *reasoning by analogy;* (9) *reasoning from special cases;* (10) *generalizing inductively from too few cases,* or from an inadequate sample.

EXERCISE 2–4

1. State the contrapositive of each of the following:

(a) If two triangles are similar, the corresponding sides are proportional.
(b) If it is a bicycle, it has two wheels.
(c) If he is an athlete, he is not a cripple.
(d) If angle A is a right angle, it is not an acute angle.
(e) If Smith is elected, he will increase social security benefits.

2. Explain by means of a diagram why the converse and the opposite of the implication $p \rightarrow q$ are logically equivalent; that is, show that $(q \rightarrow p) \leftrightarrow (\sim p \rightarrow \sim q)$.

3. Show the same relation (in number 2) symbolically instead of by using a diagram.

4. In each of the following examples, show how advertisers and propagandists make use of logical equivalence by saying one thing and hoping you will act on the contrapositive:

(a) Good citizens do not litter the streets.
(b) Experienced workmen use "Best-Made" tools.

(c) Good Scouts do one good deed each day.

(d) If I am elected, you will have more playgrounds.

(e) The best always costs more.

5. Bring in examples of advertisements and slogans gathered from newspapers, magazines, etc. Write the contrapositives, and discuss their validity, their truth, and their probable effectiveness.

6. If you want to prove the converse of each of the following statements, what other statement is it permissible to prove instead?

(a) If two sides of a triangle are unequal, the opposite angles are unequal.

(b) If a point is on the perpendicular bisector of a line, it is equidistant from the ends of the line.

(c) If a point is on the bisector of an angle, it is equidistant from the sides of the angle.

(d) If alternate interior angles are not equal, the lines are not parallel.

(e) If two chords of a circle are unequal in length, they are unequally distant from the center.

7. Give an example: (a) of a false conclusion obtained from a valid syllogism; (b) of a true conclusion obtained from an invalid syllogism.

8. The converse of every definition is true, as you have seen. Explain, by using diagrams, why the opposite of every definition is also true.

9. In each of the following, state a likely assumption that is missing; then write the three steps of the syllogism:

(a) We use seasoned wood in all our cabinets.

(b) Helen's hair always looks so lovely because she uses X-brand hair wash.

(c) We serve only home-grown vegetables.

(d) Fashionable women buy their gowns at the W-shop.

(e) A-brand apple sauce is made from ripe apples.

10. Discuss each of the following:

(a) "Bully blankets are best—Bully blankets are 100% wool!" What assumption does this slogan make?

(b) Use our mouthwash—it contains no (ingredient X). What assumption is the reader of this advertisement expected to make?

(c) Mrs. Cooper bought brand "A" maple syrup because it cost 4¢ more per pint than brand "B" maple syrup. What did Mrs. Cooper assume about these two brands?

(d) Mr. Whyte decided to buy the "W" washing machine because last year it had the greatest sales of all makes of washing machines. What two assumptions did Mr. Whyte make?

11. In each of the following, explain how the fallacy of "circular reasoning" has been made:

(a) "I can prove that these two lines must be parallel, because the alternate interior angles are equal," said John. "But how do you know that the alternate interior angles are equal?" asked Betty. "Because the lines are parallel, silly," replied John.

(*b*) Barbara said she could prove that a straight line is the shortest distance between two points. "How?" asked her friend. "Because the sum of any two sides of a triangle is greater than the third side," replied Barbara. "But why do you say that?" "Because," said Barbara triumphantly, "a broken line between two points is longer than a straight line between those points!"

(*c*) "It was a waste of money to install a burglar alarm system," exclaimed Mr. Parker, "for there hasn't been a burglary since the alarm was installed."

(*d*) What a piece of good luck that Pittsburgh—the great center of the steel industry—is located so near the coal mines of Pennsylvania.

12. Explain why each of the following is an example of poor reasoning:

(*a*) Every good tennis player has good muscular coordination. Henry has excellent muscular coordination. He should be a good tennis player.

(*b*) Democracies have elected legislatures. "Neoland" has an elected legislature. Therefore, "Neoland" is a democracy.

(*c*) If a company spends more for television commercials its sales will increase. The King Company's sales increased last year. Therefore they must have spent more for television commercials.

(*d*) At the Beverly School all seniors belong to the Fellowship Club. Helen Hall must be a senior, because she is a member of the Fellowship Club.

13. Explain why the converse of a given proposition is not necessarily true, even though the proposition is true; do the same for the opposite of the given proposition. Use diagrams.

14. In advertising, sales talk, and propaganda arguments, we are frequently asked to believe that the opposite of a proposition is true. To be sure, it is usually done in a roundabout way. In each of the following, what statement are we asked to believe in addition to the given statement?

(*a*) "Delta" brand fabric will not fade.
(*b*) Our washing machine will not tear the wash.
(*c*) X-Y-Z television sets will not distort the picture.
(*d*) This lacquer will dry almost instantly.
(*e*) "Ace" tires will give 20,000 miles of service.
(*f*) This insulation will last as long as the house stands.

15. "If all rectangles are parallelograms, and if this particular figure is not a parallelogram, then it is not a rectangle." Is this reasoning valid or not? Explain by means of a diagram.

16. "All A's are B's, and all C's are B's; therefore all A's are C's." Is this reasoning valid or not? Explain.

17. Show informally by means of a diagram that $(p \rightarrow q) \leftrightarrow \sim [p \wedge (\sim q)]$.

18. Given the statement: "If John can vote, then John is over 21," which of the following statements is then necessarily true?

(*a*) If John cannot vote, he is not over 21.
(*b*) If John is over 21, he can vote.
(*c*) Either John can vote, or he is not over 21.

(*d*) Either John can vote, or he is over 21.

(*e*) If John is not over 21, he cannot vote.

19. Using appropriate diagrams, determine whether each of the conclusions below is valid or not valid; if your answer is "not valid," explain why:

Hypotheses: (*a*) All C's are A's; (*b*) all A's are B's; (*c*) some D's are not B's. (*Note:* In logic, "some" does *not* mean "some, but not all," as it does in everyday use; "some" tells us nothing about "the rest.")

Conclusions: (1) All C's are B's; (2) some D's are not C's; (3) Some D's are not A's; (4) all D's are not B's.

20. For each of the following arguments, select the diagram below which corresponds to the argument:

(*a*) $\left\{\begin{array}{l}\text{All broadjumpers are athletes.} \\ \text{All athletes have long legs.} \\ \text{All broadjumpers have long legs.}\end{array}\right.$

(*b*) $\left\{\begin{array}{l}\text{All athletes are broadjumpers.} \\ \text{Some persons with long legs are not broadjumpers.} \\ \text{Some persons with long legs are not athletes.}\end{array}\right.$

(*c*) $\left\{\begin{array}{l}\text{All broadjumpers are athletes.} \\ \text{No persons with long legs are athletes.} \\ \text{No persons with long legs are broadjumpers.}\end{array}\right.$

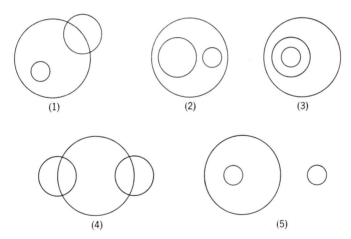

(1)   (2)   (3)

(4)   (5)

Fig. 2-15

FOR FURTHER READING AND STUDY

1. Allendoerfer, C. B. and Oakley, C. O. *Principles of Mathematics.* New York: McGraw-Hill, 1955. Chapter 1: "Logic."

2. Banks, J. Houston. *Elements of Mathematics*. Boston: Allyn and Bacon, 1956. Chapter 4: "Mathematical Proof."
3. Holmes, Roger W. *The Rhyme of Reason*. New York: D. Appleton-Century, 1939. Pages 276–296.
4. Keyser, C. J. *Thinking About Thinking*. New York: E. P. Dutton, 1926.
5. Lazar, Nathan. "The Logic of Indirect Proof in Geometry." *The Mathematics Teacher,* 40:225–240; 1947.
6. National Council of Teachers of Mathematics. Twenty-third Yearbook: *Insights into Modern Mathematics*. Washington, D. C.: The Council, 1957. Chapter 4: "Deductive Methods in Mathematics."
7. Rosskopf, Myron and Exner, R. M. "Some Concepts of Logic and their Application in Elementary Mathematics." *The Mathematics Teacher,* 48:290–298; 1955.
8. Stabler, E. R. *An Introduction to Mathematical Thought*. Cambridge, Mass.: Addison-Wesley, 1953. Chapter 3: "Essentials of Logical Reasoning."

CHAPTER 3

Geometry

It has fallen to the lot of but one people, the ancient Greeks, to endow human thought with two outlooks on the universe neither of which has blurred appreciably in more than two thousand years . . . The first was the explicit recognition that proof by deductive reasoning offers a foundation for the structures of number and form.

—E. T. Bell

EMPIRICAL GEOMETRY

geometry before the Greeks

Geometry is one of the oldest intellectual pursuits of man. Its origins can be traced to the early Babylonians and Egyptians, for whom geometry was essentially an empirical science cultivated solely for its utility. This utility had to do with the art of practical measurement as applied, for example, to the repeated surveying of land necessitated by the annual inundation of the Nile Valley, to the building of engineering structures such as bridges, aqueducts and the Pyramids, to irrigation and drainage problems, to military activities, and to various astronomical and geographic measurements. Indeed, the word geometry literally means "earth measure." To say that pre-Hellenistic geometry was essentially empirical is to say that the methods and results (often inaccurate) were arrived at by rule-of-thumb procedures. The element of logical thinking was completely lacking. More explicitly, we could say that their geometry was a collection of geometric "facts" based upon experience, observation, measurement, experimentation, and intuition. Thus both "trial-and-error" considerations and inductive inferences (perhaps unwittingly) played a major role.

In presenting geometry to the beginner, sound pedagogy suggests that we similarly use an empirical approach. We first discuss what might be called "physical geometry," which is concerned with the size, shape, and location of physical objects. Thus we observe the floor of a room or a pane of glass and call them "planes." We look at the edges of a box or the creases in a folded sheet of paper and call them "lines." The corners of a box, or the tip of a sharpened pencil, are called "points." We make dots of chalk on the blackboard or streaks of graphite on paper and call them "points" and "lines." But upon closer inspection the "point" is revealed as a solid clump of material having volume and mass; the "line," supposedly having length only, is found to have width and thickness as well.

observation, intuition, experimentation, and measurement

Our intuition is a body of sensory impressions and motor experiences which make it comparatively easy to "accept" generalizations such as those suggested below. Indeed, it is probably no exaggeration to say that scores of additional "facts" and relations of this sort can readily be adduced by "intuition" or "observation."

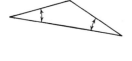

Fig. 3-1

Recourse may also be had to "experimentation" or manipulation of geometric shapes or configurations in the form of models made of cardboard, wires, rods, strings, rubber bands, etc. Many interesting and useful properties and relations may be discovered, understood and accepted in this way. For example, appropriate physical models will readily reveal some of the properties of (a) the midjoin of a triangle; (b) the diagonals of a parallelogram; (c) the midjoins of a general quadrilateral; (d) the constancy of any angle inscribed in

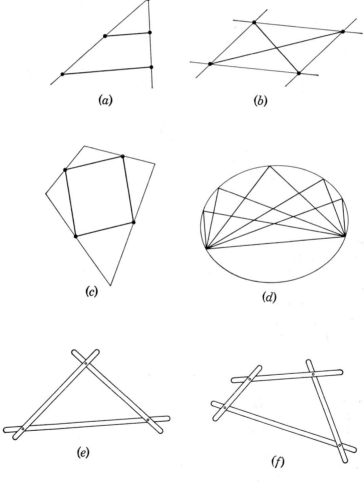

Fig. 3-2

the segment of a circle; (*e*) the rigidity of a triangle; and (*f*) the deformability of a quadrilateral.

By suitable manipulations and experiments one can easily "show" (1) that the sum of the interior angles of a triangle equals 180°; (2) that the sum of the exterior angles of a convex polygon equals 360°; (3) the properties of symmetric figures; (4) that polygons of more than three sides may be equilateral without being equiangular, and conversely; and many other relations.

Finally, we can "verify" intuitively a considerable number of metric properties of both plane and solid geometric figures by direct measurement and computation: for example, that the sum of the interior

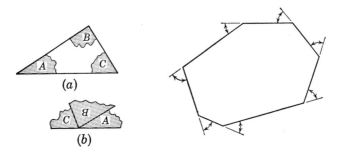

(a)

(b)

Fig. 3-3

angles of a triangle is 180°; that the median of a right triangle drawn to the hypotenuse equals one-half the hypotenuse; that the area of a triangle equals one-half that of a parallelogram with an altitude and base equal to those of the triangle; that the volume of a circular cone is one-third that of a circular cylinder having a base and altitude equal to those of the cone; that the circumference of a circle is very nearly 3.1 times its diameter; and many other relations.

EXERCISE 3-1

1. (*a*) Is a flat surface always level?
   (*b*) Does "perpendicular" mean the same as "vertical"?
   (*c*) Can a plumb line ever be oblique?
   (*d*) Does "level" mean the same as "horizontal"?
   (*e*) Can perpendicular lines ever be oblique?
   (*f*) Can a straight line ever lie wholly in the curved surface of a cylinder? in the curved surface of a cone? in the surface of a sphere?

2. (*a*) In a plane, can three distinct lines meet in a single point so that each line is perpendicular to each of the other two? (*b*) Can three distinct lines in space ever meet in a single point and be mutually perpendicular, each to the other two? (*c*) Can four distinct lines in space meet in a single point and be mutually perpendicular, each to the other three?

3. Discuss at least *three* different ways of showing intuitively or experimentally that the sum of the interior angles of a triangle equals 180°.

4. What is meant by point symmetry? by line symmetry? by plane symmetry? Give two examples of each.

5. State three specific devices which illustrate (*a*) the rigidity (or "mechanical strength") of a triangle; (*b*) give three practical applications which illustrate or utilize the property that a quadrilateral is a deformable figure.

6. Explain why a three-legged stool always rests solidly on the floor, whereas a four-legged stool or chair may be wobbly.

7. Find out what is meant by (1) *geometric dissections;* (2) *tangrams;* (3) the *Platonic solids.*

8. Find out what Cavalieri's theorem is about; show how you could use a stack of books or cards to illustrate the theorem.

9. The diameter of a circle in Fig. 3–4 is 20 inches. Any point *P* on the circle is selected at random; perpendiculars *PR* and *PS* are then dropped from *P* to the horizontal and vertical axes, respectively. The feet of the perpendiculars are then connected by the line *RS*. What is the length of *RS?* Did you find this exercise easy or difficult? Why?

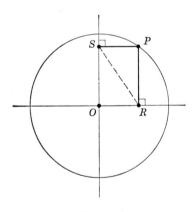

Fig. 3-4

10. Explain how the principles of line symmetry might be used with this fold-up model to show that the sum of the interior angles of any triangle is 180°. Here *ABC* is any triangle; *AR = RB, AS = SC,* and *RS, RP* and *SQ* are used as axes of symmetry; simply fold along the dotted lines. Make an actual model.

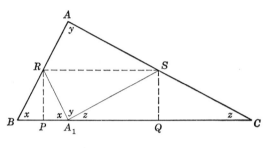

Fig. 3-5

the Greek contribution

In retrospect, then, geometry before the Greeks was empirical and dealt with concrete realities—with "physical geometry." There was no hint either of logical proof nor of abstract concepts. It was the idea of logical demonstration, of substituting deductive reasoning for inductive inference, which was the great contribution of Greek mathematics to civilization. It began about 600 B.C. with Thales and Pythagoras, who took the empirical knowledge of the Babylonians, Egyptians, and other ancient cultures and remolded it. From the very outset it became a systematic development of general principles instead of a collection of specific properties, with insistence upon deductive patterns rather than arbitrary trial-and-error methods. This Greek spirit is to be found at its best in Euclid's *Elements* (about 300 B.C.).

How can we account for this distinct shift in emphasis? Unquestionably it was the philosophical temperament of the ancient Greeks, for the deductive method is an essential tool of the philosopher. More specifically, the Greeks were concerned with systematic orderliness, with intellectual consistency, with the ideal of perfection, with the validity of discourse, with certainty and conviction, and with desired predictability.

The subsequent development of Greek mathematics lasted until about 300 A.D., reaching its zenith some four or five centuries earlier with the work of such geometers as Archimedes, Apollonius, Hipparchus, and Hero of Alexander. Then, for more than a thousand years, no significant change in geometry took place—not until the momentous contribution of Descartes in the middle of the 17th century. The history of geometry falls into four periods: (1) the synthetic geometry of the Greeks; (2) the analytic of Descartes; (3) geometry as used in the calculus; and (4) modern pure geometry.

DEMONSTRATIVE GEOMETRY

the classical approach

As we have already suggested, if we wish to set up a deductive system, any statement made in an argument must be derived from previous statements, and these in turn must have been derived from still more previous statements, and so on. But we cannot press back indefinitely without incurring the risk of engaging in "circular reasoning," that is, first deducing statement A from statement B, and subsequently deducing B from A. Hence it is essential to decide in advance upon a set of acceptable primitive statements, making no attempt to prove them, and then to deduce all other statements from these primitives by deductive reasoning. This is the essence of *postulational* or *demonstrative* geometry—indeed, of all modern mathematics. The classical method followed by the Greeks is known as the *synthetic* method. We shall present a very brief "sample" of classical, synthetic, demonstrative geometry in what follows.

To begin with, then, Euclid adopted as primitives (1) about two dozen definitions, (2) a short list of postulates, and (3) a short list of axioms, or "common notions," essentially as follows:

Postulates

1. A straight line can be drawn from any point to any point.

2. A finite straight line can be produced continuously in a straight line.

3. A circle may be described with any center and any distance.

4. All right angles are equal to one another.

5. If a straight line falling on two straight lines makes the interior angles on the same side together less than two right angles, the two straight lines, if produced indefinitely, meet on that side on which the angles are together less than two right angles.

Axioms

1. Things which are equal to the same thing are also equal to each other.

2. If equals be added to equals, the sums are equal.

3. If equals be subtracted from equals, the remainders are equal.

4. Things which coincide with one another are equal to one another.

5. The whole is greater than the part.

Both the postulates and the axioms were regarded by the Greeks as self-evident truths—undeniable, eternal verities. The postulates were specifically concerned with geometric relations; the axioms were not limited to the content of geometry, but were general truths which were applicable to relations outside of geometry as well. It is to be noted that in both the postulates and in some of the Euclidean definitions, certain terms occur, such as *point, straight line, extremity, inclination, plane,* which are nowhere defined, and which must also be regarded as primitives (undefined terms). We shall learn shortly about the serious limitations of Euclid's primitives, how naive and inadequate they are from the modern point of view. Meanwhile, we shall present a brief "sample" sequence of theorems.

In order to illustrate the nature of a sequence or chain of related theorems, we shall plunge into classical geometry by beginning with the concept of parallels and show how a short sequence of ten related theorems can be developed from the preceding assumptions and definitions (and some others which have not been explicitly stated here). We give the proofs in somewhat abbreviated form, primarily to indicate the procedure followed in building a postulational system of geometry, by synthetic methods, and within certain limitations of logical rigor to be commented upon later. The particular sequence we have chosen deliberately bypasses the matter of congruence and deals with parallelism and similarity.

parallelism

Theorem T_1. An exterior angle of a triangle is greater than either remote interior angle (Fig. 3-6).

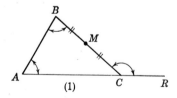 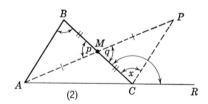

Fig. 3-6

Given: Exterior $\angle BCR$ of $\triangle ABC$.
To Prove: $\angle BCR > \angle B$, and $\angle BCR > \angle A$.
Proof: Join A with M, the midpoint of BC, and extend AM to P so

that $AM = MP$; join P with C. In △ AMB and CMP, we have: $BM = MC$, $AM = MP$, and $\angle p = \angle q$. Hence $\triangle AMB \cong \triangle CMP$[1] (s.a.s.), and, since corresponding parts of congruent figures are equal, $\angle x = \angle B$. But since $\angle BCR > \angle x$, $\angle BCR > \angle B$. In a similar manner it can be shown that $\angle BCR > \angle A$.

Theorem T₂. If alternate interior angles made by a transversal to two lines are equal, then the two lines are parallel (Fig. 3-7).

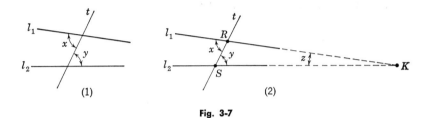

Fig. 3-7

Given: Lines l_1 and l_2; transversal t; $\angle x = \angle y$.
To Prove: $l_1 \parallel l_2$.
Proof: By the law of the excluded middle, either $l_1 \parallel l_2$ or $l_1 \not\parallel l_2$. Suppose l_1 and l_2 were *not* parallel; then they would have a point K in common and would form $\triangle RKS$. Now $\angle x$ is an exterior angle of $\triangle RKS$, and hence $\angle x > \angle y$, by Theorem T₁. But this contradicts the hypothesis that $\angle x = \angle y$; therefore the supposition that $l_1 \not\parallel l_2$ is false, and must be rejected. Hence $l_1 \parallel l_2$, since it is the only other possible supposition.

Theorem T₃. If alternate interior angles made by a transversal to two lines are not equal, then the two lines are not parallel (Fig. 3-8).

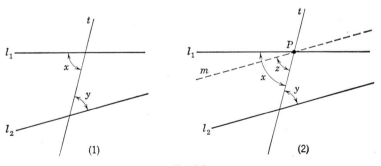

Fig. 3-8

[1] The symbol "$\cong$" means "is congruent to."

Given: $\angle x \neq \angle y$.
To Prove: $l_1 \not\parallel l_2$.
Proof: Since by hypothesis $\angle x \neq \angle y$, assume that $\angle x > \angle y$. In that case, let m be a line through P such that $\angle z = \angle y$. Then by Theorem T_2, $m \parallel l_2$. But if m is parallel to l_2, then l_1 cannot be parallel to l_2, by the assumption that through a point not on a line, there can be only one parallel to the line.[2]

Theorem T₄. If two lines are parallel, alternate interior angles made by a transversal to the two lines are equal (Fig. 3-9).

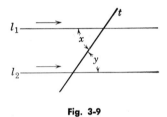

Fig. 3-9

Given: $l_1 \parallel l_2$.
To Prove: $\angle x = \angle y$.
Proof: Either $\angle x = \angle y$, or $\angle x \neq \angle y$. Suppose $\angle x \neq \angle y$; then by Theorem T_3, lines l_1 and l_2 would not be parallel. But l_1 and l_2 *are* parallel, by hypothesis; hence the supposition that $\angle x \neq \angle y$ is false. Only one other possibility remains, namely, that $\angle x$ *is* equal to $\angle y$.

Theorem T₅. The sum of the measures of the angles of a triangle equals the measure of a straight angle, or 180° (Fig. 3-10).

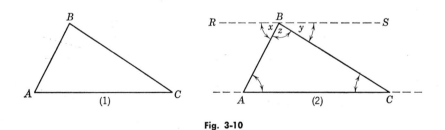

Fig. 3-10

Given: $\triangle ABC$.
To Prove: $\angle A + \angle B + \angle C = 180°$.

[2] This assumption is a modern counterpart of Euclid's fifth postulate.

Proof: Let RS be a line through B, parallel to AC. We then have: $\angle x = \angle A$; $\angle z = \angle z$; $\angle y = \angle C$. But $\angle x + \angle z + \angle y = 180°$; hence $\angle A + \angle B + \angle C = 180°$.

Theorem T₆. If two angles of one triangle are equal respectively to two angles of another triangle, the third angle of the first triangle equals the third angle of the other triangle.

This theorem obviously foll ws at once from theorem T_5.

similar figures

By definition, two polygons are similar if their corresponding angles are respectively equal and if their corresponding sides are respectively proportional. It can be proved that, if the three angles of one triangle are respectively equal to the three angles of another triangle, then the corresponding sides of the two triangles *are* in proportion, hence by definition, the two triangles are similar. Thus the equality of the angles is a sufficient condition for similarity. This statement is *not* true of polygons having more than three sides; the angles of a square are equal to the angles of a rectangle, for example, yet the square and the rectangle are not similar. In short, the equality of angles of two polygons (other than triangles) is not a sufficient condition for similarity. This fact is related to the rigidity of the triangle and to the deformability of polygons having more than three sides.

An alternative procedure is possible, which is to define similar triangles as follows: two triangles are similar if and only if their corresponding sides are proportional. Starting with this definition, it is possible to prove the theorem: if two triangles are similar, their corresponding angles are respectively equal. The converse theorem can also be proved, that is: if the corresponding angles of two triangles are equal, the triangles are similar. We shall not give these proofs here; but in what follows we shall assume that two triangles are similar if the three angles of one are equal respectively to the three angles of the other.

Theorem T₇. Two triangles are similar if two angles of the one are equal respectively to two angles of the other.

This theorem follows at once as a consequence of Theorem T₆.

Theorem T₈. In a right triangle, the altitude upon the hypotenuse is the mean proportional between the segments of the hypotenuse (Fig. 3-11).

Given: Right triangle ABC; altitude $CD = h$.

To Prove: $p/h = h/q$, or $h^2 = pq$.

Proof: Place the given $\triangle\ ABC$ (III) and $\angle$ I and II in similar positions as shown below:

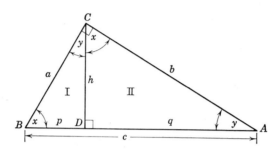

Fig. 3-11

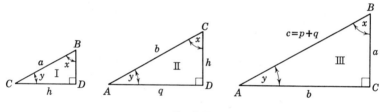

Fig. 3-12

Clearly, right $\angle$ I, II, and III are all similar to one another by Theorem T_7. From $\angle$ I and II, therefore, since corresponding sides of similar triangles are proportional:

$$p/h = h/q, \quad \text{or} \quad h^2 = pq.$$

Theorem T_9. In a right triangle, either arm is the mean proportional between the hypotenuse and the adjacent segment cut off by the altitude to the hypotenuse.

Given: Right triangle ABC; altitude $CD = h$.

To prove: (1) $a^2 = pc$, (2) $b^2 = qc$.

Proof: (Refer to the diagram for Theorem T_8.) From similar $\angle$ I and III:

$$p/a = a/c, \quad \text{or} \quad a^2 = pc.$$

From similar $\angle$ II and III:

$$q/b = b/c, \quad \text{or} \quad b^2 = qc.$$

the Pythagorean theorem

Theorem T_9 enables us to prove one of the most celebrated theorems of geometry, namely, the Pythagorean relationship.

Theorem T_{10}. In any right triangle, the sum of the squares of the arms equals the square of the hypotenuse (Fig. 3-13).

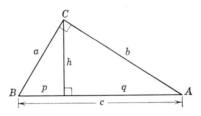

Fig. 3-13

Given: Right triangle ABC.
To Prove: $a^2 + b^2 = c^2$.
Proof: By Theorem T_9, we have:

$$a^2 = pc, \tag{1}$$
$$b^2 = qc. \tag{2}$$

Combining (1) and (2):

$$a^2 + b^2 = pc + qc$$
$$= (c)(p + q)$$

But $\qquad\qquad (p + q) = c;$

Hence $\qquad\quad a^2 + b^2 = c^2. \tag{3}$

EXERCISE 3–2

1. Complete the second part of the proof of Theorem T_1, showing that $\angle BCR > \angle A$; use the diagram given below (Fig. 3-14a).

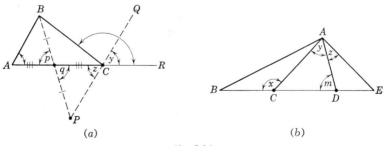

(a) $\qquad\qquad\qquad\qquad\qquad$ (b)

Fig. 3-14

2. If BE is a straight line, prove that $\angle x > \angle y$; also, that $\angle x > \angle z$ (Fig. 3-14b).

3. If two lines are both perpendicular to a third line, prove that they are parallel to each other.

4. If a line is perpendicular to one of two parallel lines, prove that it is perpendicular to the other also.

5. If two angles have their sides respectively parallel, prove that the angles are either (1) equal or (2) supplementary (Fig. 3–15a).

6. If two angles have their sides respectively perpendicular, prove that the angles are either (a) equal or (b) supplementary (Fig. 3–15b).

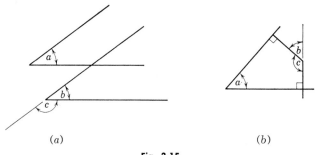

       (a)   (b)

Fig. 3-15

7. In the proof of Theorem T_8, explain why $\angle x$ in $\triangle$ I equals $\angle x$ in $\triangle$ III. Why does $\angle x$ in $\triangle$ II equal $\angle x$ in $\triangle$ III? Why does $\angle y$ in $\triangle$ I equal $\angle y$ in $\triangle$ III? Why does $\angle y$ in $\triangle$ II equal $\angle y$ in $\triangle$ III?

8. (a) Draw two general quadrilaterals whose angles are respectively equal, and which are similar in shape; (b) draw two general quadrilaterals whose angles are respectively equal, but which are *not* similar.

9. In the diagram, AB is an inclined plane; AC is horizontal; BC and SR are vertical; $ST \parallel AB$; and $SN \perp AB$. Explain why $\angle RSN = \angle BAC$ (Fig. 3-16).

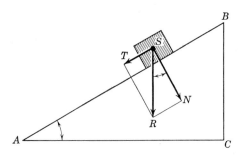

Fig. 3-16

10. Find the altitude of an equilateral triangle whose side is equal to 12 inches.

11. Prove that the altitude of an equilateral triangle of side s is given by

$$h = \frac{s}{2}\sqrt{3}.$$

12. If the diagonals of a general quadrilateral are perpendicular to each other, then the sum of the squares of two opposite sides is equal to the sum of the squares of the other two sides.

MODERN GEOMETRY

weaknesses in Euclid

Although the thirteen books of Euclid's *Elements* constitute a monumental work of profound significance in the history of thought for some two thousand years, we must realize that it was a pioneer work, and should therefore not be too surprised that it is shot through with serious logical limitations and shortcomings. The principal weaknesses are as follows:

1. Euclid's definitions leave much to be desired—some terms are inadequately defined (for example, "a point is that which has no parts"), and some are tacitly defined only by implication.

2. Euclid failed to formulate explicitly the axiomatic basis on which the congruence theorems depend. Thus "superposition" of line segments and angles (particularly the latter) was glibly glossed over with a fuzzy allusion to the "motion of rigid bodies." (If a point is a *location*, how can a point be *moved* and still be the same point!) In short, superposition is not only a logically unsound and defective idea, it is completely misleading and deceptive.

3. Euclid failed to recognize the necessity of making formal assumptions concerning order or "betweenness." This serious omission was pointed out by C. F. Gauss about 1835 and corrected by M. Pasch about 1880. We now know that order relations in geometry, particularly the order of points on a line and of regions in a plane, are essential if rigor is to be achieved. For example, one order property of the line which is indispensable is as follows: If the point S lies between the points R and T, then T does not lie between R and S. Such an assumption automatically rules out the concept of a straight line having the properties of a closed curve.

4. Euclid tacitly assumed (*a*) that a line is of infinite extent; (*b*)

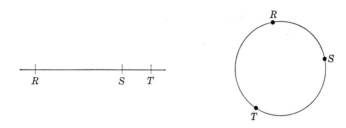

Fig. 3-17

the property of "continuity"; and (*c*) the "Archimedean property" that, given two unequal linear segments, there exists a finite multiple of the shorter segment which is longer than the other. The concept of continuity (or "denseness") has to do with the relation between the points on a line and the system of real numbers. The Archimedean postulate has to do with the possibility and nature of measurement.

5. Euclid's methods often suffered from the lack of adequate algebraic symbolism and techniques which had not as yet been developed.

It should also be pointed out that a deductive system is more than just a collection of generalizations. It involves a very special organization, in that all the statements (theorems) in the system other than the assumptions (postulates or unproved propositions) can be derived from those assumptions and from them alone. Thus we may truly say that without assumptions, there is no such thing as proof. Furthermore, everything in the system is implicit in the assumptions, that is, we cannot get more out of the assumptions than there is in them, albeit many of the relations are not immediately discernible. Indeed, the basic, undefined terms acquire their meanings from the postulates in which they occur. Great care is taken to make the assumptions self-consistent, insofar as that is possible. If at any stage in the development of the deductive system any additional assumption, knowingly or otherwise, is allowed to enter the discussion, the entire system is vitiated.

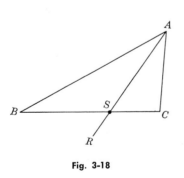

Fig. 3-18

Since we already "know" many of the relations and generalizations which constitute the system—that is, they are intuitively familiar —two considerations are forever present. In the first place, we may unwittingly employ some property or relation as a tacit assumption, as, for example, when we draw the bisector of angle A of the triangle and assume that AR will intersect BC in a point S which lies *between* B and C. Secondly, as we build up the system, we must pay close attention to the sequence in which the generalizations are deduced, always proceeding as if we did not "know what was coming," that is, we cannot "use" any relation, however plausible or familiar, until it has been logically deduced from previously established (or assumed) relations. Pupils studying geometry in high school often find that the latter requirement causes considerable difficulty.

geometry in modern times

For nearly 1300 years after the era of Greek mathematics, nothing of great significance was achieved until about the middle of the seventeenth century, when Descartes invented analytical geometry; we shall have something to say about that shortly. Significant as that invention was, which ushered in the beginnings of modern mathematics (calculus and analysis), it was overshadowed by a still more momentous discovery about the middle of the nineteenth century, that of non-Euclidean geometry, made in rapid succession by Gauss, Lobachevsky, and Bolyai. Without going into details, suffice it to say that this development is perhaps one of the greatest achievements of man's intellect; liberated from the restrictions of the parallel postulate, it became possible, at the close of the century, to make geometry an abstract postulational system, completely formal and logically rigorous. This advance was due to the pioneer work, about 1890–1900, of Pasch, Peano, Hilbert, Veblen, Huntington, and others.

abstract geometry

To distinguish between concrete or "physical geometry," on the one hand, and abstract or formal geometry on the other, we note that when the mind generalizes experience, some abstraction may also take place. Even apparently simple innocent notions such as that of a straight line may lead to an ideal construct or a pure abstraction, picturesquely suggested by the following excerpt from a delightful article by Professor Goetz[3] of the Massachusetts Institute of Technology:

[3] Billy E. Goetz. The Usefulness of the Impossible," *Bulletin, American Association of University Professors,* 42:275–277; 1956.

A straight line has no width, no depth, no wiggles, and no ends.

There are no straight lines. We have ideas about these non-existent impossibilities: we even draw pictures of them. But they do not exist.

Ask a draftsman to draw a straight line. Place his product under a microscope. Observe the variable width; the darkness and lightness which mark its varying depth; the wiggles, both lateral and vertical, where the line plunges and climbs and wriggles among the fibers . . .

A point has no dimensions, no existence, and no definition. A picture of a point is a ragged area of uncertain extent on a rough surface. By refining the picture, the area diminishes. Finally, we can refine no more. We place the portraits side by side in the sequence of successive refinement. Then we point far to the side and say, "The picture that belongs there, where refinement has been carried to the ultimate and the dimensions have entirely vanished; that picture, if it existed, would be a true dimensionless point."

Every mathematical science or axiomatic system begins with a relatively small number of words which are left undefined, although we may wish to explain or "interpret" them intuitively. Although no formal definitions of these words are given, they are nevertheless subject to the restrictions imposed upon them by the assumptions given later.

It should be understood at this point that the choice of undefined terms as well as the choice of assumptions may be influenced by certain conditions which may do violence to the mathematician's sense of fitness, but which are conceivably justifiable on pedagogical grounds. Thus the mature mathematician is intent on holding the number of undefined terms and unproved propositions to a minimum; but it may well be to the immature learner's advantage to forego such mathematical rigor for the time being and adopt some additional assumptions at first, even though these assumptions may be derivable from the others.

With these considerations in mind, we suggest the following list of undefined terms and assumptions to place elementary plane geometry upon a reasonably rigorous basis for the beginner.

Undefined Terms

1. *point*	**2.** *line*	**3.** *plane*
4. *on*	**5.** *between*	**6.** *number*
7. *equal*	**8.** *congruent*	**9.** *distance*

Assumptions

A₁. *Two distinct points determine a line.* Given any two distinct points A and B, there exists one and only one straight line containing both A and B.

A₂. *Two distinct lines have at most one point in common.* This assumption does not say that two distinct lines *must* have a point in common. They may not have any point in common; but if they do, they cannot have more than one.

A₃. *Every line is scaled.* The point on a straight line may be numbered so that the absolute values of number differences measure distances.

A₄. *Every line has two sides.* A line "separates" or divides the plane into two parts, much as a point on a line divides the line into two parts, called *rays*.

A₅. *Every circle is scaled.* An angle consists of two rays having a common endpoint. All rays having the same endpoint can be numbered so that number differences measure angles.

A₆. *A triangle is uniquely determined when two sides and the included angle are given* ("s.a.s.").

A₇. *A triangle is uniquely determined when two angles and the included side are given* ("a.s.a.").

A₈. *Through a point not on a line there exists one and only one line parallel to the given line.* Two intersecting lines cannot both be parallel to the same line. This is the famous "Parallel Postulate."

the foundations of geometry

One of the principal contributions to the development of modern geometry was the publication of the *Foundations of Geometry* by David Hilbert in 1899. His approach to the postulational basis of geometry has since become a classic. It is extremely rigorous. Hilbert employed only five undefined terms: *point, line, on, between, congruent.* He then enunciated fifteen postulates. The first two postulates are essentially the same as A_1 and A_2 above.

The next four postulates have to do with the notions of order and betweenness. It is here that some of the glaring, logical weaknesses of Euclid were corrected. These four postulates read as follows:

1. If point C is between points A and B, then A, B, C are all on the same line, and C is between B and A, and B is not between C and A, and A is not between C and B.

2. For any two distinct points A and B there is always a point C which is between A and B, and a point D which is such that B is between A and D.

3. If A, B, C are three distinct points on the same line, then one of the points is between the other two.

4. A line which intersects one side of a triangle but does not pass through any of the vertices of the triangle must also intersect another side of the triangle.

These four postulates provide for the indefinite extension of a line; they provide for the existence of an infinite number of points on a line; and they provide that the points on a line shall be in serial order rather than in cyclic order. The fourth postulate obviates the logical difficulties alluded to in the previous section, where, in the absence of an explicit postulate, we tacitly drew upon our intuition. In particular, this postulate permits us to prove Theorem T_1, since it can then be asserted that CP lies "between" CB and CR.

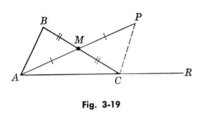

Fig. 3-19

The next six postulates deal with the concept of congruence. They are rather technical and refined, and we shall not discuss them here. Suffice it to say that these six postulates get around the logical difficulties posed by the ideas of "rigid motion" and "superposition" so largely used in less rigorous developments of geometry.

The thirteenth postulate is the parallel postulate.

The last two postulates have to do with the concept of continuity of a line. Technically stated, these two postulates could be replaced by a single postulate proposed by another German mathematician, Richard Dedekind, and which can be paraphrased as follows:

If all points of a straight line fall into two sets, such that every point of the first set lies to the left of every point of the second set, then there exists one and only one point which creates this division into two sets, that is, cuts the straight line into two parts.

This concept of continuity makes possible the idea of measurement. It also enables us to set up a one-to-one correspondence between the set of real numbers and the set of points on a line, thus making possible analytic geometry.

a miniature geometry; isomorphism

We shall pursue the idea of axiomatic structure a bit further by depicting what might be called a miniature or finite geometry, that is, a geometry, which, by the nature of the assumptions on which it is based, deals with a finite number of points and lines. In this miniature geometry, the undefined elements are "point" and "line"; the undefined relation is "on," where "point on line" and "line on point" are to be understood as having the same meaning. The following five assumptions are then made:

A₁. Each pair of lines is on at least one point.
A₂. Each pair of lines is on not more than one point.
A₃. Each point is on at least two lines.
A₄. Each point is on not more than two lines.
A₅. The total number of lines is 4.

We shall refer to the above system of two undefined elements, one undefined relation, and five assumptions as the axiom system S_0. Certain theorems can easily be proved from these assumptions; for example:

T₁. Not all lines pass through the same point.
T₂. Two distinct lines have exactly one point in common.
T₃. Exactly two lines pass through each point.
T₄. Every line contains (passes through) exactly three points.

It will be realized that the geometric configuration shown below can be regarded as a concrete model of the axiom system S_0. That it is entirely consistent with all five assumptions can readily be verified by the reader. However, this geometric interpretation (S_1) is by no means the only possible "practical interpretation" or concrete model of the axiom system S_0. By attributing appropriate meanings to the undefined elements and the undefined relation, it is possible to construct

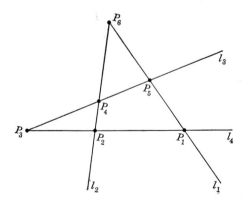

Fig. 3-20

other models by using, in turn, (1) lines and planes; (2) numbers and number pairs; (3) musical notes and chords; (4) colors and color schemes; (5) containers and assortments of objects to be put into them; (6) people and committees; etc. For example: we might let the "points" represent the officers of a club and the "lines" represent the standing committees, thus yielding another model, S_2:

I. *Officers*

P_1: Archer $\qquad$ P_2: Brown
P_3: Crosby $\qquad$ P_4: Daly
P_5: Ellis $\qquad$ P_6: Fuller

II. *Standing Committees*

Membership Committee (Archer, Ellis, Fuller)
Rules Committee (Brown, Daly, Fuller)
Entertainment Committee (Crosby, Daly, Ellis)
Tournament Committee (Archer, Brown, Crosby)

The assumptions in model S_2 would of course be interpreted as follows:

A₁. Each pair of committees shall have at least one officer in common.

A₂. Each pair of committees shall have not more than one officer in common.

A₃. Each officer shall serve as a member of at least two committees.

A₄. Each officer shall not serve on more than two committees.

A₅. There shall be four standing committees.

It is important to distinguish between a formal, abstract axiomatic system, on the one hand, and any one or more specific, concrete interpretations or models of the system, on the other. The formalization of the abstract structure requires:

1. Language, including a given logic, or set of rules of inference for deducing new statements.

2. Undefined words or symbols, designating the elements as well as operations on them, or relationships among them.

3. A set of assumptions which characterize the undefined words.

4. The necessary appropriate definitions.

5. A body of theorems about the undefined terms deduced from the assumptions and definitions in accordance with the language and logic agreed upon.

In view of the foregoing structure, we cannot very well speak about the "truth" of the assumptions or the theorems. The undefined words are actually "meaningless," as are the various statements involving them. However, the moment we give these undefined words specific meanings by associating them with words or symbols in some other system, whether real or abstract, we are interpreting the statements in the system by constructing a concrete model. As we have already seen, a given axiomatic system may have a variety of concrete interpretations, some of which may seem to be quite different, superficially, from the abstract structure. But two different models or interpretations of the same system may reveal the same essential structure, differing chiefly in the names or ideas associated with the undefined elements and relationships. If two such models are alike in this sense, we call them *isomorphic*. In other words, if in two given concrete interpretations S_n and S_k the terms of one of them can be placed in one-to-one correspondence with the terms of the other in such a way that all true statements in S_n can be translated into true statements in S_k by the mere substitution of corresponding terms, the two systems are isomorphic. This is the case with the geometric model of the axiomatic system S_0 and the model of the club committees.

mathematical rigor

It should be clear that in an "elementary" treatment of logical or demonstrative geometry we lean heavily upon intuition—we allow ourselves to be influenced by the appearance of the diagram. Yet the diagram that we draw is only a physical interpretation of the undefined elements and relationships; what we are really interested in is a logical investigation of whether certain conclusions can be deduced validly on the basis of the assumptions—we are not interested in the ink marks or the chalk lines we make. For example, we frequently make tacit assumptions—sometimes without even being aware of them—just by looking at the diagram. Thus, we might say, let PQ, the bisector of $\angle P$, meet the side AB in point Q (Fig. 3-21).

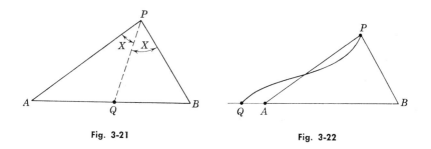

Fig. 3-21   Fig. 3-22

How do we *know* that PQ might not lie as shown in Fig. 3-22, so that Q is *not between* A and B? Or again, in proving that two sides of a triangle are unequal if the angles opposite them are unequal, we might say, in Fig. 3-23 since $\angle BAC > \angle C$ by hypothesis, draw AR so that $\angle CAR = \angle C$. Then, since $BR + RA > AB$, and $RA = RC$, $\therefore BR + RC > AB$; that is, $BC > AB$. But how can we be sure (other than by looking at the picture) that point R must fall *between* B and C? One more example must suffice. Let us say that we want to prove that the diagonals of a parallelogram bisect each other. We draw the diagram as shown in Fig. 3-24a and find that the diagonals AC and BD intersect inside the parallelogram and that both diagonals lie wholly within the quadrilateral $ABCD$. We may be tempted to assume that what is true for a parallelogram must necessarily be true of other quadrilaterals. That this assumption cannot be made is demonstrated in Fig. 3-24b.

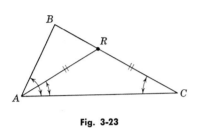

Fig. 3-23

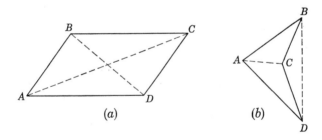

(a) (b)

Fig. 3-24

These considerations are what a bright geometry pupil once referred to as objectionable, since, as he put it, in geometry "you can *see* too much." When the tacit assumptions arising from intuitive, sensory experiences are replaced by explicit assumptions, we thereby make our mathematics more rigorous. The less we depend upon intuition, and the more we formulate the system in terms of precise abstractions, the greater the degree of rigor. This is one of the chief goals of modern mathematics. It is thus possible to write an entire book on logical geometry without making use of a single drawing or diagram. This would have been virtually unthinkable one hundred fifty years ago.

GEOMETRY AND LOGIC

related theorems

In an earlier chapter you learned that a given proposition $p \rightarrow q$ is logically equivalent to its contrapositive; also, that the opposite and the converse of a given proposition are logically equivalent. If two propositions are logically equivalent, a proof of either one is sufficient to establish the other proposition. Consider the following theorems:

PROPOSITION	CONVERSE
If alternate interior angles made by a transversal are equal, the lines are parallel.	If lines are parallel, alternate interior angles made by a transversal are equal.

OPPOSITE	CONTRAPOSITIVE
If alternate interior angles made by a transversal are *not* equal, the lines are *not* parallel.	If lines are *not* parallel, alternate interior angles made by a transversal are *not* equal.

Turning back to our "sample sequence," we note that Theorem T_3 is the opposite of Theorem T_2, and that Theorem T_4 is the converse of Theorem T_2. Upon proving T_2 and T_3, we need not have bothered to prove T_4 independently, since it is logically equivalent to T_3, just as the proof of T_2 automatically establishes the contrapositive theorem: If lines are not parallel, then alternate interior angles made by a transversal are not equal.

These considerations suggest that sometimes two theorems can be combined into a single statement, utilizing the idea of necessary and sufficient conditions; thus, for example: *Alternate interior angles made by a transversal to two lines are equal if and only if the lines are parallel.* Of course, it is also possible to assert the following: *Two lines are parallel if and only if alternate interior angles made by a transversal are equal.* Can you explain why the latter statement is true?

a word about locus theorems

Somewhat similar observations can be made with regard to locus theorems. For the reader who may have forgotten, a locus is the set containing all points which satisfy one or more specific conditions, and only such points. A locus may be a line, several lines, one or more isolated points, etc. Since by definition the locus of points satisfying one or more given conditions is the figure which contains all the points that satisfy the given conditions, and which contains no other points except these, it will be seen that a locus is both *inclusive* and *exclusive*. Hence, to prove that a given figure is a required locus, we must show that the figure includes certain precisely described points, and at the same time excludes all other points. A locus proof therefore always consists of *two parts*. There are two alternative methods of procedure.

Method I. Prove both *a* and *b*, as follows:

(*a*) that every point on the figure meets the given conditions, and

(*b*) that every point which meets the given conditions lies on the figure.

Note that this method involves the proof of a theorem and the proof of its converse. For example: consider the two theorems:

(*a*) If a point lies on the perpendicular bisector of a line segment, it is equidistant from the ends of the segment, and

(*b*) If a point is equidistant from the ends of a line segment, it lies on the perpendicular bisector of that segment.

Taken together, these two theorems constitute a complete proof that the perpendicular bisector of a line segment is the locus of all points equisdistant from the ends of the segment. This illustrates Method I for proving a locus theorem.

Method II. This consists of proving both *a* and *b*, as follows:

(*a*) that every point on the figure satisfies the given conditions, and

(*b*) that every point not on the figure does not satisfy the given conditions.

It will be seen that this method involves proving a theorem and also proving the opposite of the theorem. For example, consider the two theorems:

(*a*) If a point lies on the perpendicular bisector of a line segment, it is equidistant from the ends of the segment, and

(*b*) If a point does not lie on the perpendicular bisector of a line segment, it is not equidistant from the ends of the segment.

Taken together, these two theorems constitute an alternative but also complete proof that the perpendicular bisector of a line segment is the locus of all points equidistant from the ends of the segment. This illustrates Method II for proving a locus theorem.

indirect proof

The scheme of inference used in ordinary "direct" proof in demonstrative geometry is already familiar to the reader. Stated informally, we reason by saying: "A is true if B is true; but B is true, therefore A is true." More technically, this kind of scheme is known as *modus ponens*, and says, essentially: from the statement "If p then q" and the statement "p," we can infer the statement "q"; in symbols,

$$
\begin{aligned}
&1.\ p \rightarrow q \\
&2.\ p \\
\hline
&3.\ \therefore\ q
\end{aligned}
$$

It is, however, frequently necessary or desirable to use a scheme of "indirect" proof. Methods of indirect reasoning are often regarded as somewhat less adequate than direct reasoning. But with proper safeguards, indirect proofs are logically just as valid as direct proofs. Moreover, they are extremely useful not only in mathematics, but also in scientific thinking, in legal argumentation, and occasionally in everyday situations. For convenience, we recognize three types of indirect reasoning:

1. Proof by elimination of all possibilities but one.
2. Proof by proving the contrapositive.
3. Proof by showing that the hypothesis and the denial of the conclusion are contradictory.

The first type is perhaps the simplest, and is fairly common. It consists essentially of stating all the possibilities and then showing that all but one of these possibilities is false; hence the remaining one must be true. For example, a proposition may state that under certain conditions, two lines are parallel. We assert that there are only two possibilities: either the lines are parallel, or they are not parallel.

We then proceed to show that they cannot be parallel under the given conditions and in terms of the proof structure described earlier; it then follows, since there is only one possibility left (namely, that the lines are parallel) that this conclusion must be true. In symbols:

$$p \lor (\sim p)$$
$$\underline{\sim (\sim p)}$$
$$\therefore p$$

Generalizing, we are using the so-called double rule of inference: if $p \lor q$ is true, then the other proposition must be true.

(a) $p \lor q$ $\qquad\qquad\qquad$ (b) $p \lor q$
$\underline{ \sim q}$ $\qquad\qquad\qquad\qquad$ $\underline{ \sim p}$
$\therefore p$ $\qquad\qquad\qquad\qquad\quad$ $\therefore q$

Or again, we can assert that, with respect to two quantities A and B, one and only one of these three statements is true:

$$A > B, \quad A = B, \quad \text{or} \quad A < B.$$

If it can be proved that any two of these three possibilities are false, then clearly the third must be true. This is what we might have expressed, in our earlier notation, as follows:

$$p \lor q \lor r$$
$$\sim q$$
$$\underline{\sim r }$$
$$\therefore p$$

The two essential points in this type of proof, therefore, are these:

1. We must be certain, at the outset, that all of the n possibilities have been considered.

2. We must have a valid reason for asserting that each of $(n - 1)$ possibilities is false before we can assert that the nth possibility must be true.

These two qualifications are easily met in mathematics, as a rule; but when reasoning about everyday, non-mathematical matters, it is not always easy to be sure about meeting them, especially the first. A good example of this kind of indirect reasoning is the proof of Theorem T_2 in our sample sequence above (if alternate interior angles made by a transversal to two lines are equal, the lines are parallel).

In the second type of indirect reasoning we simply make use of the logical equivalence $(p \to q) \leftrightarrow (\sim q \to \sim p)$. An example of this procedure is the proof of Theorem T_4 (*if two lines are parallel, the alternate interior angles formed by a transversal are equal*). Instead of proving this implication directly, we prove instead the implication stating that *if the alternate interior angles formed by a transversal are not equal, then the lines are not parallel*. (See the proof of Theorem T_3 above, which automatically establishes Theorem T_4).

In the third type of indirect reasoning we make use of the logical equivalence $(p \rightarrow q) \leftrightarrow \sim [p \wedge (\sim q)]$. In order to prove a theorem "If p, then q" by this method, we show that is impossible to have the hypothesis and the denial of the conclusion both true.

Example.

Prove: From a point outside a line, only one line can be drawn perpendicular to a line.

Given: $PS \perp AB$; to prove PR is not $\perp AB$. If PR were $\perp$ to AB while $PS \perp AB$, we would have a triangle (PRS) with two right angles, which is clearly impossible in view of Theorem T_5.

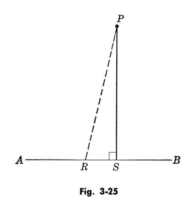

Fig. 3-25

EXERCISE 3–3

1. The terms *axiom, postulate,* and *assumption* are synonymous. Show how their etymological derivations are related to this meaning.

2. Trace the dictionary meaning of each of the following words and show how this points up the impossibility of defining every word in the logical sense of definition: (*a*) *soft*, (*b*) *heavy*, (*c*) *round*, (*d*) *point* (*geometric meaning*).

3. Discuss the oft-quoted dictum of Bertrand Russell: "Mathematics may be defined as the subject in which we never know what we are talking about, nor whether what we are saying is true."

4. What is meant (*a*) by *autonomous* thinking, (*b*) by *hypothetico-deductive* thinking?

5. What is the significance of the word "distinct" in Assumptions A_1 and A_2 on pages 76–77?

6. Discuss the general nature or "structure" of proof in demonstrative geometry.

7. What is meant by the genealogy or "family history" of the proof of a theorem?

8. Consider the list of Assumptions A_1–A_8, page 77, as applying to the surface of a sphere, where "points" are thought of as points on the sphere, where "lines" are thought of as great circles on the sphere, and where a "plane" is thought of as the surface of a sphere. With this interpretation, explain the following:

(*a*) that it is possible to have two distinct lines joining the same two points.

(*b*) that all perpendiculars drawn to a given line on the same side of the line intersect in a point.

(*c*) that there are no parallel lines.

(*d*) that it is possible for a triangle to contain two or even three right angles.

9. A noted authority on mathematical education once indicated his conviction that

". . . geometry as a school subject has been taken too seriously. Geometry is not a model of how to think—at any rate, school geometry is not. There are about thirty results in Euclid that one needs to know for use in other branches of mathematics, and these can be sketched on one large sheet of paper. . . . Our prejudice is simply against geometry treated solemnly as a training in logical thinking. We do not believe it is."

Discuss the pros and cons of the above passage. What are its implications for geometry instruction on the junior and senior high school level?

10. Referring to the quotation in Number 9 above, make a list of the 30 "results" (that is, theorems or relations) which you consider essential for use in other branches of mathematics, as, for example, trigonometry, analytic geometry, and related mathematics used in shop work, mechanics, mechanical drawing, etc.

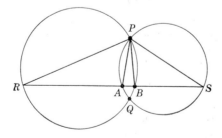

Fig. 3-26

11. Find the fallacy in the following proof that there are two perpendiculars from a point to a line. Let any two circles intersect in P and Q; let PR and PS be the respective diameters; and let the line joining R and S intersect the circles in A and B. Then angles PBR and PAS are right angles, being inscribed in semicircles. Hence PA and PB are both perpendicular to RS.

12. Find the fallacy in the following proof that an obtuse angle is equal to a right angle. Let $ABCD$ be any rectangle; let CE be drawn outside the rectangle and equal in length to CD; let PR and PS be the perpendicular bisectors of BC and AE, respectively. Then triangles PBA and PCE are congruent, since the three sides of one are equal to the three sides of the other. Therefore $\angle PBA = \angle PCE$, and hence, by subtracting the equal angles x and y, the obtuse angle ECR equals the right angle ABR.

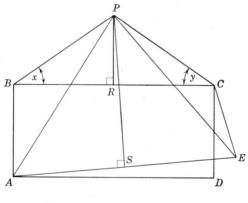

Fig. 3-27

ANALYTIC GEOMETRY

another approach to geometry

Analytic geometry, also called *coordinate geometry,* invented by Descartes in the first half of the seventeenth century, is a momentous milestone in the history of mathematics. Its significance lies in the fact that it consists of another mode of thinking about geometry. The concept of coordinates was not new. Fixing the position of a point by means of coordinates was already known to the ancients: the Egyptians and the Romans used the idea in surveying, and the Greeks employed the device in making maps. The crux of the new idea, contributed by Descartes, is the identification of algebraic symbols with geometrical configurations. More explicitly, the essence of analytic geometry is the recognition that every equation corresponds to some geometric locus, and that every geometric locus corresponds to some equation. Stated a little differently, and in more modern terms, the basic idea is that to every ordered pair of real numbers there corresponds a unique point in the plane, and that every point in the plane can be uniquely identified by an ordered pair of real numbers. This recognition constitutes a unifying principle which turns out to be a powerful tool for discovering relations and properties, to say nothing of applications of mathematics to science and technology.

In analytical geometry the postulational approach is also used, but it is combined with algebraic techniques. Moreover, the terms point, line, and surface are not left undefined. From this point of view a point is an algebraic entity, and is defined as an ordered pair of numbers, that is, a pair of coordinates; in a three-dimensional space a point is defined as an ordered triple of numbers. Certain classes of points are called lines, certain others, planes, and still others, circles, ellipses, cylindrical surfaces, spherical surfaces, and so on. Properties of these algebraic entities, and relations among them, are then studied by the analytic method; this is distinctly different from the methods used either in the physical or the synthetic approach of classical Euclidean geometry. Finally, the algebraic imagery is translated back to its geometric counterpart.

The correspondence between ordered pairs of numbers and points in a plane is a simple enough idea. The pair of numbers constitute the coordinates of the point. We divide the plane into four quadrants by means of two perpendicular lines, called the x axis and the y axis; their point of intersection is called the *origin.* The points on the horizontal scale are numbered, using the real numbers. By convention, those to the left of the origin are considered negative, those to the right, positive. The points on the vertical scale are similarly numbered; those counting upward from the origin are considered positive, those downward, negative. With these conventions, it is a simple matter to identify any point in the plane by means of a unique pair of ordered numbers; the first number of the pair, or x distance, is called the *abscissa,* and the second number, or y distance, is called the *ordinate.* The two ordered numbers are the coordinates of the point. Thus, in Fig. 3-28, point P corresponds to the ordered pair $(4, 5)$; the coordinates of point Q are $(-6, 4)$; R $(-5, -8)$; etc. Conversely, to every ordered pair of real numbers there corresponds one and only

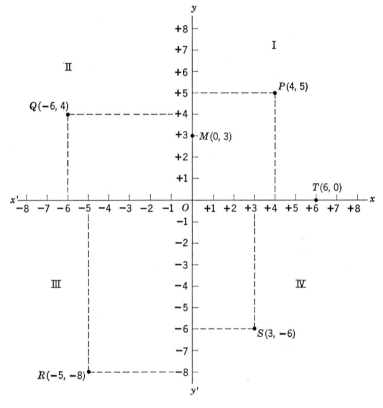

Fig. 3-28

one point in the plane. The entire device is known as a system of rectangular coordinates, or Cartesian coordinates, in honor of Descartes. It is also possible to use other systems of coordinates, such as oblique coordinates or polar coordinates (a circular system), but the basic principle is the same.

the equation of a locus

A curve which passes through all points that satisfy a given condition or description, and through no other points, is called the locus of the points satisfying that condition. A "curve," as used here, means any continuous line, whether curved or straight. A locus may even comprise two or more curves. Thus all the points in a plane may be

divided into two sets: (1) those which satisfy a given condition, and
(2) those that do not; set 1 is the required locus. A locus may also be
regarded as the path of a "moving point" which is thought of as
successively taking all the possible positions which satisfy a given condition. As the point moves about, subject only to the restriction of
the given condition, it traces the desired locus. From this point of
view, we use the singular and speak of "the locus of a point" as it
moves, etc. Both the "set" idea and the "path" idea lead to the same
concept. In the latter case, we imagine the point $P(x,y)$ following
the desired path; the given condition determines the nature of the
equation which is identified with that path or locus.

It is not difficult to understand how a geometric locus can be
described by an algebraic equation. For example, all the points which
are 4 units above the x axis lie on a line which is parallel to the x axis;
the equation of this line is clearly $y = 4$. Similarly, the equation

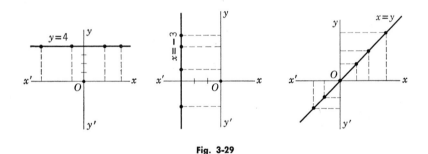

Fig. 3-29

$x = -3$ is the algebraic "description" of all points which are 3 units
to the left of the y axis. Or again, the equation $x = y$ describes the
locus of all points that are as far from the x axis as they are from the
y axis. The locus of the equation $x^2 + y^2 = r^2$ is a circle whose center
is at the origin $(0, 0)$, and whose radius equals r. Similarly, the equations of ellipses, parabolas and hyperbolas are also equations of the
second degree in two variables, such as $x^2 = ky$, $y^2 = kx$, $ax^2 + by^2 = k$,
$x^2 - y^2 = k$, and $xy = k$, where k is a constant.

Thus there are two fundamental problems in analytic geometry:

1. to plot the locus of a given equation.
2. to find the equation of a curve which is defined as the locus of a
point satisfying one or more given conditions.

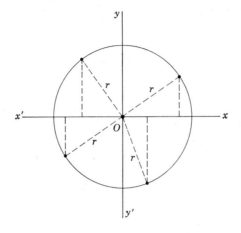

Fig. 3-30

the significance of analytic geometry

Probably enough has been suggested to indicate the general nature of analytic geometry; this has been our major purpose. The two fundamental considerations are:

1. for every specified geometric locus there is a unique algebraic equation or analytic expression, and
2. for every given algebraic equation or analytic expression there is a corresponding geometric locus or configuration.

We shall soon learn that the points on a line can be ordered; also, that the real numbers of algebra (generalized arithmetic) can also be ordered. In short, there is a one-to-one correspondence between the points on a line and the real numbers.[4] The isomorphism between the real numbers and the points on a line leads to a one-to-one correspondence between the real numbers and the totality of points in the plane. The essence of analytic geometry is the identification of the algebraic correlation with geometric locus. This concept is made possible by the isomorphism of the points on a line and the real numbers, which in turn enables us to represent all the points in a plane by ordered pairs of real numbers. In short, analytic geometry is

[4] The concept of "real numbers" will mean more to the reader when he has completed his study of Chapters 3 and 4.

not another kind of geometry, nor another branch of geometry; rather, it is another method of thinking about geometry. The crucial concept is that of assigning algebraic meanings (that is, numbers and operations) to the undefined terms of geometry: *point, line, on, between,* and *congruent.* In this way the postulates of geometry are transformed into algebraic statements or analytic expressions. Thus a geometric point becomes an ordered pair of real numbers; a straight line becomes an equation of the form $ax + by + c = 0$ (where a and b are not both equal to zero); a point is said to lie on a line if and only if its coordinates satisfy the equation of the line; and so on. We can therefore properly speak of the method of analytic, or algebraic, geometry, and also of the method of geometric algebra. Neither the Greeks nor the Romans had the slightest insight into the nature of the real number system; this is a distinctly modern concept. The superiority of the analytic method over the synthetic method of the ancients lies in vastly greater power and economy, due to the use of algebraic language to describe spatial relations. The pattern or structure of number and of form are thus intimately related. Deductive or postulational thinking furnishes the basis for this recognition.

EXERCISE 3–4

Plot the locus of each of the following equations:

1. (a) $x = 6$ (b) $y = -5$ (c) $y = 2x$
   (d) $x = 2\frac{1}{2}y$ (e) $3x = 4y$ (f) $y = x + 4$
   (g) $x = y - 3$ (h) $x - y = 4$ (i) $3x + 2y = 6$ (j) $x = 0$

2. (a) $y = \dfrac{12}{x}$ (b) $x = \dfrac{8}{y}$
   (c) $xy = 48$ (d) $xy = 1$

3. (a) $x^2 = 4y$ (b) $y^2 = 9x$ (c) $y = (x + 2)^2$
   (d) $x = (y - 4)^2$ (e) $x^2 = 2y + 4$ (f) $y^2 = 3x - 6$

4. (a) $x^2 + y^2 = 64$ (b) $y = x^2 - x - 6$ (c) $4x^2 + 9y^2 = 36$
   (d) $4x^2 - 9y^2 = 36$ (e) $x^2 - y^2 = 0$

5. Write an equation which can be identified with each of the following loci:

   (a) A line parallel to the x axis and 10 units above the x axis.
   (b) A line parallel to the y axis and 8 units to the left of the y axis.
   (c) The x axis.
   (d) The locus of all points whose abscissas and ordinates are alike except for sign.
   (e) A circle whose center is at the origin and whose radius equals 5.

6. What is the equation of the locus of a point which moves so as to be equidistant from the lines $x = 4$ and $x = 11$? Equidistant from the lines $y = -6$ and $y = 4$?

7. A point moves so that its distance from the x *axis* is always 3 times its distance from the y *axis*. What is the equation of the locus?

8. What is the equation of the locus of the centers of all circles which are tangent to the x *axis* at the point $(6, 0)$?

9. Write some of the points whose abscissa is 6 more than twice their ordinate. Now write the equation which represents all such points.

10. In Fig. 3–31:

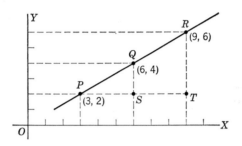

Fig. 3-31

(a) What are the coordinates of P? of Q? of S?
(b) How long is PS? QS?
(c) What is the ratio of QS to PS?
(d) What are the coordinates of T? How long is RT? PT? What is the ratio of RT to PT?
(e) From your answers, what can you infer, intuitively, about the slope (or slant) of line PR?

11. In Fig. 3–32:

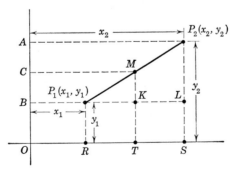

Fig. 3-32

(*a*) If M is the midpoint of P_1P_2, why is T the midpoint of RS? Why is C the midpoint of AB?

(*b*) What are the coordinates of T? of C?

(*c*) Prove that the abscissa of M is $\dfrac{x_1 + x_2}{2}$, and that the ordinate of M is $\dfrac{y_1 + y_2}{2}$.

12. Prove that the distance (*d*) between any two points such as P_1 and P_2 is given by the expression $d = \sqrt{(\triangle x)^2 + (\triangle y)^2}$, where $\triangle x = P_1R = x_2 - x_1$, and $\triangle y = P_2R = y_2 - y_1$.

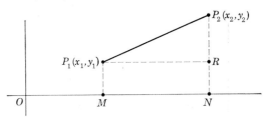

Fig. 3-33

FOR FURTHER READING AND STUDY

1. Bell, E. T. *Mathematics, Queen and Servant of Science.* New York: McGraw-Hill, 1951. Chapter 7: "Pictorial Thinking."
2. Eaves, J. C. and Robinson, A. J. *Introduction to Euclidean Geometry.* Cambridge, Mass.: Addison-Wesley, 1957.
3. Eves, Howard and Newsom, Carroll. *An Introduction to the Foundations and Fundamental Concepts of Mathematics.* New York: Rinehart, 1958. Chapter 1: "Mathematics before Euclid"; Chapter 2: "Euclid's Elements."
4. Hemmerling, Edwin. *College Plane Geometry.* New York: Wiley, 1958.
5. Holmes, Roger W. *The Rhyme of Reason.* New York: D. Appleton-Century Co., 1939. Chapter 9: "Mathematics as a Game."
6. Kline, Morris. "The Straight Line." *Scientific American,* March 1956, pp. 105–114.
7. Meder, A. E. "What Is Wrong with Euclid?" *The Mathematics Teacher* 51:578–584; December 1958.
8. Whitehead, A. N. *An Introduction to Mathematics.* New York: H. Holt, 1911; Dover Publications, 1957. Chapter 9: "Co-ordinate Geometry."

CHAPTER 4

The Number Concept

Correspondence and succession, the two
principles which permeate all mathematics—nay, all realms of exact
thought—are woven into the very fabric of our number system.

—Tobias Dantzig

WHAT ARE NUMBERS?

numerals versus numbers

No one has ever seen a number. Of course you can see the symbol
"3" that someone has written, and which stands for the number three.
But the number itself does not exist physically, any more than a geometric point exists physically. You cannot see or touch a point;
neither can you see or feel a number. Numbers are something we
think. Numbers exist only in people's minds; they are abstractions.
When we talk about numbers, we use words or make marks on paper:
for example, *four* dollars, *5* pounds, *14*, *¼*, *3½*, *0*, *218*, and so on.
But these words and marks are not the numbers; they are only symbols which stand for the numbers we are thinking.

In mathematics, as elsewhere, it is often very important to be sure whether (*a*) we are talking about the *thing* to which a word or symbol refers, or whether (*b*) we are talking about the word or *symbol* being used to designate that thing. This matter is not a trivial one. An easy way to make sure whether we mean the thing itself or merely its symbol is to use quotation marks. For example:

1. Helen is a girl. "Helen" is a girl's name.
2. Trees have leaves. "Trees" has five letters.
3. If you put poison on your tongue, you will be sorry. If you put "poison" on the label, you will be safe.

Remember also that the name given to a thing is not necessarily a property of the thing.

When the thing we are talking about is a number, the symbol that stands for the number is called a *numeral*. Thus the numeral "5" stands for the number 5. Remember that a number is an idea—an abstract concept. We said you couldn't see a number. The numeral "5," which you can see, stands for the number 5. The number 5 means "fiveness"—something which does not belong to any particular set of objects, but which is characteristic of *all* the sets of objects which can be matched with the fingers of one hand. Any particular number may be represented by several different symbols—whether words or marks. Each of the symbols in the following array is a name for the same number:

Fig. 4-1

We are not quibbling when we distinguish between a numeral and a number. Study the following sentences; they will help to make these ideas clear:

(*a*) "9" is a numeral for 9.
(*b*) You can put "9" on the blackboard.
(*c*) 9 is an odd number.
(*d*) You can't put 9 on the blackboard.
(*e*) 9 is divisible by 3.

(f) "9" is not a number.

(g) "5 + 4" is a numeral for 9.

Notice in the last sentence that a composite symbol was used for the number 9. When a mathematician sees the composite numeral "5 + 4," he does not always hasten to write "9." Instead of regarding "5 + 4" as an addition example, he considers the addition operation as having already been completed; the answer is "5 + 4." In other words, "5 + 4" is just another symbol for the number 9. Obviously there is an endless number of ways of writing the number 9; for example, "1 + 8," "2 + 7," "3 + 6," "10 − 1," "11 − 2," and so on.

We have suggested that it is impossible to say exactly what a number is. "Number" cannot be defined. But just because the "whole numbers" of arithmetic are so familiar, it is difficult to appreciate how they came to have meaning for us. Of one thing we may be sure: although our understanding of numbers grows out of experience with "real" objects, eventually numbers become abstract ideas.

The idea of number is one of the most abstract concepts that the mind of man has ever evolved. Number is not a fact of "reality." Number is not a quality of an object or of a collection of objects, as is their shape, their size, and their color. No physical aspects of objects, or of our impressions, can ever suggest the idea of number. Number is something that the mind creates, or invents, not by contemplating the qualities of the objects, but rather by deliberately disregarding their qualities. Thinking with numbers is therefore a mental process of the highest order. Counting, computing, and using numerical relations are among the most significant of all human achievements. The concept of number, like the idea of the wheel, is not the contribution of a single individual, but rather the product of a gradual social evolution. The number system which man painstakingly created over thousands of years is an unbelievably abstract invention which enables him to deal more effectively with reality than he could without it.

how many are there?

Long before man grasped the idea of number it was perfectly possible for him to distinguish between few and many, even as animals can discriminate between the number of objects when the number is rather small. One does not need to count, for example, to observe that a single article in a familiar setting is missing, or that all the members of one's family are present, or that a small collection of items has been increased by one. The earliest step in enumeration is simply the act of identifying or naming, even as shepherds in remote times kept track of their flocks by naming the individual sheep. Using a roster of names is obviously a form of enumeration, but it lacks generality. If correspondence is obtained, it is known without using numbers that the collection is complete.

As a matter of fact, it is very easy to tell something about the "number" of things in two sets without using numbers or numerals. All we have to do is compare the two sets. Sometimes the comparison can be made by a simple observation; for example, a mere glance at the two configurations in Fig. 4-2 shows at once that there are more dots in *a* than in *b*.

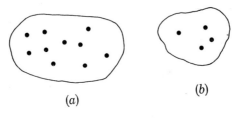

(a)

(b)

Fig. 4-2

We may compare two sets in a more sophisticated way. Every passenger in the bus is wearing one hat and only one hat; we know at once that there are just as many hats in the bus as there are passengers. Or again: I am seated in an auditorium and observe (1) that no person in the auditorium is standing, (2) that every seat is occupied by one and only one person, and (3) that there are no vacant seats; then, without using a number word or symbol, I can be certain that there are equally as many persons as seats in the auditorium. Similarly, a child could tell, without counting or using numbers, that there are just as many flowers as flower pots in Fig. 4-3. Or, for that matter, that he had just as many fingers as toes. In short, it is possible to tell (at least for "small" collections) whether they are equally numerous, without using numbers, by a simple process of pairing.

Such a pairing of the members of two sets is called matching. Two sets are matchable if they can be paired against each other with no

Fig. 4-3

members of either set left over. We say that to each member of the first set there corresponds one and only one member of the second set, and, conversely, to each member of the second set there corresponds one and only one member of the first set. Technically, two sets that match are said to be in *one-to-one correspondence*. Such matching sets are *equivalent;* that is, they are equally numerous. On the other hand, one set is "smaller" than another if and only if it is matchable with a proper subset of the second set, but is not matchable with the second set itself.

cardinal number

How, then, do we use numbers to tell how many members there are in a set? The device is simplicity itself. Suppose that some very familiar sets of objects are associated with arbitrary but conventional symbols—either words or numerals (see Fig. 4-4 on the following page). Clearly, each of these sets can be identified and symbolized by a word (*one, two, three,* etc.), or by a numeral (*1, 2, 3,* etc.). To tell how many objects there are in some other given set, say the objects lying on the table, we simply match that set with one of the familiar sets above. The symbol of the matching "standard" set then tells how many objects there are on the table. It's as simple as that.

The symbol used for any one of the standard sets is called the *cardinal number* of that set. Consider the following sets of objects: set of five different coins and a set of any five objects on the desk—they don't even have to be similar objects. Clearly, each of these sets can be matched with the fingers of one hand. The symbol for this standard set—five, or 5, is the cardinal number of each of these sets. The cardinal number is the one property that all three sets have in common—"fiveness."

A pair of mittens	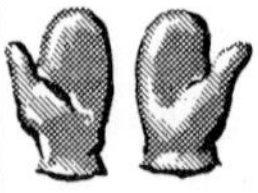	*two*	2
A place setting		*three*	3
The legs of a chair		*four*	4
The fingers of a hand		*five*	5
The faces of a cube	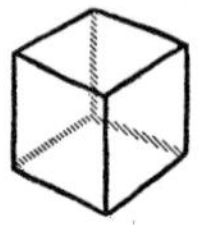	*six*	6

Fig. 4-4

ordinal number

It is possible to think of the objects in a set as arranged in some particular order; that is, a definite succession or sequence. For example, a dictionary standing on the shelf might be the fourth book from the left; or, Johnny might be the fifth boy in line waiting for the bus. This is the *ordinal* idea of number. The 102 in the upper corner of this page is an ordinal. When we refer to the sixth floor, or Apartment 29, or Tenth Avenue, we are using ordinal numbers. An ordinal tells the position of an object in a particular linear sequence or succession. Strictly speaking, when we use ordinals in this way, we are not counting; we are deciding upon a specific sequence, as when taking our places in a game: *First! Second! Third!* etc.

counting

Let us generalize the procedure described above, where certain familiar sets were used. Consider the sequence of dots:

(.), (. .), (. . .), (. . . .), (. . . . .), etc.

If a set can be matched with the set of dots in (.), we say that the number of members of the set is *one*. If the set can be matched with the set of dots in (..), the number is said to be *two*, and so on for succeeding numbers. The secret of counting, therefore, is to use a *set of conventional symbols prearranged in a fixed conventional sequence.* Instead of this awkward sequence of sets of dots, we use the familiar numerals in the standard conventional order:

$$(1) \quad (1, 2) \quad (1, 2, 3) \quad (1, 2, 3, 4) \quad \text{etc.}$$

Now when we match any given set of objects against one of *these* standard sets, we do not have to think or say the entire standard set; we merely refer to the *last numeral* in the standard set with which it is matched. Thus:

(1)	corresponds to 1;
(1, 2)	corresponds to 2;
(1, 2, 3)	corresponds to 3;
	and so on.

It should be noted that when we wish to enumerate or count a set of objects, the objects can be enumerated in more than one way (unless there are fewer than two objects in the set). For example, there are four books in this set, no matter in which one of 24 possible different ways I may arrange them. The possible orders are listed:

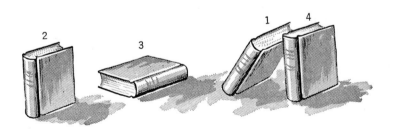

Fig. 4-5

1234	2134	3124	4123
1243	2143	3142	4132
1324	2314	3214	4213
1342	2341	3241	4231
1423	2413	3421	4312
1432	2431	3412	4321

In every case, when we have enumerated the last book, we arrive at the number 4 in our thinking. The last, or highest, ordinal reached is always the cardinal number of the set, that is, the "number of objects" in the set. In short, the cardinal number of a set is independent of the order in which they are counted. When counting we use the ordinal idea of number; the result, or the number of objects in the set, is expressed by a cardinal number.

So you see that there is an intimate connection between the ordering process and the matching process. In fact, although the two processes are quite distinct, they are subtly related, and it is virtually impossible to think of one without at the same time thinking of the other—mathematically as well as psychologically. So far as is known, no culture has ever developed the ordinal idea without simultaneously developing the cardinal idea. One might be tempted to ask, therefore, why bother to distinguish between the two processes? Why be concerned about this dual aspect of number—ordinal and cardinal? The answer is that the process of matching standard sets with numerals arranged in a conventional order holds good only for finite[1] sets; it cannot be used for infinite sets. The fact that the ordinary numbers $1, 2, 3, 4, \ldots$ can be used to designate both cardinal and ordinal numbers for finite sets is a fortunate circumstance. When dealing with finite sets, to each cardinal there belongs one and only one ordinal number. As we saw above in the case of the four books, a given set of n elements admits of various arrangements, but all these arrangements have a common ordinal structure; that is, each of these arrangements has a *first, second, third, ... nth* element and no other.

numbers and sets

The purely abstract nature of number can now be appreciated. The common property of all equivalent sets which remains after their elements have been stripped of all other properties is the cardinal number of those sets. In mathematical terms, the cardinal number of a set may be defined as that property which is common to the given set and to all other sets which are equivalent to it. The only distinction between ordinal and cardinal numbers is that the former involve order whereas the latter do not.

We may now summarize some important ideas as follows:

[1] For the time being, it will be sufficient to characterize a finite sequence as one that has a "beginning" and an "end," whereas an infinite sequence has a beginning but no end (there is no "last" element).

1. When two sets are matched so that they are in one-to-one correspondence, the sets are *equivalent*.

2. The order in which the correspondence is made is immaterial.

3. There is an endless number of sets that are equivalent to any given (finite) set.

4. The totality of all equivalent sets is itself another set.

5. A *cardinal* number is the class of all equivalent classes.

6. If set A is matched with set B and the elements of set B are not only used up, but some elements of set A are left over, we say that set A has a higher rank than set B; and conversely. Equivalent sets have the same rank. The lowest rank is a set with but a single element (excluding null or empty sets).

7. Sets may be arranged in order, according to their rank: (.), (..), (...), (....), etc.

8. Each of the sets in parentheses is given its customary name or numeral:

one,	two,	three,	four,	etc.
1	2	3	4	etc.

9. Each of these cardinal numbers represents an entire class of equivalent classes.

10. The new set of ordered classes in 9 can be used as a basis for matching against any other given set, with the added restriction that the order of the numerals must not be changed.

11. All equivalent sets that can be put into one-to-one correspondence in order (that is, for A–a, B–b, C–c, etc., we know that if A precedes B then a precedes b, etc.) are known as *similar* sets.

12. An *ordinal* number is the class of all similar classes.

Thus it may be said that the concept of *set* is even more fundamental than the concept of *number* itself. Indeed, most modern mathematicians regard the general theory of sets and relations as the very foundations upon which the concept of number is built. Today the various branches of mathematics—arithmetic, algebra, trigonometry, calculus, higher analysis, function theory, and much of geometry are all based upon the concept of number. This modern outlook is referred to as the "arithmetization" of mathematics.

EXERCISE 4–1

1. In each of the following sentences insert quotation marks wherever they are necessary; explain why you think they should be used:

(*a*) Add 6 and 4.
(*b*) Twenty-six is an even number.
(*c*) You can write 15 instead of writing $10 + 5$.
(*d*) Thirty-five is divisible by seven.
(*e*) You can write the numeral 15 when you mean the number $10 + 5$.
(*f*) The 6 on this typewriter is badly worn.
(*g*) The teacher cancelled the 8 and wrote 2.
(*h*) To multiply by 10 you annex a 0.
(*i*) The license number of the car is 88633.
(*j*) On the license plate we saw 88633.
(*k*) To divide 37.5 by 100, you move the decimal point 2 places to the left.
(*l*) You can find the sum of 4 and 7, but you can't find the sum of 4 and 7.

2. Name three non-mathematical symbols (*a*) that stand for things or ideas; (*b*) three symbols that stand for processes or operations.

3. Name three mathematical symbols (*a*) that stand for things or ideas; (*b*) three symbols that stand for processes or operations.

4. Explain the difference between a number and a numeral.

5. In each of the following, tell whether the word "figure(s)" refers to numerals or numbers:

(*a*) "Let's check the figures," said the bookkeeper.
(*b*) "The figure in ten's place is wrong," said the teacher.
(*c*) "This piece of work has been measured to 3-figure accuracy," said the machinist.
(*d*) "This is what the figures show," said the executive.
(*e*) "He needs practice in adding 3-figure numbers."
(*f*) "This measurement has 3 significant figures."
(*g*) "Write your figures legibly."
(*h*) "Put the figures directly one under the other."

6. Explain the precise meaning of each of the following terms as used in mathematics:

(*a*) arbitrary   (*b*) abstract   (*c*) sequence   (*d*) conventional
(*e*) fixed   (*f*) unique   (*g*) distinct.

7. When matching two sets to tell if they have the same number, is it sufficient to see that to every number of the first set there is a corresponding number in the other set? Why, or why not?

8. In the early literature of the subject, one-to-one correspondence was called "one-to-one reciprocal correspondence"; what was the purpose of the word "reciprocal"?

9. Give an example of one-to-one correspondence which shows that two sets have the same cardinal number; an example of two sets with different cardinal numbers, as shown by matching, not by "counting."

10. (*a*) Do all the objects that constitute a set have to be alike or of the same kind? (*b*) Do the elements of a set have to be alike in order to count them? (*c*) Does the order in which you count the elements of a set affect the number of elements in the set?

11. You can see the beginning of a column of soldiers, but not the end of the column. If you are told that "positively" every soldier is carrying one rifle and only one, and that no soldier is without a rifle, what fact can you assert, even if you can never see the end of the column? Why?

12. In the light of the present discussion, explain the meaning of: (*a*) *enumerate*, (*b*) *tally*, (*c*) *count-off*.

THE COUNTING NUMBERS

the counting numbers

The numbers represented by the sequence of numerals
$$1, 2, 3, 4, 5, \ldots 99, 100, 101, \ldots$$
may appropriately be called "counting numbers," since they are the only numbers we need in order to count how many. When we use zero to denote the fact that there aren't any, zero is not a counting number, since in counting the number of elements in a set there is no element before the first element. Through experience we observe certain properties of the counting numbers; we agree as to how the counting numbers "behave." In the first place, we feel that although the sequence 1, 2, 3, . . . has a beginning, it has no end, that is, there is no last counting number in the ordered sequence. Such an unending set we call an infinite set.

addition with counting numbers

In the second place, we can "add" counting numbers. Thus addition is thought of as putting two sets together to form one set. When we add 3 and 5 we "obtain" 8. Actually, we don't get "more" when we add; we already have 8 when we begin with one set of 3 and another set of 5. All we do is regard the two sets as one set. That is what was meant earlier when we said the composite numeral "5 + 4" is just another symbol for the number 9. In short, addition is a form of counting: it means counting the elements of the set obtained by combining two sets whose respective cardinal numbers are known. The operation of addition is denoted by the symbol +.

It is always possible to add counting numbers; intuitively we "know" that when any counting number is added to another counting number, the resulting number is also a counting number. Moreover, for any pair of counting numbers, there exists one and only one counting number which is their *sum*.

We observe, too, that addition is *commutative*, which means that we can commute or reverse the order in which two numbers are added without affecting their sum. (A commuter is a traveler who alternately reverses his trip.) Thus when we say $3 + 5 = 5 + 3$, we admit that the results of the two operations are the same, although we recognize that the operations are different; in one case we add 5 to 3, whereas in the other we add 3 to 5, which is not at all the same operation. Not all operations are reversible in this sense: adding water to sulfuric acid and adding sulfuric acid to water produce very different results, as every student of chemistry knows.

Finally, addition is also *associative*, which means, for example, that

$$3 + (5 + 7) = (3 + 5) + 7,$$
$$\text{or} \quad 3 + 12 = 8 + 7.$$

A parenthesis placed about the indicated sum of two numerals emphasizes the fact that those two numerals are to be regarded as a symbol for one number. For example: $(2 + 3) + 8$ means $5 + 8$, or 13; or, $4 + (6 + 1)$ means $4 + 7$, or 11. When numerals are enclosed in a parenthesis, the operation indicated within should be performed first; in this way, the compound numeral is replaced by a single numeral which stands for the same number. In other words, we get the same result whether we add the sum of the first and second number to the third, or add the first number to the sum of the second and third. The word "associate" suggests that when adding three numbers we may put a parenthesis around the first pair or the second pair, as we wish; the resulting sum is the same whichever way they are associated.

multiplication with counting numbers

Intuitively, we know that multiplication with counting numbers is always possible; when any two counting numbers are multiplied, the result is another unique counting number called their *product*. Multiplication is a sort of short cut. We have before us some boxes of paper clips; we count the set of boxes and find that there are 12; the set of clips in each box has already been counted, and numbers 100. We do not have to empty all the boxes and count the number of clips in the new set of clips made by combining the sets in each box. Instead, we multiply and say the product is 12×100, or 1200. In effect, the multiplication of two numbers is simply a form of addition, or counting, in which we count a number of sets, knowing that the number of elements in each set is the same. and so find the total number of elements in the combination of all the equivalent sets. The two numbers which are multiplied are called *factors*. By common consent, 12×100 is read "12 times 100," that is, 100 "taken" 12 times; or, "100 multiplied by 12." This operation is not at all the same as 100×12, which means "12 taken 100 times," or 100 sets each containing 12 elements. In other words, by convention, the first factor in the product of two numbers denotes the number of equivalent sets we are adding or counting, whereas the second factor denotes the number of elements in each of the equivalent sets.

We observe (again through experience) that multiplication is reversible, or commutative: $3 \times 4 = 4 \times 3$. Although the two operations are not at all the same, we recognize that the product in each case is the same. For example, consider a dozen objects packed in a box as

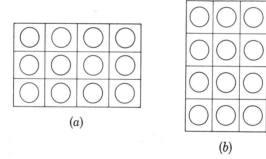

(*a*)

(*b*)

Fig. 4-6

shown. In *a* there are 3 rows (sets) of 4 elements each; merely by turning the box through 90°, we have in *b* 4 rows (sets) of 3 elements each, yet the product (or total number of elements in the large set) has been unaffected. Although the operation is commutative, the order of operation may affect the meaning of the product when the numbers refer to realities. Thus, although four 3-cent stamps cost the same as three 4-cent stamps, there is a difference in the number and type of letters that can be mailed with the stamps.

Multiplication, like addition, is also associative. This means, for example, that $(3 \times 4) \times 5 = 3 \times (4 \times 5)$. Again, by convention, an operation within a parenthesis must be performed first, so that the compound numeral is replaced by a single numeral representing the same number. In other words, we obtain the same product whether we multiply the third number by the product of the first two, or multiply the product of the last two by the first number. The word "associate" suggests that when multiplying three numbers we may put a parenthesis around the first and second, or around the second and third, as we wish; the resulting product is the same in either case.

There is still another property exhibited by counting numbers, one which "ties together" the operations of addition and multiplication. This is the so-called *distributive* property; accordingly,

$$\underbrace{(3)}_{\text{(factor)}} \times \underbrace{(5 + 7)}_{\text{(factor)}} = \underbrace{(3 \times 5)}_{\text{(term)}} + \underbrace{(3 \times 7)}_{\text{(term)}}.$$

Reading from left to right transforms the product of two factors into a sum of two terms; reading from right to left changes the sum of two terms to a product of two factors. We say that multiplication is distributive with respect to addition; that is, in the example above, the factor "3" distributes itself over both terms ("5" and "7") of the other factor. Thus the area of a new rug made by sewing together two rugs of the same width is the same as the combined areas of the original rugs (Fig. 4-7):

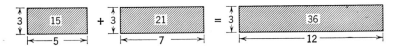

Fig. 4-7

THE NATURAL NUMBERS

a model of the counting numbers

The counting numbers which we have been discussing in the previous sections are based upon experience with real things. Their properties are accepted on the basis of intuition and experience, and although they appear to be plausible and consistent, these properties cannot be proved mathematically. When setting up a system of abstract numbers, therefore, we adopt the counting numbers, together with their familiar numeral symbols, as a model, and call them the *natural numbers*. We then *assume* that the natural numbers will behave just as the counting numbers do. In short, we postulate that the natural numbers shall have the same properties that the counting numbers have.

The natural numbers should not be called "integers," [2] for, as we shall soon see, the integers constitute a different set from the set of natural numbers. The natural numbers are not a subset of the set of integers. Zero is not a natural number. However, if we include zero with the natural numbers, we obtain the so-called "whole numbers" of school arithmetic.

mathematical operations

In mathematics, many kinds of operations are possible. In general, the word "operation" is left undefined; but the nature of any given operation and its characteristics are determined by the specific assumptions which we choose in connection with that operation. Technically, an operation on a set S of elements is a rule which assigns to each ordered subset of elements of the set S a unique element of the same set S.

In building the logical foundations of elementary mathematics, we use just two operations: addition and multiplication. They are assumed to be binary operations. A *binary operation* is an act which, when performed on any two ordered elements a and b of a given set S, produces a unique element c which is also an element of the same set S.

Example 1. If N represents the set of natural numbers, then the operation of addition, performed on any two natural numbers a and b, yielding their sum, $(a + b) = c$, is a binary operation, since c is also a member of the set N. Thus, $3 + 5 = 8$, and since 8 is a natural number, the operation of addition is a binary operation.

Example 2. Again using the set N of natural numbers, the operation of multiplication, performed on any two natural numbers a and b, yielding their product $a \times b = c$, is a binary operation, since c is also a member of set N. Thus, $4 \times 7 = 28$, and since 28 is a natural number, multiplication is a binary operation.

Example 3. If we take a and b as any two natural numbers, the operation of subtraction, yielding the remainder $a - b = c$, is *not* a binary operation, since c may or may not be a member of N. Thus if $a = 6$ and $b = 2$, $c = 4$, which is a natural number. But if $a = 6$ and $b = 6$, or if $a = 6$ and $b = 8$, then c is not a natural number, for neither 0 nor -2 are included in the set N.

---

[2] The natural numbers should not even be confused with "the positive integers"; for example, "+6" does not mean the same as "6" with the plus sign "understood."

Example 4. Again, if we take a and b as any two natural numbers, the operation of division, yielding the quotient $a/b = c$, is *not* a binary operation, since c may or may not be a member of N. Thus if $a = 8$ and $b = 2$, $c = 4$, which is a natural number; but if $a = 3$ and $b = 5$, then $c = 3/5$, which is not a natural number.

Example 5. Extracting the square root of a from the natural number yields $\sqrt{a} = c$, which is *not* a binary operation, since c may or may not be a member of N. Thus if $a = 9$, $c = 3$, which is a natural number. But if $a = 2$, $c = \sqrt{2}$, or $1.414 \ldots$, which is not a natural number.

the assumptions of equality

Before setting down the assumptions which will characterize the natural number system, we shall take another look at the apparently simple notion of equality, which is more subtle than it might seem to be. Equality may be regarded as a basic concept of logic, without definition, that is, as a primitive notion; or, it may be characterized mathematically by the following assumptions, sometimes called the assumptions of equality. We apply them here to the natural numbers.

P₁. If a is a natural number, then $a = a$.

You will recognize this as the law of identity. It asserts that a thing is equal to itself. This is not a trivial notion, but rather an intrinsic idea of logical self-consistency.

P₂. If a and b are any two natural numbers and $a = b$, then $b = a$.

You will recognize this as the law of symmetry. It means that an equality can be read from right to left as well as from left to right. When we say a "equals" b, we are saying that a and b are different symbols for the same natural number; they are simply different names for the same thing. This is the essential meaning of equality, mathematically speaking.

P₃. If a, b and c are natural numbers, and if $a = b$ and $b = c$, then $a = c$.

You will recognize this as the law of transitivity. It is often quoted by saying: Things equal to the same thing are equal to each other (a and c are both equal to b). For the sake of brevity, we often say "by substitution" when referring to this assumption. Thus we may substitute c for a, or a for c. Assumption P₃ also permits us to say that if $a = b$, $b = c$, $c = d$, and $d = e$, then $a = e$.

P₄. If $a = b$ and $c = d$, where a, b, c and d are natural numbers, then $a + c = b + d$.

You will recognize this as the familiar axiomatic rule: "If equals are added to equals the results are equal."

P₅. If $a = b$ and $c = d$, where a, b, c and d are natural numbers, then $ac = bd$.

You will recognize this as the familiar rule: "If equals are multiplied by equals, the results are equal."

fundamental assumptions for the natural numbers

We are now ready to choose the assumptions which we wish the abstract natural numbers to obey. Remember that number is an undefined term, and that the two basic operations of addition and multiplication are also undefined, except insofar as they will be characterized by the assumptions. By choosing the assumptions we are about to make, we shall determine the structure of the arithmetic we are about to build up. We shall present and discuss the twelve necessary assumptions in four groups: (1) the assumptions for closure; (2) the assumptions for addition; (3) the assumptions for multiplication; and (4) other needed assumptions.

the assumptions for closure

Assumption C₁. For every pair of natural numbers a and b, there exists a unique natural number s, called the sum of a and b; or, $s = a + b$.

While "s" is just another name for the number $(a + b)$, the number s is also an element of the same set which contains a and b, that is, the set of natural numbers.

Assumption C₂. For every pair of natural numbers a and b, there exists a unique natural number p, called the product of a and b; or $p = a \times b$.

While "p" is another name for the number $a \times b$, or ab, the number p is also an element of the set of natural numbers.

These two assumptions, C_1 and C_2, make provision for what is known as *closure*. This means that both operations, addition and multiplication, respectively, when applied to natural numbers, will always yield a natural number. In other words, the set of natural numbers is "closed" as far as addition and multiplication are concerned. Since these are the only two operations about which we make any assumptions, no further assumptions for closure are necessary. The concept of closure is an important one. Not all sets are closed with respect to a given operation. For example, the set of *even* numbers is closed with respect to addition, but the set of *odd* numbers is not closed to addition, since the sum of two odd numbers is not in the set. Again, the set of natural numbers is not closed to subtraction, nor is it closed to division, as we have already noted when defining a binary operation. There is no natural number $(5 - 8)$, for example, nor is there a natural number $\frac{2}{3}$ or $\frac{7}{4}$.

the assumptions for addition

Assumption A$_1$. If a and b are any two natural numbers, then $a + b = b + a$.

This is the *commutative law* for the addition of natural numbers. It is the basis for saying that addition is "reversible," or that "the addition facts come in pairs."

Assumption A$_2$. If a, b and c are any natural numbers, then $a + (b + c) = (a + b) + c$.

This is the *associative law* for the addition of natural numbers. It makes possible the addition of three or more natural numbers, as shown below.

$$\begin{array}{ll} 8 & a \\ 3 & b \\ \underline{9} & c \\ 20 & \end{array}$$

Fig. 4-8

Several important points should be noted here in connection with the assumptions for addition. In the first place, adding a column of numbers either "downward" or "upward" and getting the same result illustrates the use of the commutative and associative laws. Adding downward means $(8 + 3) + 9$; adding upward means $(9 + 3) + 8$. In other words, this implies that $(a + b) + c = (c + b) + a$. Is this true? Here is the proof:

$$\begin{aligned} (a + b) + c &= a + (b + c) && \text{[by Assumption A}_2\text{]} \\ &= (b + c) + a && \text{[by Assumption A}_1\text{]} \\ &= (c + b) + a && \text{[by Assumption A}_1\text{]} \end{aligned}$$

In the second place, we have assumed only that $a + (b + c) = (a + b) + c$. Nothing has been said as yet about the number $(a + b + c)$. But, $a + (b + c)$ has a meaning; it is the unique natural number obtained by adding two natural numbers, by Assumption C$_1$. Similarly for the meaning of $(a + b) + c$. Since these two expressions are assumed to be equal, we define $(a + b + c)$ to be the natural number obtained by inserting parentheses in either way. This idea can be extended still further. It is not difficult, on the basis of our assumptions, to prove the theorem that if a, b, c, and d are natural numbers, then

$$[(a + b) + c] + d = (a + b) + (c + d).$$

The theorem can be extended further to apply to the sum of any number of natural numbers: $a + b + c + d + \ldots + k$.

In the third place, although the commutative and associative laws may seem trite, they are not. For example, subtraction as you know it (for we have not yet admitted it as an operation) is neither commutative nor associative:

$$(a) \ 3 - 10 \neq 10 - 3$$
$$(b) \ (9 - 6) - 2 \neq 9 - (6 - 2)$$

Finally, with these assumptions it is possible to prove other simple relations between the natural numbers.

Example. Given that a, b, and c are natural numbers, prove that

$$b + (a + c) = c + (a + b).$$

Proof:

$$
\begin{aligned}
b + (a + c) &= b + (a + c) \quad \text{[by identity (P$_1$)]} \\
&= (a + c) + b \quad \text{[by (A$_1$)]} \\
&= (c + a) + b \quad \text{[by (A$_1$)]} \\
&= c + (a + b) \quad \text{[by (A$_2$)]}
\end{aligned}
$$

the assumptions for multiplication

Assumption M$_1$. If a and b are any two natural numbers, then

$$a \times b = b \times a.$$

This is the *commutative* law for the multiplication of natural numbers. It may also be written $ab = ba$. It is the basis for saying that multiplication is "reversible," or that "the multiplication facts come in pairs."

Assumption M$_2$. If a, b, and c are any natural numbers, then $(a \times b) \times c = a \times (b \times c)$.

This is the *associative* law for the multiplication of natural numbers. It may also be written $(ab)c = a(bc)$. Just as the associative law for addition could be generalized for any number of natural numbers, so the associative law for multiplication with natural numbers can be extended. Thus, abc means $(ab)c$ or $a(bc)$; and $[(ab)c]d = (ab)(cd)$, etc.

Assumption M₃. If a, b, and c are natural numbers, then $a \times (b + c) = (a \times b) + (a \times c)$.

This is the *distributive* law for multiplication with respect to addition. It can also be written: $a(b + c) = ab + ac$. By extension, it can be proved that $a(b + c + d) = ab + ac + ad$.

It is this law which is involved when multiplying numbers with two or more places. For example:

1. $3 \times 27 = 3 \times (20 + 7) = 3 \times 20 + 3 \times 7$
$$= \quad 60 \quad + \quad 21 \quad = 81$$

2. $\begin{array}{r} 324 \\ 6 \\ \hline 1944 \end{array}$ $\begin{aligned} 6 \times 324 &= 6 \times (300 + 20 + 4) \\ &= 6 \times 300 + 6 \times 20 + 6 \times 4 \\ &= 1800 + 120 + 24 = 1944 \end{aligned}$

3. $\begin{array}{r} 14 \\ 25 \\ \hline 70 \\ 28 \\ \hline 350 \end{array}$ $\begin{aligned} 25 \times 14 &= (20 + 5) \times 14 \\ &= (5 + 20) \times 14 \\ \\ &= 5 \times 14 + 20 \times 14 \\ &= 70 + 280 = 350 \end{aligned}$

other needed assumptions

It might seem as though these seven assumptions would provide for all the properties of the natural numbers and the operations with these numbers as we ordinarily use the counting numbers of arithmetic. But such is not the case. We list five remaining assumptions that are still needed.

Assumption O₁. There exists a natural number, designated as "1," with the property that $a \times 1 = 1 \times a = a$, where a is any natural number.

This is clearly suggested by intuitive experience; $1 \times 3 = 3$, $1 \times 4 = 4$, etc. The "1" is called the *identity element*.[3] None of the previous assumptions provided for this relationship.

Assumption O₂. For any two natural numbers a and b, one and only one of the following alternatives holds:

---

[3] The identity element is also sometimes called the unit element; in this text we shall call it the identity element.

1. $a = b$.

2. There is a natural number x such that $a + x = b$.

3. There is a natural number y such that $a = b + y$.

This is a technical way of saying that for any two natural numbers a and b, exactly one of these statements is true: (1) $a = b$; or (2) $a < b$; or (3) $a > b$. This idea of order or rank will be seen later to be very important.

Assumption O₃. For all natural numbers, if $a + c = b + c$, then $a = b$.

This is the law of cancellation for addition.

Assumption O₄. For all natural numbers, if $a \times c = b \times c$, then $a = b$.

This is the law of cancellation for multiplication.

Assumption O₅. If a set of natural numbers includes 1 and also includes $k + 1$ whenever it includes k, then the set includes every natural number.

This is sometimes called the law of finite induction, or the principle of *mathematical induction*. What it means, essentially, is this: if whatever holds true for any n also holds true for $n + 1$, then it holds true for all n. This assumption will be found useful when extending the number system to include more than the natural numbers.

SUMMARY OF ASSUMPTIONS FOR THE NATURAL NUMBERS

We now restate briefly for the reader's convenience the twelve basic assumptions which are necessary for the system of natural numbers.

C₁. For every a and b, there is a unique sum s, equal to $a + b$. Closure for Addition

C₂. For every a and b, there is a unique product p, equal to ab. Closure for Multiplication

A₁. $a + b = b + a$. Commutative Law for Addition

A₂. $a + (b + c) = (a + b) + c$. Associative Law for Addition

M₁. $ab = ba$. Commutative Law for Multiplication

M₂. $a(bc) = (ab)c.$ Associative Law for Multiplication

M₃. $a(b + c) = ab + ac.$ Distributive Law for Multiplication over Addition

O₁. $a \times 1 = 1 \times a = a.$ Identity Element

O₂. $a = b,$ or $a > b,$ Assumption of Order
or $a < b.$

O₃. If $a + c = b + c,$ then $a = b.$ Cancellation Law for Addition

O₄. If $ac = bc,$ then $a = b.$ Cancellation Law for Multiplication

O₅. If what holds for any n also Principle of Mathematical Induction
holds for $n + 1,$ it holds for
all $n.$

EXERCISE 4–2

1. Explain the term *closure*. Are the natural numbers closed with respect to subtraction? with respect to division?

2. Consider the set of natural numbers 1, 2, 3, . . . 20, inclusive. Is this set closed with respect to addition? with respect to multiplication?

3. Which of the following sets are closed?

(a) The even numbers with respect to multiplication.
(b) The even numbers with respect to division.
(c) The odd numbers with respect to multiplication.
(d) The odd numbers with respect to division.
(e) The squares of the natural numbers.

4. State the assumption or assumptions which justify each of the following statements, where the letters represent natural numbers:

(a) $1 + 2 = 2 + 1$
(b) $p + q = q + p$
(c) $(m + n)$ is a natural number
(d) $(5 + 1) + 4 = 5 + (1 + 4)$
(e) $a + (x + y) = (a + x) + y$
(f) $(5 + 9) + 3 = 3 + (5 + 9)$

5. Which of the following are commutative?

(a) Leaving the house and arriving at the office.
(b) Stepping on the gas and putting on the brake.
(c) Signing your name and address.
(d) Signing your name and blotting the signature.

6. Prove each of the following, with the letters representing natural numbers; justify each step or transformation by reference to a specific assumption from the basic list:

(a) $(m + n) + (p + q) = (p + q) + (m + n)$
(b) $(a + b) + c = a + (c + b)$
(c) $(x + y) + z = z + (x + y)$
(d) $(a + b) + c = b + (a + c)$
(e) $(m + n) + p = (m + p) + n$
(f) $(c + a) + b = (a + b) + c$
(g) $[(a + b) + c] + d = (a + b) + (c + d)$

7. Explain the associativity of multiplication by using as a model the volume of a rectangular solid and showing "intuitively" that $V = l(wh) = (lw)h$.

8. State the assumption or assumptions which justify each of the following statements, where the letters are natural numbers:

(a) $(8 \times 9) \times 3 = 8 \times (9 \times 3)$ (b) $(3 + 5) \times 7 = 7 \times (3 + 5)$
(c) $7(3 + 5) = 7 \times 3 + 7 \times 5$ (d) $(6 \times 8) \times 2 = 6 \times (8 \times 2)$

9. Find the value of each of the following:

(a) $4 \times (3 + 7)$ (b) $4 \times 3 + 7$
(c) $4 + 3 \times 7$ (d) $(4 + 3) \times 7$

10. State the assumption(s) which justify each of the following statements, where the letters stand for natural numbers:

(a) $uv = vu$ (b) $(xy)z = x(yz)$
(c) $x(y + z) = xy + xz$ (d) $ap + aq = a(p + q)$
(e) $(x + y)z = z(x + y)$ (f) $(m + x) + k = m + (x + k)$

11. Find the value of each of the following without using pencil and paper; try to use an appropriate assumption as a short cut:

(a) $(873 \times 2) \times 5 = ?$ (b) $(129 \times 6) + (129 \times 4) = ?$
(c) $698 + (456 + 2) = ?$ (d) $(37 \times 92) + (37 \times 8) = ?$

12. Prove each of the following, where the letters represent natural numbers; justify each step or transformation by reference to a specific assumption from the basic list:

(a) $(a + b) = ac + bc$ (b) $a(b + c) = (c + b)a$

13. Prove or disprove the statement:

$$m + (pq) = (m + p)(m + q).$$

14. Which of the following expressions represent a natural number? (a) $(8 - 5)$; (b) $(6 \div 3)$; (c) $(5 - 8)$; (d) $(5 \div 2)$; (e) $(2 \div 5)$; (f) $(3 \div 6)$.

15. If m and n represent natural numbers, which of the following expressions always represent a natural number? $(m + n)$; $(m - n)$; mn; $(m \div n)$. In the case of those which do not, what condition must be fulfilled by m and n in order that those expressions will always represent natural numbers?

16. Does the commutative law hold for subtraction when using the natural numbers? Does it hold for division?

17. Does the associative law hold with natural numbers for subtraction? For division?

18. We have assumed a distributive law "for multiplication with respect to addition," (M_3), which states that $a(b + c) = ab + ac$. Can you state a distributive law "for addition with respect to multiplication"? Does it hold for the natural numbers? Illustrate. Compare your answers to your solution for number 13.

19. What is meant by the generalized distributive law for multiplication over addition? Express it in symbolic form.

20. Show how each of the following expressions could be true by inserting parentheses in appropriate places:

(a) $72 \div 4 \cdot 2 + 1 = 6$
(b) $72 \div 4 \cdot 2 + 1 = 10$
(c) $72 \div 4 \cdot 2 + 1 = 8$
(d) $72 \div 4 \cdot 2 + 1 = 37$

21. Show by means of sets of points designated by A and B in Fig. 4–9a that the commutative law holds for addition and for multiplication. (Addition may be interpreted as the union of two sets, $P \cup Q$; multiplication as the intersection of two sets, $P \cap Q$).

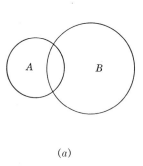

(a)   (b)

Fig. 4-9

22. Show by use of point sets that the associative law holds for addition and for multiplication (Fig. 4–9b).

23. By using point sets, illustrate or verify the distributive law for multiplication, $A(B + C) = AB + AC$ (Fig. 4–9b).

24. Given the example $5 + 3 \times 4 = $?, three pupils gave the following answers:

(a) $5 + 3 \times 4 = 8 \times 4 = 32$
(b) $5 + 3 \times 4 = 5 + 12 = 17$
(c) $5 + 3 \times 4 = (5 + 3) \times (5 + 4) = 72$

Which is correct? Generalize the three "solutions" and show by point sets why they are correct or incorrect.

25. Discuss the meaning and significance of the statement: "Number is a synthesis of the inclusion of categories and of serial order."

THE POSITIVE AND NEGATIVE INTEGERS AND ZERO

inverse operations

An operation which "restores" what another operation has done is called an *inverse* operation. Boiling water changes it to steam; condensing (cooling) the steam restores it to water; these are inverse operations. The inverse of addition is subtraction; the inverse of multiplication is division; the inverse of raising a number to the *n*th power is finding the principal *n*th root. Any two inverse operations performed in succession leave the number unchanged.

In the light of the above, we may define the operation of subtraction by means of the equations

$$a - b = x \quad \text{if} \quad b + x = a. \tag{1}$$

These equations say, in effect, that a new number represented by $a - b$ is the result of a new operation, subtraction. They tell us further that this new number, which is designated either by $(a - b)$ or by x, is such that when it is added to b the result is a. We thus define the operation of subtraction in terms of the operation of addition. There is nothing strange about that; every youngster "knows" that if you subtract 2 from 8 the resulting 6 is what you have to add to 2 to get the 8 back again.

The rub comes that when dealing with the natural numbers, we are at a loss to say what, for example, $3 - 7$ means. By the definition of subtraction, $(3 - 7)$ means that number which, when added to 7, gives 3. But there is no such number among the natural numbers. Remember that although addition is undefined, it implies the concept of an ordered sequence. It is clear then that we could never arrive at 3 by *counting* beyond 7. In short, subtraction in the realm of natural numbers is not always possible. Using the twelve postulates set forth above for the natural numbers, the operation of subtraction, as indicated by $a - b$, where a and b are natural numbers, is possible only if $b < a$; if $b \geqq a$, the operation is meaningless, since there is no natural number produced by the operation. In other words, the natural numbers are not closed under subtraction. This is a serious gap in the number system, for it is desirable that an operation be omni-possible in any system under consideration.

The only other operation included in our set of postulates for the natural numbers is multiplication, also undefined. The inverse of multiplication is division. We did imply that multiplying might be regarded as repeated addition, that is, the addition of equal sets; hence division can be regarded as repeated subtraction, or as the subtraction of equal sets. But just as we defined subtraction in terms of addition by saying $(a - b)$ is the number which, when added to b, gives a, so we may define division[4] in terms of multiplication by saying

$$\frac{a}{b} = x \text{ if } bx = a; \tag{2}$$

That is, a/b is the number which, when multiplied by b, gives a, provided $b \neq 0$. Here again we find that when dealing with the natural numbers, the operation of division is not always possible. What, for example, is the natural number which corresponds to $\frac{7}{5}$? What natural number when multiplied by 5 gives 7? Surely not 1, nor 2, nor any natural number greater than 2. Thus the operation of division is not omnipossible in the realm of natural numbers. The natural numbers are not closed under division. And so we have another serious gap which needs our attention.

The first of these two limitations can be remedied by taking two significant steps: (1) by creating the number zero, and (2) by creating the positive and negative integers.

the role of zero

As we shall see in Chapter 6, one role assigned to the symbol zero, 0, is that of a placeholder in our system of numeration. This is a very significant meaning and use for the symbol. In this capacity, zero is merely a numeral or a digit; it is neither a counting number nor a natural number. But it will now serve our purpose well if we assign an additional role or meaning to zero. We shall deliberately make zero a number by calling it a number. By thus creating the number zero, we have clearly enlarged or extended our conception of what a number is. In its new role, zero now means "none," that is, zero as a

---

[4] Note that $\frac{a}{b}$ is to be read "a divided by b"; the notation $\frac{a}{b}$ instead of $a \div b$ for the operation of division is generally considered preferable.

number may be regarded as the cardinal number of the null set, or of all empty sets. In this sense it tells "how many" books there are on an empty shelf, or how many home runs the baseball team made in a scoreless inning.

We may therefore define zero as a number in terms of natural numbers and the basic undefined operations of addition and multiplication by means of the equations:

$$a + 0 = a \tag{3}$$
$$\text{and} \quad a \cdot 0 = 0, \tag{4}$$

where a is any natural number. These definitions of zero are consistent with the original meanings of the counting numbers, and so "fit in" with the natural numbers. Thus if a is any number in our newly enlarged system, namely, the natural numbers and zero, it is clear that both the commutative and the associative principles hold for addition:

$$0 + a = a,$$
$$a + 0 = a;$$
$$\text{and} \quad (a + b) + 0 = a + (b + 0) = a + b;$$
$$\text{also,} \quad 0 + 0 = 0.$$

Furthermore, $a - 0 = a$, since by definition, we must add a (the "remainder" or difference) to 0 to obtain a (the minuend). Accordingly, we see that $a - a = 0$, since we must add the zero to the second a to obtain the first a. In other words, in our enlarged number system we can now subtract a number from itself; it is still not possible, however, to subtract a larger number from a smaller number.

In the same way, the commutative, associative, and distributive laws for multiplication also hold in our enlarged system of natural numbers and zero. Thus

$$a \cdot 0 = 0 \cdot a = 0$$
$$\text{and} \quad 0 \cdot 0 = 0.$$

Also,
$$(ab) \cdot 0 = 0,$$
$$(ab) \cdot 0 = a(b \cdot 0) = a \cdot 0 = 0,$$
$$\text{and} \quad 0(a + b) = 0.$$

Finally,
$$0(a + b) = 0 \cdot a + 0 \cdot b = 0 + 0 = 0,$$
$$\text{and} \quad a(0 + b) = a \cdot 0 + ab = 0 + ab = ab.$$

Although these laws could be given physical interpretations, we need not be concerned here about such interpretations since we are saying, in effect, "let these be the assumptions" governing our enlarged system, just as we did earlier when we set forth the properties of the natural numbers by stating twelve basic postulates.

We note also that the effect of 0 in addition is the same as that of 1 in multiplication, that is, they both leave a number unchanged:

$$a + 0 = a,$$
$$\text{and} \quad a \cdot 1 = a.$$

We call 0 the *identity element* for addition, just as we called 1 the *identity element* for multiplication.

division with zero

A little reflection will show why we cannot satisfactorily *define* what we mean by using zero as a divisor. Consider the following indicated operations:

$$(1) \ \frac{0}{a} \qquad\qquad (2) \ \frac{a}{0} \qquad\qquad (3) \ \frac{0}{0},$$

where $a \neq 0$. In **1** the result must be a number such that, when multiplied by a, the product is 0. Whatever number is multiplied by zero, the product is 0; hence if one factor of a product is a, the other factor must be 0. Thus since $a \cdot 0 = 0$, we see that $0/a = 0$.

But with **2** and **3** the situation is quite different. In **2**, we are forced to deny that $a \cdot 0 = 0$, and in **3** the result could consistently be any number at all. Hence, in these two cases, *where the divisor is zero*, we can get nowhere within the framework of our definitions and assumptions. So we conclude that division by zero cannot be defined; we leave it undefined. And since we do not define the operation of dividing by zero, it is not admitted as a legitimate operation. When it is admitted, division by zero leads to inconsistencies and paradoxes.

We are now at the point at which zero has been introduced as a number with the same properties (by postulation) as the natural numbers except that zero can never be used as a divisor. This conclusion suggests an additional assumption of equality, as follows:

P₆. If $a = b$ and $c = d$, where $c \neq 0$ and $d \neq 0$, then $a/c = b/d$.

In words, *if equal numbers are divided by equal numbers other than zero, the results are equal.*

We would like to add a final assumption of equality, namely, that if equal numbers are subtracted from equal numbers, the results are equal. But as our number system now stands, we cannot postulate this, for, even when $a = b$ and $c = d$, we can say that $a - c = b - d$ only if $c \leq a$ and $d \leq b$; if $c > a$ and $d > b$, the results are (as yet) undefined. At this juncture we take the second step by creating the positive and negative integers in order to make subtraction omnipossible.

the integers

Keeping the symbolism that $(a - b)$, the difference of two natural numbers, represents another number (natural or not), we note intuitively that $(3 - 5)$ is the same as $(6 - 8)$. It seems "reasonable" that whatever is added to 5 to give 3 is the same as what must be added to 8 to give 6. We are led to say, intuitively, that the two pairs, $(3 - 5)$ and $(6 - 8)$, are equal; that is, they are different names for the same number. We call this number "-2" (read "negative two"); we could just as well represent it by $(5 - 7)$, or $(30 - 32)$, or $(98 - 100)$. Notice that the number $(5 - 7)$ is different from the number $(7 - 5)$. The number $(7 - 5)$, $(32 - 30)$, or $(100 - 98)$ is called "$+2$" (read "positive two") to distinguish it from the number $(5 - 7)$, $(30 - 32)$, or $(98 - 100)$. When we use pairs of natural numbers in this way (by ordering them), we are using *integers*.

An integer is defined as an ordered pair of natural numbers (a, b). There are two ways of designating an ordered pair of natural numbers to represent an integer: the symbol (a, b) in this connection means the same as the symbol $(a - b)$. The reader should be aware that both methods are in common use; some writers use one, some the other, despite the fact that the notation (a, b) resembles the notation used in analytic geometry to designate a point in a system of coordinates. The context generally avoids possible confusion. You may think it rather peculiar to represent an integer (a new kind of number) by means of an ordered pair of natural numbers, say $(3 - 4)$; but this is no more peculiar than representing a fraction (also a new kind of number) by means of an ordered pair of natural numbers and writing it, say, as $\frac{3}{4}$ or $3 \div 4$, or $3/4$.

equality of integers

Any integer, be it positive, zero, or negative, can be represented as the difference $(a - b)$ of two natural numbers a and b. If $a > b$, then the number $(a - b)$ is a positive integer; if $a = b$, then $(a - b)$ is the zero integer; if $a < b$, then $(a - b)$ is a negative integer.

We define the equality of two integers $(a - b)$ and $(c - d)$ as follows:

$$(a - b) = (c - d) \text{ if and only if } (a + d) = (b + c). \qquad \textbf{(D}_1\textbf{)}$$

For example, $(7 - 11) = (2 - 6)$ because $7 + 6 = 11 + 2$; both pairs represent the integer $^-4$. Similarly, $(8 - 5) = (12 - 9)$ because $8 + 9 = 5 + 12$; both pairs represent the integer $^+3$.

Equality of two integers does not mean that the symbols used are identical, but rather that the different symbols used to designate the integers are different names for the same integer. It can be shown that the equality of integers is reflexive, symmetric and transitive; in other words, using the alternative notation for integers:

1. $(a, b) = (a, b)$.
2. If $(a, b) = (c, d)$, then $(c, d) = (a, b)$.
3. If $(a, b) = (c, d)$ and $(c, d) = (e, f)$, then $(a, b) = (e, f)$.

properties of the integers

It cannot be overemphasized that the integers are *ordered pairs*. The ordering may be defined formally as follows:

$$(a, b) \gtreqless (c, d) \text{ respectively, according as } (a + d) \gtreqless (b + c). \qquad \textbf{(D}_2\textbf{)}$$

For example:

$(8, 5) > (7, 6)$, since $8 + 6 > 5 + 7$, or $14 > 12$.
$(5, 2) < (9, 2)$, since $5 + 2 < 2 + 9$, or $7 < 11$.
$(6, 9) < (8, 8)$, since $6 + 8 < 9 + 8$, or $14 < 17$.
$(8, 5) = (11, 8)$, since $8 + 8 = 5 + 11$, or $16 = 16$.

We define the operation of addition for integers by the equation

$$(a, b) + (c, d) = (a + c, b + d). \qquad \textbf{(D}_3\textbf{)}$$

For example:

$(6, 4) + (8, 3) = (6 + 8, 4 + 3)$, or $^+2 + {}^+5 = {}^+7$.
$(2, 5) + (10, 2) = (2 + 10, 5 + 2)$, or $^-3 + {}^+8 = {}^+5$.
$(5, 1) + (3, 10) = (5 + 3, 1 + 10)$, or $^+4 + {}^-7 = {}^-3$.
$(2, 7) + (8, 12) = (2 + 8, 7 + 12)$, or $^-5 + {}^-4 = {}^-9$.

Now we can see why subtraction with the integers is omnipossible. By definition of subtraction, to subtract (c, d) from (a, b) means to find an integer (m, n) such that

$$(a, b) = (c, d) + (m, n). \tag{1}$$

By addition, we get: $(a, b) = (c + m, d + n).$ \hfill (2)

From the definition of equal integers, we have:

$$a + d + n = b + c + m. \tag{3}$$

But equation (3) is true only if:

$$m = a + d \text{ and } n = b + c. \tag{4}$$

From (1) we have:

$$(a, b) - (c, d) = (m, n). \tag{5}$$

Substituting from (4) in (5) gives:

$$(a, b) - (c, d) = (a + d, b + c). \tag{6}$$

And since a, b, c and d are natural numbers, the sums $a + d$ and $b + c$ always exist. Hence $(a, b) - (c, d)$ always exists, that is, subtraction is omnipossible.

Having established the operation of subtraction as always possible, we can now state the final assumption of equality without restrictions.

P₇. If $a = b$ and $c = d$, then $a - c = b - d$, where a, b, c and d are integers, not natural numbers.

In other words, in the realm of the integers, if equal numbers are subtracted from equal numbers, the results are equal.

Finally, we can define the operation of multiplication of integers as follows:

$$(a, b) \cdot (c, d) = (ac + bd, bc + ad). \tag{D_4}$$

For example:

$$(6, 2) \cdot (8, 3) = (48 + 6, 16 + 18), \text{ or } (^+4) \cdot (^+5) = {}^+20$$
$$(10, 7) \cdot (4, 6) = (40 + 42, 28 + 60), \text{ or } (^+3) \cdot (^-2) = {}^-6$$
$$(5, 9) \cdot (7, 4) = (35 + 36, 63 + 20), \text{ or } (^-4) \cdot (^+3) = {}^-12$$
$$(2, 5) \cdot (4, 9) = (8 + 45, 20 + 18), \text{ or } (^-3) \cdot (^-5) = {}^+15$$

Notice carefully that we did not *prove* the "rule of signs" for multiplying the integers; it derives from the definition of multiplication in the system of assumptions and definitions we have used here. In effect, we postulate that "minus times minus is plus," or that the product of two negative integers is a positive integer. However, in other systems of assumptions and definitions this principle can be proved.

the system of positive and negative integers and zero

The integers, together with zero, can be ordered as follows:

... $(a, a + 3)$; $(a, a + 2)$; $(a, a + 1)$; (a, a); $(a + 1, a)$; $(a + 2, a)$; ...

Or, in more conventional form:

$$..., {}^-n, ... {}^-3, {}^-2, {}^-1, 0, {}^+1, {}^+2, {}^+3, ... {}^+n, ...$$

Together, the positive and negative integers and zero constitute a *different number system* from the system of natural numbers. We have enlarged the system not merely by adding "negative numbers" and zero to the basic system of natural numbers, but by modifying the nature of the numbers through changes in postulates and definitions. It is true that the natural number 2, for example, "looks like" the integer $^+2$; indeed, they have many properties in common. Nevertheless they belong to different number systems.[5] In a sense, the integers may be regarded as different kinds of numbers. Actually, the integers $^+1$ and $^-1$ represent *relations;* $^+1$ is the relation of $n + 1$ to n, and $^-1$ is the relation of n to $n + 1$. On the other hand, the signless natural number 1 is not a relation at all, but a *cardinal number*, that is, a class of classes. Thus the positive integers should not be identified with the signless natural numbers.

EXERCISE 4–3

1. Prove the reflexivity of equal integers; that is, prove that $(a, b) = (a, b)$.

2. Prove the symmetric property of equality of integers; that is, prove that if $(a, b) = (c, d)$, then $(c, d) = (a, b)$.

3. Prove the transitivity of equal integers; that is, prove that if $(a, b) = (c, d)$ and $(c, d) = (e, f)$, then $(a, b) = (e, f)$.

4. Prove that the sum of two positive integers is always a positive integer.

5. Prove that the sum of two negative integers is always a negative integer.

6. By using general number pairs, illustrate the "rules" for subtraction of positive and negative integers.

7. Prove that the commutative law for multiplication holds for the integers; that is, prove that $(a, b) (c, d) = (c, d) (a, b)$.

8. Show, by using general number pairs, that the product of any integer and zero is zero.

---

[5] In another sense, because of isomorphism, the natural numbers are "embedded within the integers"; but that need not concern us here.

9. Prove the associative law for addition of the integers; that is, prove that

$$(a, b) + [(c, d) + (e, f)] = [(a, b) + (c, d)] + (e, f).$$

10. Prove that $(b, c) = (m, m)$ if and only if $b = c$.

11. Prove that the integer $(a + 1, a)$ is greater than zero; that is, prove that $(a + 1, a) > (a, a)$.

12. Prove that no integer exists between 0 and $^+1$.

13. (a) Discuss the two meanings of zero alluded to in this chapter; (b) explain why division by zero is not admitted as an operation.

14. Find the fallacy in the following:

Let
$$a = x;$$
Then
$$a^2 = ax,$$
$$a^2 - x^2 = ax - x^2,$$
$$(a + x)(a - x) = x(a - x),$$
$$a + x = x,$$
$$x + x = x,$$
$$2x = x,$$
$$2 = 1.$$

15. Assume that $x + y + z = 0$; then

$$x = -y - z$$
$$y = -x - z$$
$$z = \underline{-x - y}$$

Adding:
$$x + y + z = -2x - 2y - 2z$$
$$(x + y + z) = (-2)(x + y + z)$$
$$1 = -2$$

Where is the fallacy?

FOR FURTHER READING AND STUDY

1. Adler, Irving. *The New Mathematics*. New York: John Day, 1958. Chapters 1 and 2.
2. Allendoerfer, C. B. and Oakley, C. O. *Principles of Mathematics*. New York: McGraw-Hill, 1955. Chapter 2: "The Number System."
3. Banks, J. Houston. *Elements of Mathematics*. Boston: Allyn and Bacon, 1956. Chapter 3: "What Is a Number?"
4. Dantzig, Tobias. *Number: The Language of Science*. New York: Macmillan, 1930. Chapters 1, 2, and 4.
5. Dubisch, Roy. *The Nature of Number*. New York: Ronald Press, 1952. Chapters 3–5.
6. Jones, Burton W. *Elementary Concepts of Mathematics*. New York: Macmillan, 1947. Chapter 2: "The Positive Integers and Zero."
7. Richardson, M. *Fundamentals of Mathematics*. New York: Macmillan, 1958. Chapters 3 and 4.

CHAPTER 5

Extending the Number System

God made the integers; all else is the
work of Man.

—Leopold Kronecker

THE RATIONAL NUMBERS

the need for further extension

We have seen that in order to make subtraction an omnipossible operation, the system of natural numbers had to be extended to embrace the positive and negative integers and zero. A moment's consideration will reveal that division is not omnipossible either in the system of natural numbers or in the system of integers.

Division is the inverse of multiplication, and is defined as follows: If a and b are any two numbers in a given number system, and there is a number q in the system such that $bq = a$, then q is called the *quotient* of the division of a by b, and is written $a \div b$, or preferably, a/b, where $b \neq 0$.

In the natural number system, $8 \div 4 = 2$, $\dfrac{12}{3} = 4$, etc. But there are many divisions that are not possible: for example, there is no natural number for $\dfrac{10,}{3}$ since $1 \times 3 = 3$, $2 \times 3 = 6$, $3 \times 3 = 9$,

$4 \times 3 = 12$, etc. Similarly, there are no natural numbers for $\dfrac{3}{4}$, for $\dfrac{12}{5}$,

$\dfrac{8}{6}$ or $\dfrac{18}{12}$. Likewise, in the system of positive and negative integers and zero, no quotient exists for $(6, 2) \div (5, 2)$, or for $(8, 3) \div (10, 2)$. It becomes apparent, therefore, that if division is to be made omnipossible, we shall have to create a new number system with its own definitions and assumptions. The new numbers we shall create are called the *rational* numbers, and they will be built upon the system of integers and zero.

the rational numbers

We define a rational number as the quotient of any two integers. More precisely:

A rational number is an ordered pair of integers, written (p, q) or p/q, when it is understood that $q \neq 0$.   (**D₁**)

The reader will recognize, of course, that what he has always known in school arithmetic as a common fraction, proper or improper, is simply a rational number; for example, $\frac{3}{5}$, $\frac{5}{2}$, $\frac{4}{4}$, $\frac{6}{3}$, $\frac{3}{6}$, $\frac{2}{1}$, $\frac{1}{2}$, etc. Reflexivity, symmetry, and transitivity of equality for rational numbers can be proved.

The equality of two rational numbers is readily established by definition, as follows:

Two rational numbers, (a, b) and (c, d) are equal if and only if $ad = bc$.   (**D₂**)

This is what justifies, logically, the "reduction" of fractions, upwards or downwards; for example,

$$\frac{3}{4} = \frac{6}{8} \text{ because } 3 \times 8 = 4 \times 6;$$

$$\frac{10}{25} = \frac{2}{5} \text{ because } 10 \times 5 = 25 \times 2; \text{ etc.}$$

More generally, if a, b, c, and d are natural numbers, then

$$\frac{^{+}a}{^{+}b} \text{ and } \frac{^{-}a}{^{-}b} \text{ are positive rational numbers,}$$

and $\dfrac{-a}{+b}$ and $\dfrac{+a}{-b}$ are negative rational numbers.

It will be seen from the law of signs previously referred to, together with the definition of equal fractions, that we have:

$$\frac{-a}{+b} = \frac{+a}{-b}, \quad \text{and} \quad \frac{-a}{-b} = \frac{+a}{+b}.$$

If we further agree to use only the form $(+a, +b)$ for positive rationals, and only the form $(-a, +b)$ for negative rationals, we can then order the rational numbers as follows:

$$\frac{a}{b} \underset{<}{\overset{>}{\gtrless}} \frac{c}{d} \text{ according as } ad \underset{<}{\overset{>}{\gtrless}} bc. \tag{D\textsubscript{3}}$$

From this it will be seen that:

1. Every positive rational number is greater than every negative rational number.

2. Every positive rational number is greater than the rational number $0/q$, or zero.

3. Every negative rational number is less than zero.

Note: From now on we shall omit the $+$ sign from positive integers; they should not be regarded as natural numbers, however, since we have put *them* behind us for the moment. We are now in the realm of rational numbers, built upon the integers.

Examples.

1. $\dfrac{+3}{4} > \dfrac{-5}{2}$; since $(3) \cdot (2) > (4) \cdot (-5)$, or $+6 > -20$.

2. $\dfrac{2}{3} > 0$, or $\dfrac{2}{3} > \dfrac{0}{a}$; since $(2) \cdot (a) > (3) \cdot (0)$, or $2a > 0$.

3. $\dfrac{-3}{5} < 0$, or $\dfrac{-3}{5} < \dfrac{0}{a}$; since $(-3) \cdot (a) < (5) \cdot (0)$, or $-3a < 0$.

addition of rational numbers

We define addition of rational numbers as follows:

$$\frac{a}{b} + \frac{c}{d} = \frac{ad + bc}{bd} \tag{D\textsubscript{4}}$$

For example:

$$\frac{2}{3} + \frac{4}{5} = \frac{(2)(5) + (3)(4)}{(3)(5)} = \frac{22}{15}.$$

Or, more generally, with positive and negative integers:

$$\frac{^-3}{5} + \frac{7}{8} = \frac{(^-3)(8) + (5)(7)}{(5)(8)} = \frac{^-24 + {^+35}}{40} = \frac{^+11}{40}.$$

It can also be shown, in terms of the definitions of addition and subtraction, that subtraction with the rational numbers is omnipossible.

multiplication of rational numbers

The operation of multiplication with rational numbers is defined by the relation:

$$\frac{a}{b} \cdot \frac{c}{d} = \frac{ac}{bd}. \qquad (\mathbf{D}_5)$$

Interestingly enough, whereas the commutative law for multiplication has to be assumed for the natural numbers, it can be proved for the integers and also for the rational numbers. We give the proof for the rational numbers, based on the properties of the integers:

By definition $\mathbf{D}_5$: $\qquad \frac{a}{b} \cdot \frac{c}{d} = \frac{ac}{bd},$ $\qquad (1)$

And $\qquad \frac{c}{d} \cdot \frac{a}{b} = \frac{ca}{db}.$ $\qquad (2)$

But $\qquad \frac{ac}{bd} = \frac{ca}{db},$ since $ac = ca$, and $bd = db$. $\qquad (3)$

Therefore $\qquad \frac{a}{b} \cdot \frac{c}{d} = \frac{c}{d} \cdot \frac{a}{b},$ $\qquad (4)$

(By the assumption of equality: numbers equal to the same number are equal to each other.)

It is also possible, from the definition $(\mathbf{D}_5)$ of multiplication for fractions, to prove that the inverse operation, division, is omnipossible with the rational numbers. Thus:

$$\frac{a}{b} \div \frac{c}{d} = \frac{p}{q} \text{ if } \frac{a}{b} = \frac{c}{d} \cdot \frac{p}{q} = \frac{cp}{dq},$$

or, that is, if $adq = bcp.$ $\qquad (1)$

But $\qquad adq = bcp$ if $p = ad$ and $q = bc.$ $\qquad (2)$

Hence $\qquad \frac{a}{b} \div \frac{c}{d} = \frac{ad}{bc}.$ $\qquad (3)$

Needless to say, division by zero is at all times excluded. Equation 3 justifies the familiar rule of school arithmetic that "to divide by a fraction, invert the divisor and multiply."

rational numbers and fractions

By now the reader will surely recognize the rational numbers as our old friends, the common fractions of arithmetic. The alternative notations $\frac{a}{b}$, a/b and (a, b) should no longer be bothersome. We have defined a rational number a/b as the quotient of any two integers; excluding division by zero, this definition would include not only all the common fractions, whether "proper" or "improper," but also the natural numbers, the integers, and zero. Thus $\frac{1}{3}$, $\frac{2}{3}$, $\frac{3}{1}$, $\frac{3}{2}$, $\frac{3}{3}$, $\frac{0}{3}$ are all rational numbers.

The fraction $\frac{a}{b}$ may be interpreted in several ways when applied to concrete realities.

1. Dividing a elements into b equal sets, and asking how many elements there are in each of the equal sets.

Example 1. $12/3 = ?$ means how many elements in each set if 12 elements are divided into 3 equal sets? That is: $12 = 3 \times 4$.

2. Dividing a elements into equal sets, each set to have b elements, and asking how many such sets there will be.

Example 2. $12/3 = ?$ means how many sets each containing 3 elements can we make from 12 elements? That is: $12 = 4 \times 3$.

3. Dividing one whole into b equal parts and taking a of those parts.

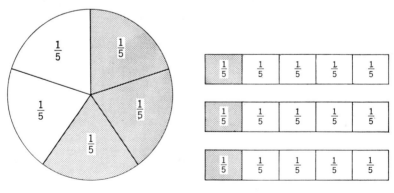

Fig. 5-1   Fig. 5-2

Example 3. $\frac{3}{5}$ means dividing one whole into 5 equal parts and then taking 3 of those equal parts; that is, $\frac{3}{5} = 3(\frac{1}{5})$, or *three fifths of one whole* (Fig. 5–1).

4. Dividing each of a wholes into b equal parts, and then taking one of those parts from each of the a wholes.

Example 4. $\frac{3}{5}$ means dividing each of 3 wholes into 5 equal parts, and then taking 1 of those parts from each whole; that is, $\frac{3}{5} = \frac{1}{5}(3)$ or $\frac{1}{5}$ of *three wholes* (Fig. 5–2).

5. Comparing a with b, that is, a is so-and-so many times as great as b, or a is what part of b.

Example 5. $\frac{3}{2}$ means 3:2, or 3 is $1\frac{1}{2}$ times as great as 2; that is, $3 = \frac{3}{2} \times 2$.

Example 6. $\frac{2}{3}$ means 2:3, or 2 is $\frac{2}{3}$ of 3; that is, $2 = \frac{2}{3} \times 3$.

As for the addition of fractions, this was defined as

$$\frac{a}{b} + \frac{c}{d} = \frac{ad + bc}{bd}. \tag{1}$$

We could just as well have defined addition of fractions as follows:

$$\frac{a}{b} + \frac{c}{d} = \frac{a + c}{b + d}. \tag{2}$$

Indeed, pupils in arithmetic and algebra classes often add fractions in this way, to their teachers' dismay. Yet both these definitions, when applied to appropriate concrete models, can be perfectly meaningful. Thus according to 1, the conventional definition, we would have

$$\frac{2}{3} + \frac{4}{5} = \frac{10}{15} + \frac{12}{15} = \frac{10 + 12}{15} = \frac{22}{15} = \frac{15 + 7}{15} = \frac{15}{15} + \frac{7}{15} = 1\frac{7}{15}$$

Here we deliberately wish the "3" in $\frac{2}{3}$ to mean 3 equal parts of something, and the "5" in $\frac{4}{5}$ to mean 5 equal parts of something else; but we cannot add 2 parts and 4 parts to say 6 parts unless we are assured that the "parts" in each case are alike; 6 parts wouldn't mean much if some of the 6 parts were different from the others. By changing them to fifteenths, however, we can then add 10 fifteenths and 12 fifteenths with the assurance that all 22 fifteenths were 22 "things of the same kind."

On the other hand, suppose a baseball player made 3 runs out of

5 times at bat on Monday, and 2 runs out of 7 times at bat on Tuesday. His combined record for the two days would be meaningfully given by the following addition,

$$\frac{3}{5} + \frac{2}{7} = \frac{3+2}{5+7} = \frac{5}{12},$$

which is the addition of fractions according to equation 2 above.

There are two reasons for preferring to define addition with fractions (or rational numbers) as given by equation 1. In the first place, this is the way in which fractions are commonly used when numbers are applied to concrete situations as *parts* of something. And in the second place, if we did not define or postulate addition as given by equation 1, the integers and the rational numbers would lose their uniqueness; for example, $\frac{3}{1} + \frac{5}{1} = \frac{8}{2}$ instead of $\frac{8}{1}$, or 8.

distribution of the rational numbers

We shall now explain a remarkable property of the rationals, namely, that between any two rational numbers there always exists another rational number. Remember that the rational number system is closed with respect to addition and multiplication, and that subtraction and division (excluding division by zero) are omnipossible. In short, the sum, difference, product, or quotient of any two rational numbers always yields another rational number. Considering this fact (Fig. 5-3), let X be a number midway between any two rational numbers A

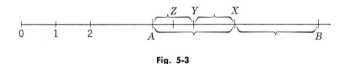

Fig. 5-3

and B, such that $X = (A + B)/2$. Then clearly X is also a rational number, since $(A + B)$ is rational, and therefore $(A + B)/2$ is rational. Similarly, a number Y halfway between the rational numbers A and X must again be a rational number; so also for $Z = (A + Y)/2$, and so on and on and on. It is clear then that between any two rational numbers, *however close they may be*, there must lie not only one more rational number, but an indefinitely large number of rational numbers. Putting it another way, the rational numbers between any two given rationals are numerous without end, or infinitely great. One need but think of all the proper fractions existing between 0 and 1:

$$\tfrac{1}{2}, \tfrac{1}{3}, \tfrac{1}{4}, \tfrac{1}{5}, \cdots; \tfrac{2}{3}, \tfrac{2}{5}, \tfrac{2}{7}, \tfrac{2}{9}, \cdots; \tfrac{3}{4}, \tfrac{3}{5}, \tfrac{3}{7}, \tfrac{3}{8}, \cdots;$$

$$\tfrac{4}{5}, \tfrac{4}{7}, \tfrac{4}{9}, \tfrac{4}{11}, \cdots; \text{etc., etc. } \cdots.$$

to realize the endless number of rationals between 0 and 1. For the time being we shall content ourselves by saying that given any definite natural number N however great one can name or imagine, the number of rational numbers between any two given rationals, however close, will exceed the number N. This means that the points on any segment of a line (no matter how short) are "packed" unbelievably close together. The mathematician says that the points on a line segment constitute a *dense set.*

This notion of the density of the set of rational numbers (or of points on a line segment) is closely related to the concept underlying Archimedes' postulate of continuity in geometry. This postulate says:

If A_1 is any point between two arbitrary points A and B of a straight line, and if points $A_2, A_3, A_4, \ldots$ be chosen so that A_2 lies between A_1 and A_3, A_3 between A_2 and A_4, etc., and if segments AA_1, A_1A_2, A_2A_3, $\ldots$ are equal, then there exists a point A_n, such that B lies between A and A_n.

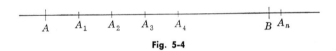

Fig. 5-4

The sense of this postulate is that no matter how small a "unit" segment AA_1 we may select, there is always an integral multiple of that unit, $n \times (AA_1)$, which is greater than any other segment AB no matter how great. In other words, every rational number can be made to correspond to a unique point on a line. This property is a necessary condition for making measurement possible. It emphasizes the distinction between counting and measuring. For the purpose of counting, the natural numbers suffice; but for measuring, neither the natural numbers nor the integers are sufficient. We must create the rational numbers before we can measure.[1]

---

[1] Even the rational numbers are not sufficient for *all* measurements, as will be seen shortly in the section on "Irrational Numbers." This is because not every point on a line can be made to correspond to a rational number.

number fields

The rational numbers are so called because a rational number can always be expressed as the *ratio* of two integers. We have just seen that in the system of rational numbers, all four fundamental operations are omnipossible. For this reason these operations are called *rational operations*. (We shall soon see that extracting a root is not always possible with the rational numbers; hence extracting a root is not a rational operation.) Whenever an operation within a system is omnipossible and always yields a number which is also in the system, we say that the system is closed with respect to that operation. The system of rational numbers is closed with respect to the four fundamental operations. Furthermore, there is an identity element for addition, namely zero, which leaves a number unchanged when added. There is also an identity element for multiplication, namely 1, which leaves a product unchanged. All these properties of a number system are characteristic of a *number field*. We may summarize them as follows, where a, b, and c are numbers in the system.

F_1. $a + b$ is uniquely defined.   Addition is omnipossible.

F_2. ab is uniquely defined.   Multiplication is omnipossible.

F_3. $a + b = b + a$.   Addition is commutative.

F_4. $a + (b + c) = (a + b) + c$.   Addition is associative.

F_5. $ab = ba$.   Multiplication is commutative.

F_6. $a(bc) = (ab)c$.   Multiplication is associative.

F_7. $a(b + c) = ab + ac$.   Multiplication is distributive over addition.

F_8. For any a, there is an element z such that $a + z = a$.   Identity element for addition; $z = 0$.

F_9. For any a, there is an element u such that $a \cdot u = a$.   Identity element for multiplication; $u = 1$.

F_{10}. For any a, there is an element a' such that $a + a' = 0$.   Inverse of addition; $a' = {}^{-}a$, or the negative of the integer a.

F_{11}. For any a, there is an element a'' such that $a(a'') = 1$.   Inverse of multiplication; $a'' = 1/a$, or the reciprocal of the integer a.

Any set of elements or any system of numbers which exhibits these eleven properties is known as a *number field,* and the properties are called *field properties.* The natural numbers do not form a field; neither do the integers. But the rational numbers do form a field.

1. Prove that the commutative and associative laws hold for the addition of rational numbers.

2. Prove that the commutative and associative laws hold for the multiplication of rational numbers.

3. Prove that the distributive law holds for multiplication over addition with respect to rational numbers.

4. Prove, in general, by using ordered pairs of integers, that every positive rational number is greater than zero.

5. Explain why the natural numbers do not form a field.

6. Explain why the integers do not form a field.

7. Prove that if two fractions have the same numerator, the fraction with the larger denominator is the smaller fraction.

8. Prove that if two fractions have the same denominator, the one with the larger numerator is the larger fraction.

9. Which is greater: $7/19$ or $13/31$? How can you tell?

10. Find a rational number between $3/8$ and $4/9$.

11. Prove that if $a/b > x/y$ and $x/y > c/d$, then $a/b > c/d$, where a, b, c, d, x, and y are natural numbers.

12. If the addition of fractions is defined as

$$\frac{a}{b} + \frac{c}{d} = \frac{a+c}{b+d},$$

where a, b, c, and d are integers, prove that the associative law for addition still holds.

13. Explain the difference in meaning between $3\left(\frac{1}{4}\right)$ and $\frac{1}{4}(3)$ when these expressions refer to concrete applications of number. Prove that, in general' $(m)\left(\frac{1}{k}\right) = \left(\frac{1}{k}\right)(m)$, where m and k are any integers.

14. Explain the difference in meaning between $3\left(\frac{1}{4}\right)$ and $\frac{3}{4}(1)$ when referring to concrete applications. Prove that, in general, $a\left(\frac{1}{b}\right) = \left(\frac{a}{b}\right)(1)$, where a and b are any integers.

THE IRRATIONAL NUMBERS

powers and roots

When a product consists of several factors, all of which are alike, the product is called a *power* of that factor. Thus if $r \cdot r \cdot r \cdot \ldots n$ times equals a, we write $r^n = a$, and say: "the *n*th power of r is a."

This process is called *involution*. The inverse operation is called *evolution;* it may be defined as finding a number r, if it exists, such that if repeated n times as a factor it gives a specified number a. We write

$$r = \sqrt[n]{a},$$

and say: "r is the *nth* root of a."

It is quickly seen that with the natural numbers (or the integers) the operation of finding a given root of a given number is not omnipossible. For example, $\sqrt{9} = 3$; but what is the $\sqrt{10}$? There is no natural number which when squared gives 10. Similarly, the $\sqrt[3]{8}$ is 2, but $\sqrt[3]{9}$ does not exist among the natural numbers, that is, there is no natural number k such that $k \cdot k \cdot k = 9$. If we turn to the integers, because of the law of signs when multiplying positive and negative integers, we note that $\sqrt{+9} = {}^{+}3$ and $^{-}3$, that is, there are *two* square roots of $^{+}9$. Or again: there is no cube root of $^{+}9$; only one cube root of $^{+}27$ (among the integers, that is); and no square root of $^{-}9$. (Why?)

The desire to make the operation of finding a root omnipossible forces us to extend the number system again, creating two kinds of new numbers: the *irrational numbers* and the *complex numbers*.

the existence of non-rational numbers

Are there numbers which are not rational? Over two thousand years ago Pythagoras proved that $\sqrt{2}$ was not a rational number, or that $\sqrt{2}$ cannot be expressed as the quotient of two integers. His proof ran essentially as follows. Suppose that $\sqrt{2}$ were rational; that is,

$$\sqrt{2} = \frac{a}{b},$$

where a and b are integers that are relatively prime, that is, a and b have no common factor. Then

$$2 = \left(\frac{a}{b}\right)^2 = \frac{a^2}{b^2},$$

$$\text{or} \qquad 2b^2 = a^2. \qquad (1)$$

From equation 1 we see that a^2 is an even number, since it equals $2b^2$, which is divisible by 2. Hence a is also an even number, since the square of an odd number is always odd. Now if a is an even number, it may be represented by $2k$, where k is any positive integer; hence

$$2b^2 = a^2 = (2k)^2 = 4k^2,$$
$$\text{or } b^2 = 2k^2.$$

Hence b^2 is even, and therefore b is even. Since both a and b are even, the assumption that a and b are relatively prime is contradicted, and therefore the supposition that $\sqrt{2} = a/b$ must be false. Thus there is no rational number which, when squared, gives the rational number 2. This method of proving that the square roots of certain numbers are not rational can be generalized for any rational, integral number N, where N is not the square of another integer.

Simple concrete representations of irrationals such as $\sqrt{2}$ or $\sqrt{3}$ given by the geometric figures in Fig. 5-5, which are self-explanatory.

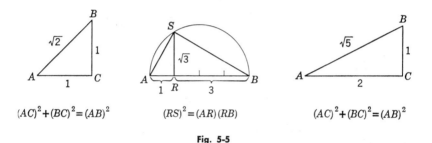

$(AC)^2+(BC)^2=(AB)^2$ $\qquad$ $(RS)^2=(AR)(RB)$ $\qquad$ $(AC)^2+(BC)^2=(AB)^2$

Fig. 5-5

the real numbers

As already intimated, to make the operation of finding the nth roots of numbers an omnipossible operation, two further extensions of the number system are necessary: (1) to make omnipossible the finding of the nth root of *positive* numbers we shall need the *irrational numbers;* and (2) to make omnipossible the finding of the nth root of *negative* numbers, where n is an even integer, we need the *complex numbers.* Let us now turn our attention to problem 1. (See Fig. 5-6.)

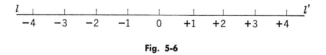

Fig. 5-6

If all the integers are represented by points on the line ll', it is clear that the integers are not only ordered, but also that they are *discrete;*

that is, there are gaps between them. Or, stated a little differently, the integers are successively adjacent; given a specific integer, there is a "next" one, with no other integers between it and its successor (or predecessor).

But this is not true of the rational numbers. If the rationals are represented by points on a line, they form a dense set, as we have already seen. Rational numbers are not adjacent. There is no "next" greater or smaller rational to a given rational number; they are packed tightly so that between any two rationals, however close, there is an infinite number of other rationals. It is easy to prove that no two rationals can be adjacent in the sense that there is no third rational between them. Suppose m/n and p/q were two such adjacent rationals, with $m/n < p/q$. Now let us form a new rational number,

$$K = \frac{m + p}{n + q}.$$

Then according to D_3:

$$\frac{m + p}{n + q} > \frac{m}{n}, \text{ since } mn + np > mn + mq, \text{ or } np > mq;$$

That is $\qquad\qquad\qquad\qquad mq < np;$

Also $\quad \dfrac{m + p}{n + q} < \dfrac{p}{q}$, since $mq + pq < np + pq$, or $mq < np$

But $mq < np$ by hypothesis (since we assumed $\dfrac{m}{n} < \dfrac{q}{p}$; therefore there is another rational number, K, between them, and the supposition that they m/n and p/q are adjacent (or next to each other) is false.

Let us now imagine that all the rational numbers have been identified or placed along a line. The question may then be asked: Have *all* the points on the line been accounted for? Or are there still some gaps? It is a temptation to say yes, all the points on the line have been accounted for. Are not the rational numbers crowded so closely that there are infinitely many more rational numbers between any two given rationals? But wait! Where on the line is the point that corresponds to the number $\sqrt{2}$? Surely there must be such a point! And there is: it is point B, which can be constructed from the diagonal of the square whose side is 1, by swinging the arc AB with point O as a center.

Now we are going to ask you to believe intellectually what neither you nor anyone else can possibly imagine or visualize intuitively. Despite the fact that the rational points are a dense set, they are not a *continuous* set. Contrary to intuition and experience, there are *holes* in the line on which we have labelled all the rational points. We shall see presently that there are infinitely many such gaps; but we are getting ahead of our story.

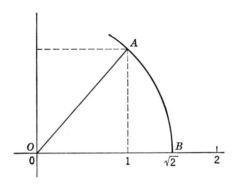

Fig. 5-7

The explanation of these gaps is frankly not easy to understand. We shall not attempt to be rigorous, and will deliberately shun technicalities. We shall say that the gaps are filled by *irrational* numbers. And we shall look upon the points of a line with new eyes. (After all, a line was never defined; it is an utter abstraction.) Think once more of the rational numbers and their point counterparts on a line.

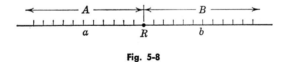

Fig. 5-8

Let us suppose that the point R represents a rational number. We can think of a point as separating all the rational numbers into two sets, A and B, such that (1) both sets contain numbers, (2) every number in B is greater than every number in A, and (3) there is no greatest number in A. This last point is perhaps the most difficult to grasp, but a number such as R,[2] fulfilling these three conditions is called a *cut* in the rational number system.

A cut may be rational or irrational. For example: if set A includes all numbers less than 2, and set B includes all other numbers, then there is a least number in B, namely 2, and we say the cut is *rational*. But it can be proved that there may not be a least number in B, in which case we call the cut *irrational*. For example, if A contains all the negative rational numbers, zero, and all those positive rationals whose square is less than 2, and set B contains all the other rational numbers, then there is no greatest rational in A and no least rational in B. In this case we call the cut $\sqrt{2}$; it is called an *irrational real number* (Fig. 5-9).

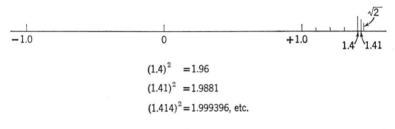

$$(1.4)^2 = 1.96$$
$$(1.41)^2 = 1.9881$$
$$(1.414)^2 = 1.999396, \text{ etc.}$$

Fig. 5-9

The entire set of rational and irrational cuts form a system of numbers called the *real numbers*. At last we have filled all the gaps in the line; it is now not only dense, but *continuous*. A geometric line may now be transformed, so to speak, or be interpreted, in terms of the real numbers. Every point on a line corresponds to a real number; conversely, every real number corresponds to some point on a line. This suggests the Dedekind continuity postulate:

If all points on a line fall into two classes, such that every point in one class lies to the left of every point in the other class, then there exists one and only one point which effects this division of all points into two classes, or which cuts the line in two.

[2] If there were a greatest rational number in A, call it k. Form the number $\dfrac{R+k}{2}$; it is rational. (Why?) Now $k < R$. (Why?) So, $\dfrac{R+k}{2} > k$, but $< R$; so, there is a number greater than k, but still in set A. Thus, there is no greatest rational number in (A).

This is what we mean by a line's being continuous. When we are referring to the points on a line as representing the real numbers, it is called the *continuum*. This concept, a cornerstone of modern mathematical analysis, makes analytical geometry possible.

representing numbers in decimal notation

An *infinite repeating decimal* is a decimal in which a sequence of one or more digits recurs indefinitely; for example, these are repeating decimals:

$$0.3333\ldots \qquad 0.129129\ldots$$
$$0.454545\ldots \qquad 2.8603603\ldots$$

So-called terminating decimals, such as 0.5, 0.72, 0.0387, may be regarded as *finite* repeating decimals. Thus we may say:

$$0.5 \quad = 0.5000\ldots \quad = 0.4999\ldots$$
$$0.72 \quad = 0.72000\ldots \quad = 0.71999\ldots$$
$$0.0387 = 0.0387000\ldots = 0.0386999\ldots$$

If a and b are relatively prime integers, the rational number a/b, when expressed in decimal form, always turns out to be either a finite or an infinite repeating decimal.

In our scale of notation (base 10), the repeating decimal "terminates" if and only if the denominator of a/b is a product of the form $2^m \cdot 5^n$, where m and n are integers 0, 1, 2, 3, ...; that is, if the denominator is the product of multiples of 2 and 5.

Examples.

$$\frac{4}{5} = 0.8 \qquad \frac{5}{16} = 0.3125 \qquad \frac{3}{4} = 0.75 \qquad \frac{3}{25} = 0.12$$

If the denominator is not of this form, then the repeating decimal is infinite.

Examples.

$$\frac{2}{3} = 0.6666\ldots \qquad \frac{5}{11} = 0.454545\ldots \qquad \frac{5}{13} = 0.384615384615\ldots$$

We can see, then, that every rational number can be expressed as a repeating decimal. The converse is also true; that is, every repeating decimal represents a rational number.

Examples.

1. Given: $N = 0.2727 \ldots$; to find $\dfrac{a}{b} = N$.

$$100N = 27.272727 \ldots$$
$$N = 0.2727 \ldots$$

Subtracting:

$$100N - N = 27$$
$$99N = 27$$
$$N = \frac{27}{99} = \frac{3}{11} = \frac{a}{b}, \text{ the corresponding rational fraction}$$

2. Given: $N = 0.03646464 \ldots$; to find $\dfrac{a}{b} = N$.

$$10{,}000N = 364.6464 \ldots$$
$$100N = 3.6464 \ldots$$

Subtracting:

$$9900N = 361$$

$$N = \frac{361}{9900} = \frac{a}{b}.$$

3. Given: $N = 2.3515151 \ldots$; to find $\dfrac{a}{b}$.

$$1000N = 2351.5151 \ldots$$
$$10N = 23.5151 \ldots$$

Subtracting:

$$990N = 2328$$

$$N = \frac{2328}{990} = \frac{388}{165} = \frac{a}{b}.$$

Irrational numbers differ from rational numbers in that an irrational number always yields a non-terminating, non-repeating decimal. This is a perfectly general principle which may be stated as follows without proof (although it can be proved):

1. Every irrational number results in and only in an infinite non-repeating decimal; and

2. Every non-repeating infinite decimal represents an irrational number.

For example, $\sqrt{2} = 1.41421 \ldots$ is a non-terminating (that is, infinite) decimal in which no sequence of digits ever repeats itself systematically. This does not mean, however, that carrying out the computation of a square root to a "sufficient" number of decimal places can be used, in general, as a test of irrationality.

Any irrational number such as $\sqrt{2}$ or $\sqrt{3}$ can be approximated as closely as desired by any one of several methods. Thus

$$\sqrt{2} = 1.4 \qquad \sqrt{3} = 1.7$$
$$= 1.41 \qquad = 1.73$$
$$= 1.414 \qquad = 1.732$$
$$= 1.4142 \qquad = 1.7321$$
$$= \text{etc.} \qquad = \text{etc.}$$

Each of these decimal approximations terminates and is therefore a rational number. The irrational number $\sqrt{3}$ lies somewhere between rational approximations approaching it from "above" and "below"; thus, for $\sqrt{3}$, we have:

$$(1)^2 \qquad = 1.0 \qquad\qquad < 3 < 4.0 \qquad\qquad = (2)^2$$
$$(1.7)^2 \qquad = 2.89 \qquad\qquad < 3 < 3.24 \qquad\qquad = (1.8)^2$$
$$(1.73)^2 \qquad = 2.9929 \qquad\qquad < 3 < 3.0276 \qquad\qquad = (1.74)^2$$
$$(1.732)^2 \qquad = 2.999824 \qquad < 3 < 3.003289 \qquad = (1.733)^2$$
$$(1.7320)^2 \ = 2.99982400 \qquad < 3 < 3.00017041 \qquad = (1.7321)^2$$
$$(1.73205)^2 = 2.9999972025 < 3 \ < 3.0000318436 = (1.73206)^2$$

There are not many theorems which enable us to tell whether a given number is rational or irrational. However, when using approximate numbers such as $\sqrt{3} = 1.732$, or $\pi = 3.14$, the scientist or the engineer is using rational numbers. When measuring, he is only interested in, and can only be concerned with rational numbers which are approximations to the magnitude he is measuring. In his computations he uses these rational numbers or approximate numbers, to as many decimal places as he desires. This is not to say, however, that he does not use the irrational numbers in his theoretical discussions, when, for example, he is dealing with relations such as

$$t = 2\pi \sqrt{\frac{l}{g}} \quad \text{or} \quad f = \frac{1}{2\pi \sqrt{LC}}.$$

We have seen that the positive integers, which are a subset of the integers, are isomorphic with the natural numbers. We also know that the rational numbers, which are a subset of the real numbers, are isomorphic with repeating decimals. It is important to emphasize that every real number is either rational or irrational. There are many more irrational numbers than there are rational numbers, as we shall see in the next section. In fact, most of the quantities encountered in science and technology are represented by irrational numbers.

EXERCISE 5–2

1. Prove that the square of any odd number is always an odd number. (Hint: let the expression $(2n + 1)$ represent any odd number.)

2. Prove that $\sqrt{3}$ is irrational by a method similar to Pythagoras' proof that $\sqrt{2}$ is irrational.

3. Show that there is always a rational number between any two given rational numbers by expressing them as repeating decimals.

4. Express each of the following as a repeating decimal:

(a) $\frac{7}{9}$ (b) $\frac{10}{11}$ (c) $\frac{11}{6}$
(d) $5\frac{1}{8}$ (e) $\frac{1}{7}$ (f) $\frac{5}{13}$

5. Find the rational fraction represented by each of the following:

(a) $0.8181\ldots$ (b) $0.225225\ldots$ (c) $0.888\ldots$
(d) $0.4999\ldots$ (e) 0.017979 (f) $1.25454\ldots$

6. Why must the sum, difference, product, or quotient of any two rational numbers always be a rational number?

7. Which of the following are rational and which are irrational?

(a) $2\sqrt{5} + 2$

(b) $\dfrac{\sqrt{5}}{2\sqrt{5}}$

(c) $2 \div \sqrt{2}$

(d) $\dfrac{2}{\sqrt{3}} \div \dfrac{\sqrt{3}}{5}$

(e) $(5 + \sqrt{2})(5 - \sqrt{2})$

(f) $\sqrt{24} \cdot \sqrt{6}$

8. The identity $a^2 - b^2 = (a + b)\ (a - b)$ holds true when a and b are rational numbers. Does it still hold true if either a or b is irrational?

9. We sometimes say that $x^2 - 3$ is not "factorable," and sometimes we say that it is "factorable." Explain the difference between these two meanings of the word *factorable* as used here.

10. Find out what you can about the rationality of the number π; also, to how many decimal places it has been calculated.

counting the infinite

We have seen that the essence of counting finite sets lies in the concept of one-to-one correspondence with a standard set, that is, the idea of equivalent sets. The cardinal number of a set is based on the notion of equivalent sets. We shall now extend these ideas to infinite sets. Finite sets are always ordered; they have a beginning and an end, a "first" and a "last" element. When the elements of a finite set are put into one-to-one correspondence with the natural numbers, the multiplicity of elements in the set is indicated by the last or highest number, which is the cardinal number of the set. Some infinite sets can also be ordered. If two infinite sets can be put into one-to-one correspondence we say they are equivalent. Such sets have the same cardinal number, in these cases, called *transfinite numbers*.

We begin our discussion of transfinite numbers by asking: how many natural numbers are there? Since there is a first, but no last natural number, we might be tempted to say, intuitively, an infinite number. Unfortunately, the word "infinite" is often used rather loosely, as in "infinite patience," or "an infinite number of grains of sand," etc., when all that is meant is a very, very large number. Let us be somewhat more rigorous. Consider all the natural numbers:

(A) $1, 2, 3, 4, 5, \ldots m, \ldots n, \ldots$

Now consider all the "even" natural numbers:

(B) $2, 4, 6, 8, 10, \ldots 2m, \ldots 2n, \ldots$

Our first impulse would be to say that there are only "half as many" even numbers as all natural numbers, since we've selected only "every other one" from set A to form set B. Yet a moment's reflection should convince us that the two sets, A and B, can obviously be put into one-to-one correspondence; clearly every element of A has a unique mate in B, namely, *its double;* and conversely, every element in B has a unique mate in A, namely, *its "half."* No number that you can name in either set is *without* its corresponding element in the other set; no number in either set corresponds to *two* elements in the other set. The two sets are definitely and indisputably equivalent in multiplicity. How then, explain the apparent anomaly that there are *just as many* elements in half of a set as there are in the entire set! No, we do not have to visit a psychiatrist. We simply use this property as the criterion to distinguish finite sets from infinite sets. Stated informally:

1. For finite sets, the whole set is always greater than any part[3] of the set.

2. For infinite sets, a part can have the same number as the whole.

In other words, a set is infinite if part of the set can be put into one-to-one correspondence with the entire set. If a part of a collection is removed and the number of elements in the set is not "diminished," the set is infinite; or, putting it in another way, an infinite set can never be exhausted by removing one element at a time, nor even by repeated removals of subsets, however large. Perhaps you begin to see, now, somewhat more forcibly, the meaning of mathematical infinite.

[3] That is, any proper subset.

Stated more formally, we speak of any set as being *denumerable* if it can be put into one-to-one correspondence with the ordered set of natural numbers. If a set cannot be matched with the natural numbers, it is non-denumerable. All finite sets are therefore denumerable. Furthermore:

1. A denumerable set is *infinite* if the entire set can be put into one-to-one correspondence with a part of itself.

2. A denumerable set is *finite* if the entire set cannot be put into one-to-one correspondence with itself.

denumerability of the rational numbers

It is fairly easy to see that the positive and negative integers and zero can be put into one-to-one correspondence with the natural numbers, and therefore constitute a denumerably infinite set. We simply combine the two infinite sequences A and B into set C, as shown:

(A) 0, $^+$1, $^+$2, $^+$3, . . . ^+n, . . .
(B) $^-$1, $^-$2, $^-$3, . . . ^-n, . . .
(C) 0, $^-$1, $^+$1, $^-$2, $^+$2, $^-$3, $^+$3, ... ^-n, ^+n, . . .

The equivalence of set (C) with the set of natural numbers is then easily established, and we conclude that there are just as many integers (positive, negative, and zero) as there are natural numbers. Hard to believe? Or are you getting used to the idea of the infinite? The mathematician says that the set of integers and zero, like the set of natural numbers, is *countably infinite*, that is, denumerably infinite.

We shall now show that the set of rational numbers is also denumerably infinite. Let the positive rationals be ordered as shown in Fig. 5-10.

The arrows indicate the order of counting the rational numbers; the one-to-one matching with the natural numbers is indicated below:

1	2	3	4	5	6	7	8	9	10	11	12	13	14	...
$\frac{1}{1}$	$\frac{1}{2}$	$\frac{2}{1}$	$\frac{3}{1}$	$\frac{2}{2}$	$\frac{1}{3}$	$\frac{1}{4}$	$\frac{2}{3}$	$\frac{3}{2}$	$\frac{4}{1}$	$\frac{5}{1}$	$\frac{4}{2}$	$\frac{3}{3}$	$\frac{2}{4}$	...

The particular way in which the correspondence is set up is not important; other ways are possible. The fact that each rational number appears in the array an infinite number of times ($\frac{1}{1} = \frac{2}{2} = \frac{3}{3} = \frac{4}{4} = \dots$; $\frac{2}{1} = \frac{4}{2} = \frac{6}{3} = \frac{8}{4} = \dots$; etc.) also does not matter. The important consideration is that there has been *some sort of systematic method* for matching the positive rationals with the natural numbers.

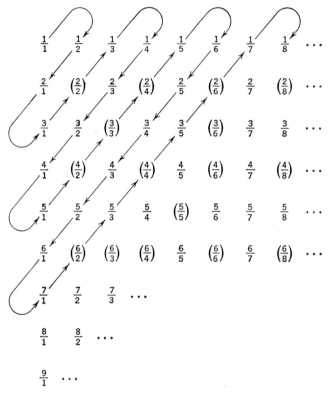

Fig. 5-10

We have thus shown that the positive rational numbers are denumerably infinite. Hence the entire set of rational numbers—positive, negative, and zero, can also be shown to be denumerably infinite. This is one of the most remarkable and significant theorems of modern mathematics, first systematically expounded by G. Cantor toward the close of the nineteenth century.

non-denumerability of the real numbers

We have now seen that the set of integers and the set of rational numbers can both be put into one-to-one correspondence with the natural numbers, and that they are therefore both denumerably infinite sets. We have also learned that if sets are equivalent or similar, then they have the same cardinal number. The cardinal number of denumerably infinite sets has been designated by mathematicians as $\aleph_0$, read "aleph null." [4] It is the "first" transfinite number, or the first infinite cardinal. We shall now show that there are other infinite cardinals that are infinitely greater than $\aleph_0$; in other words, there are sets which are *not* denumerable.

Let us consider *all* the real numbers between 0 and 1, that is, all real numbers r, where $0 < r < 1$. We recall that every repeating decimal is a rational number, and conversely, every rational number can be expressed as a repeating decimal (for example $\frac{1}{2} = 0.4999\ldots$, and $\frac{2}{3} = 0.6666\ldots$); recall also that all irrational numbers when expressed decimally are non-repeating infinite decimals. Assume that the real numbers between 0 and 1, expressed as decimals, have been ordered as suggested by the following schematic arrangement,

$$1 \leftrightarrow r_1 = 0.a_1a_2a_3a_4a_5a_6a_7a_8a_9 \ldots a_k \ldots$$
$$2 \leftrightarrow r_2 = 0.b_1b_2b_3b_4b_5b_6b_7b_8b_9 \ldots b_k \ldots$$
$$3 \leftrightarrow r_3 = 0.c_1c_2c_3c_4c_5c_6c_7c_8c_9 \ldots c_k \ldots$$
$$4 \leftrightarrow r_4 = 0.d_1d_2d_3d_4d_5d_6d_7d_8d_9 \ldots d_k \ldots$$
$$5 \leftrightarrow r_5 = 0.e_1e_2e_3e_4e_5e_6e_7e_8e_9 \ldots e_k \ldots$$

$$n \leftrightarrow r_n = 0.n_1n_2n_3n_4n_5n_6n_7n_8n_9 \ldots n_k \ldots$$

in which the a's, b's, c's, $\ldots$ represent specific digits. It would at first seem that such an array, extending as it does indefinitely to the right and indefinitely downward, must of necessity include every possible decimal between 0 and 1. The ordering would seem foolproof. The particular letter indicates the position of the decimal in the ordered sequence of decimals, and the subscript indicates the position of a digit in the particular decimal in which it stands. The entire array of decimals would appear to have been put into correspondence with the natural numbers, and we might well believe that the real numbers between 0 and 1 are denumerable.

But wait—as it turns out, it is possible to write a decimal which

---

[4] This symbol, $\aleph$, is the Hebrew letter *aleph,* the first letter of the Hebrew alphabet.

lies between 0 and 1 but which is *not included* in the above array! All we have to do is to form the decimal $0.m_1m_2m_3m_4m_5\ldots$, where m_1 is different from a_1, m_2 is different from b_2, m_3 different from c_3, etc. In short, this new decimal will differ from each of the decimals r_1, r_2, r_2, $\ldots r_n$ in at least one decimal place. Hence it is seen that no matter how we may try to arrange all the decimals, inevitably some decimals will not be included in the array. We are thus forced to the following conclusions:

1. The real numbers cannot be ordered as is the case with the natural numbers, the integers, and the rationals.

2. The irrationals are far more numerous than the rationals.

3. The irrationals are non-denumerable and of a greater or higher order of infinity than the rationals.

4. The real numbers between 0 and 1 are non-denumerably infinite.

5. The set of all real numbers is non-denumerably infinite.

This new transfinite cardinal, designated as **C,** is known as the *cardinal of the continuum.* It is infinitely greater than the transfinite cardinal $\aleph_0$ (and that is not a play on words). It is also known that there are transfinite cardinals greater than **C**—indeed, an infinite number of them; but it is not yet known whether there is any transfinite cardinal between $\aleph_0$ and **C**. However, lest the reader feel uncomfortable at these dizzy heights, we bring him back to earth by suggesting that the cardinal of the continuum, being greater than the cardinal of the rationals ($\aleph_0$), is of great significance in arithmetic, algebra, and analysis. Although the set of rational numbers (or rational points on a line) is *dense,* the set of real numbers (or real points on a line) is said to be *everywhere dense,* which is the mathematician's way of saying that a line is *continuous.* This concept is of fundamental importance in connection with analytic geometry.

We conclude by illustrating, in a sense, this concept of continuity. It can be shown, for example, that there are just as many points on a line segment one inch long as there are on a segment two inches long. In Fig. 5-11 *a* let AB and RS be the two given segments; let RA and SB intersect in M. Then point A corresponds to R, and R to A; also, point B corresponds to S, and S to B. To every point P_1, P_2, $\ldots$ on RS there corresponds one and only one point on AB, namely Q_1, $Q_2 \ldots$, respectively. Conversely, every point on AB has one and only one corresponding point on RS. In short, no point on either segment can be named which does not have a corresponding point on the other segment. We conclude that the two sets of points, that comprising seg-

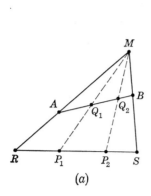

(a)

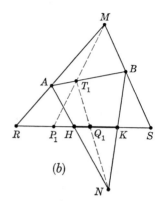

(b)

Fig. 5-11

ment AB and that comprising segment RS, must be equivalent. Or, the number of points on AB equals the number of points on RS.

This is a perfectly general relation; that is, a part of any line segment has the same number of points as the whole segment. This is easily seen from Fig. 5-11 b, where HK is any desired segment of RS, and where AH and BK intersect in N. By reasoning as before, there are the same number of points in the segment HK as in the segment AB, and therefore as in RS. The one-to-one correspondence is easily made: to every point Q_1 on HK there corresponds a unique point P_1 on RS, found by the aid of T_1, and conversely, to every point P_1 on RS there corresponds a unique point Q_1 on HK; the end points H and K are no exception, for they correspond to R and S, respectively, and conversely.

These considerations, at once amazing and intuitively difficult to comprehend, should nevertheless help us to realize the abstract concept of a point being dimensionless. They should also help to explain the difference between the questions "How many?" and "How much?" The first is concerned with counting discrete objects; the second is concerned with measuring continuous magnitudes.

EXERCISE 5–3

1. Define an *infinite* set; a *denumerable* set.

2. Show that the squares of the natural numbers are denumerably infinite.

3. Explain informally what is meant by saying that $\aleph_0 - n = \aleph_0$, when n is any finite number, however large.

4. How would you explain or justify the statement $\aleph_0 + \aleph_0 = \aleph_0$?

5. Give an illustration showing that an infinite subset of a denumerably infinite set is itself denumerable.

6. Show by a diagram that there are just as many points on a circle of finite length as there are on a straight line of infinite length.

7. (*a*) Does a straight line have a beginning and an end, that is, does it have boundaries? (*b*) Does a circle have boundaries? (*c*) Is a straight line finite or infinite in extent? (*d*) Is a circle finite or infinite in extent? (*e*) In the light of your answers to *a* through *d*, what distinction would you make between the mathematical meanings of *boundless* and *infinite?*

8. A pupil tells you that, since a point has no dimensions, it is zero units long; further, a line segment consists of an infinite number of points, each of zero length; finally, the sum of an infinite number of zeros is zero. Yet the segment has a length of (say) six inches. He wants to know "what's wrong" with his reasoning. How would you explain the apparent inconsistency?

COMPLEX NUMBERS

the imaginary number

We have seen that the creation of the real numbers—rational and irrational—sufficed to make evolution an omnipossible operation provided that we are finding the nth root of *positive* numbers. But what of the nth root of *negative* numbers, particularly when n is even? What, for example, is the meaning of $\sqrt{-9}$? Clearly in the real number system, $\sqrt{-9}$ does not exist, since by definition the product of two like numbers is always positive. Thus:

$$\sqrt{-9} \neq {}^+3, \text{ since } (^+3)^2 = (^+3)(^+3) = {}^+9;$$

and $\qquad \sqrt{-9} \neq {}^-3, \text{ since } (^-3)^2 = (^-3)(^-3) = {}^+9.$

So, if we wish to the extraction of roots an omnipossible operation, we shall have to invent a new number system in which $\sqrt{N}$ always exists, regardless of whether N is positive or negative.

Proceeding somewhat informally, we may define this new type of number, i, by means of the relations:

$$i = \sqrt{-1},$$

or $\qquad i^2 = (\sqrt{-1})(\sqrt{-1}) = {}^-1.$

Although $\sqrt{-1} = i$ is called an *imaginary number,* it is no more "imaginary" or unreal or mysterious than any of the other abstract numbers invented by man: the *integers,* the *rationals* (fractions), and the *irrationals.* As a matter of fact, it's quite simple and consistent with the idea of an inverse operation which "undoes" what has been "done," leaving a number unchanged. Thus, since involution and evolution are inverse operations, we note, in general, that:

$$\sqrt{*} \cdot \sqrt{*} = (\sqrt{*})^2 \;\; = *$$
$$\sqrt{+3} \cdot \sqrt{+3} = (\sqrt{+3})^2 = {}^+3$$
$$\sqrt{-1} \cdot \sqrt{-1} = (\sqrt{-1})^2 = {}^-1$$

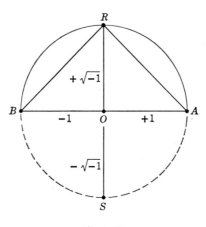

Fig. 5-12

A geometric "interpretation" of this new type of number may take away some of the mystery. Let the directed lengths of segments OA and OB represent $^+1$ and $^-1$, respectively. By geometry, the triangle ARB inscribed in the semicircle with diameter AB is a right triangle, and the altitude (OR) drawn to the hypotenuse (BA) is the mean proportional between the segments of the hypotenuse:

$$\frac{OA}{OR} = \frac{OR}{OB}$$

Substituting for OA and OB:

$$\frac{^+1}{OR} = \frac{OR}{^-1}$$

or $$(OR)^2 = (^+1)(^-1) = {}^-1$$
$$OR = \pm\sqrt{-1}$$

That is $$OR = {}^+\sqrt{-1} = {}^+i$$
And $$OS = {}^-\sqrt{-1} = {}^-i$$

In other words, we may regard the horizontal axis as the scale of real numbers, and the vertical axis as the scale of imaginary numbers.

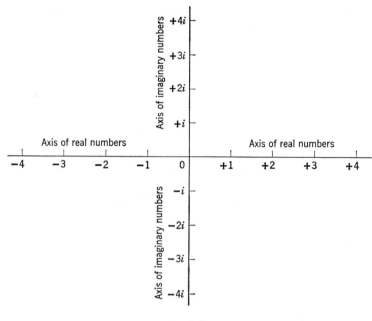

Fig. 5-13

complex numbers

A *complex number* may be defined as an ordered pair of real numbers $[m,n]$, the symbol $[m,n]$ representing a combination of the form $m + ni$. Every complex number thus consists of a "real part" and an "imaginary part." In the complex number $a + bi$, the real part is a and the imaginary part is bi. If $a = 0$ and $b \neq 0$, the complex number becomes a "pure imaginary"; if $b = 0$, $a \neq 0$, the complex number becomes a real number. Thus every real number may be regarded as a complex number of the form $a + bi$ in which $b = 0$; for example, $12 = 12 + 0 \cdot i$.

Two complex numbers $a + bi$ and $c + di$ are equal, by definition, if and only if $a = c$ and $b = d$; that is, if their respective "real parts" are equal and their respective "imaginary parts" are equal.

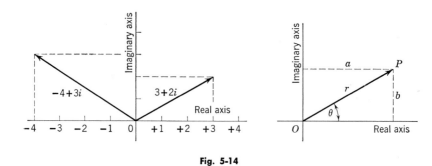

Fig. 5-14

A complex number[5] may be represented geometrically as shown in Fig. 5-14. Thus the point P, or the directed segment OP, represents the complex number $a + bi$, or the ordered pair of reals $[a, b]$. We designate the undirected length of the segment OP by r, which is called the *modulus* of the complex number; we designate the positive angle less than 360° (counter clockwise) as θ; it is called the *amplitude* of the complex number. The reader who recalls his trigonometry will see that

$$r = \sqrt{a^2 + b^2}, \quad \text{and} \quad \tan \theta = \frac{b}{a}.$$

The directed line is called a *vector*, and is designated by $\overrightarrow{OP}$.

operations with complex numbers

The *addition* of two complex numbers is defined as follows: The sum of $[a, b]$ and $[c, d]$, taken in order, is the ordered pair of real numbers $[a + c, b + d]$.

In other words:

$$
\begin{array}{ll}
a + bi & 3 + 5i \\
c + di & 4 + 3i \\
\hline
(a + c) + (b + d)i & 7 + 8i
\end{array}
$$

It can be shown that the complex number system is closed under ad-

---

[5] When we write $-5 + 2i$ we really mean $(^-5) + (^+2i)$; similarly, $3 - 4i$ is taken to mean $(^+3) + (^-4i)$, unless we deliberately wish to indicate subtraction, as in $(^+3) - (^+4i)$.

dition, and that addition is both commutative and associative. Addition of complex numbers can also be shown geometrically; it is vector addition.

Example 1. Add $5 + 6i$ and $3 - 2i$.

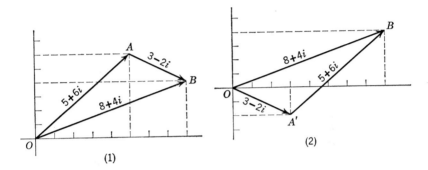

(1)

(2)

Fig. 5-15

Note that in both 1 and 2 the sum is the same, $8 + 4i$, illustrating commutativity. If 1 and 2 were to be drawn on the same set of axes (Fig. 5-16) we see the "parallelogram law" illustrated.

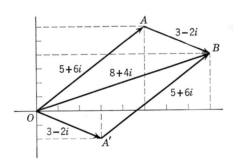

Fig. 5-16

Example 2. Add vectorially (Fig. 5-17):

$$6 + 4i; \quad -5 + 2i; \quad -3i; \quad 2 + 4i; \quad 2 - 5i.$$

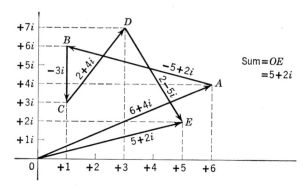

Fig. 5-17

Multiplying imaginary numbers shows the following characteristics, by definition:

$$(^+i)(^+i) = ^+(i^2) = ^+(^-1) = ^-1$$
$$(^+i)(^-i) = ^-(i^2) = ^-(^-1) = ^+1$$
$$(^-i)(^+i) = ^-(i^2) = ^-(^-1) = ^+1$$
$$(^-i)(^-i) = ^+(i^2) = ^+(^-1) = ^-1$$

From this it follows that:

$$i^1 = \qquad\qquad\qquad i$$
$$i^2 = \qquad\qquad\qquad -1$$
$$i^3 = i^2 \cdot i = (^-1)(i) \quad = ^-i$$
$$i^4 = i^2 \cdot i^2 = (^-1)(^-1) = ^+1$$
$$i^5 = i^4 \cdot i = (^+1)(i) \quad = ^+i$$
$$i^6 = i^4 \cdot i^2 \quad (^+1)(^-1) = ^-1$$
$$i^7 = i^4 \cdot i^3 = (^+1)(^-i) \quad = ^-i$$
$$i^8 = i^4 \cdot i^4 = (^+1)(^+1) \quad ^+1$$

Example 1. Simplify: $3\sqrt{-25}$.

$$3\sqrt{-25} = 3\sqrt{25} \cdot \sqrt{-1} = (3)(5)i = 15i$$

Example 2. Simplify: $\sqrt{-48}$.

$$\sqrt{-48} = \sqrt{48} \cdot \sqrt{-1} = \sqrt{16}\sqrt{3} \cdot \sqrt{-1} = 4\sqrt{3}\,i$$

Example 3. Reduce i^{26}.

$$i^{26} = i^{24} \cdot i^2 = (i^4)^6 \cdot i^2$$
$$= (+1)^6 \cdot (^-1) = ^-1$$

Example 4. Multiply: $\sqrt{-6} \cdot \sqrt{-12}$.

$$\begin{aligned}
\sqrt{-6}\,\sqrt{-12} &= \sqrt{6} \cdot \sqrt{-1} \cdot \sqrt{12} \cdot \sqrt{-1} \\
&= \sqrt{6} \cdot \sqrt{12}\; i^2 \\
&= \sqrt{6 \cdot 6 \cdot 2}\; i^2 \\
&= 6\sqrt{2}\; i^2 = {}^-6\sqrt{2}
\end{aligned}$$

The product of two complex numbers is defined as follows:

$$[a,\, b] \cdot [c,\, d] = [ac - bd,\, ad + bc]$$

It can be shown that the complex numbers are closed under multiplication, and that multiplication is commutative, associative, and distributive over addition.

Example. Multiply: $(5 + 3i)\,(4 - 2i)$.

$$\begin{array}{r}
5 + 3i \\
4 - 2i \\
\hline
20 + 12i \\
-\,10i - 6i^2 \\
\hline
\end{array}$$

Product: $20 + 2i - 6i^2$

But $i^2 = {}^-1$

Therefore, the product equals $20 + 2i - (6)({}^-1) = 26 + 2i$.

number systems in retrospect

This completes the extension of the number system, starting with the natural numbers. The scheme, in brief, followed these steps:

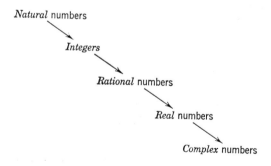

Fig. 5-18

Each successive extension from one number system to the next enlarged the scope of the mathematics. If a and b are natural numbers, the equation $x + a = b$ cannot be solved until we create the system of integers. Again, if a and b are integers $(a \neq 0)$, the equation $ax = b$ cannot be solved until we create the system of rational numbers. None of these numbers will enable us to solve the equation $x^2 = N$, where N is any number not the square of an integer, until we create the real numbers. And finally, we cannot solve the equation $x^2 = {}^-N$ until we create the complex numbers.

We conclude with a schematic classification of the related number systems by way of clarification and summary:

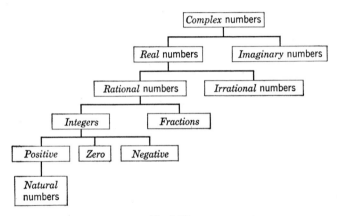

Fig. 5-19

EXERCISE 5–4

1. Write each of the following in simplest form:

(a) $\sqrt{-64}$ (b) $4\sqrt{-36}$ (c) $-\sqrt{-18}$

(d) $3\sqrt{-50}$ (e) $^-4\sqrt{-100}$ (f) $^-\sqrt{-a^2}$

(g) i^{20} (h) $-8i^6$ (i) $^-5i^4$

(j) i^{10} (k) $6i^{11}$ (l) $2i^{39}$

2. Multiply:

(a) $\sqrt{-9} \cdot \sqrt{-16}$ (b) $\sqrt{-5}\sqrt{-7}$ (c) $(\sqrt{-3})^4$

(d) $(\sqrt{-4})^3$ (e) $3i \cdot 2i \cdot 5i^2$ (f) $\sqrt{-3} \cdot \sqrt{-6} \cdot \sqrt{-2}$

3. Add algebraically:

(a) $3 + 5i, 4 - 8i, +2$ (b) $-5 + 7i, +6i, -3 - 4i$

(c) $3 + 4i; 3 - 4i; -3 + 5i; -3 - 5i$

4. Add vectorially:

(a) $(^-4 + 6i)$ and $(3 - 2i)$ (b) $8 - 3i; {}^+4i; {}^-6 + 3i$

(c) $6 + 5i; {}^-10; 4 - 3i; {}^-2i$

5. Multiply:

(a) $(4 - 3i)(6 + 2i)$

(b) $(5 + 4i)(5 - 4i)$

(c) $(1 + i)^2$

(d) $(\sqrt{-3} + 1)(\sqrt{-3} - 1)$

(e) $(i - 1)^3$

(f) $(m + \sqrt{-p})(m - \sqrt{-p})$

6. Show that the addition of complex numbers is commutative; first explain it algebraically, then geometrically.

7. Show algebraically and geometrically that addition of complex numbers is associative.

8. Show algebraically that multiplication of complex numbers is commutative.

9. Explain how you would subtract geometrically one complex number from another.

10. Solve the equation $x^2 + 20 = 0$.

11. If a number located on either the real axis or the imaginary axis is multiplied by i, what effect will this have on the number?

12. Plot the complex number $4 + 6i$. Multiply $(4 + 6i)$ by i and plot the result; repeat the process four times.

13. Bearing in mind the definition of *integer* as used in this text, how might you improve upon the quotation from Kronecker at the beginning of the present chapter? (page 130).

14. Which of the following statements is (are) correct:

(a) If $mx = a + m/c$, and $m \neq 0$, then $x = a + 1/c$.

(b) If $ax - k = m$, and $x \neq 0$, then $a = m + k/x$.

(c) If $ax \div k = m$, and $m \neq 0$, then $k = ax/m$.

15. Which of the following is (are) correct:

(a) $\dfrac{9}{1\frac{1}{3}} = \dfrac{9 \times \frac{3}{4}}{\frac{4}{3} \times \frac{3}{4}}$

(b) $9 \times 1\frac{1}{4} = 9 + 2\frac{1}{4}$

(c) $\dfrac{\frac{2}{3}}{\frac{3}{5}} = \dfrac{\frac{2}{3} \cdot \frac{10}{10}}{\frac{3}{5} \cdot \frac{6}{6}}$

(d) $\dfrac{5}{3} + 1\frac{1}{2} = \dfrac{8}{3} + \dfrac{2\frac{1}{2}}{5}$

16. Which of the following are correct, where n is a real number not equal to zero:

(a) $\dfrac{0}{n} = 0$

(b) $\dfrac{n}{0} = n$

(c) $0 \times n = 0$

(d) $\dfrac{n}{n} = 0$

(e) $n \times \dfrac{1}{n} = 1$

17. Indicate which laws (*commutative, associative, distributive*) is illustrated by each of the following:

(a) $98 + (2 + 83) = (98 + 2) + 83$

(b) $98 + (83 + 2) = 98 + (2 + 83)$

(c) $(40 \times 79) \times \frac{1}{4} = 79 \times (40 \times \frac{1}{4})$

(d) $(17 \times 63) + (17 \times 37) = 17 \times (63 + 37)$
(e) $2 \times 59 \times 5 = 59 \times (2 \times 5)$

18. Label each of the following by using the appropriate word from the following list: *rational, irrational, real, imaginary, complex.*

(a) $3 \sqrt{-4}$ (b) $3 \sqrt{4}$ (c) $3 \sqrt{5}$
(d) $3 + \sqrt{4}$ (e) $3 + \sqrt{5}$ (f) $3 + \sqrt{-5}$

19. If m and n are relatively prime integers, and $m < n$, which of the following expressions is (are) *not integers?*

(a) $n - m$ (b) $m + n$ (c) $m - n$
(d) m/n (e) $m \cdot n$ (f) n/m

20. Label each of the items below, using one or more of the following three designations which fits the description given: (a) the *natural numbers;* (b) the *positive and negative integers and zero;* (c) the *rational numbers.*

(a) A number system in which subtraction is always possible
(b) A number system in which subtraction is *not* always possible
(c) A number system which is closed under the operations of addition and multiplication
(d) A number system which is closed under the operations of addition, subtraction, multiplication, and division (except by zero)

FOR FURTHER READING AND STUDY

1. Adler, Irving. *The New Mathematics.* New York: John Day, 1958. Chapters 3–6.
2. Banks, J. Houston. *Elements of Mathematics.* Boston: Allyn and Bacon, 1956. Chapter 5.
3. Courant, Richard and Robbins, Herbert. *What Is Mathematics?* New York: Oxford University Press, 1941. Chapters 1 and 2.
4. Dantzig, Tobias. *Number: The Language of Science.* New York: Macmillan, 1930. Chapters 6, 9, and 10.
5. Dubisch, Roy. *The Nature of Number.* New York: Ronald Press, 1952. Chapters 6–8.
6. Jones, Burton W. *Elementary Concepts of Mathematics.* New York: Macmillan, 1947. Chapter 3: "Negative Integers, Rational and Irrational Numbers."
7. Kasner, Edward and Newman, James. *Mathematics and the Imagination.* New York: Simon and Schuster, 1940. Chapter 2: "Beyond the Googol."
8. Niven, Ivan. "The Concept of Number." In: *Insights into Mathematics. Twenty-third Yearbook,* National Council of Teachers of Mathematics, 1957. Pp. 7–35.
9. Reichmann, W. J. *The Fascination of Numbers.* London: Methuen and Co. 1957. Chapters 10 and 12.

CHAPTER 6

Numeration, Exponents, and Logarithms

Yet zero, first of the digits, was the last to be invented; and zero, first of the numbers, was the last to be discovered. These two events, the invention and the discovery of zero, tardy as they were in the history of number, did not occur at the same time. The invention of zero preceded its discovery by centuries.

—Constance Reid:
From Zero to Infinity

NUMBERS AND NUMERALS

systems of numeration

We have seen that the general concept of number can be arrived at without resorting to the device of counting. We have also seen that the natural numbers are most readily arrived at, historically and psychologically at least, through the act of counting or enumerating. In either case, the essence of telling "how many" lies in the idea of one-to-one correspondence. When man invented symbols, called numerals, to record the results of counting, he took the first step in creating a system of numeration. Note that the initial motive was recording, not computing.

A system of numeration should not be confounded with a number system. The latter refers to a far broader concept, namely, numbers and their properties, as governed by the postulates, irrespective of the particular notation used to denote the numbers. A system of numeration is expressly concerned with the symbols and notation used for writing the numbers, and is not concerned with their properties. Thus 206 is a natural number, preceded by 205 other natural numbers (ordinals), and has the same meaning whether written as 206, CCVI, $\bigcirc\bigcirc$||| or $2(10)^2 + 6(10)^0$.

The principal elements of a place system of numeration are (1) the base; (2) symbols for the digits, or numerals; (3) the principle of position, or place value; (4) a symbol for the empty space, or zero, which is necessitated by the positional principle; (5) the cipherization device; and, if the system is to include a notation for fractions, then (6) a decimal point or other separatrix is needed. Not all of these features need be present in a particular system, however. Our so-called Hindu-Arabic system of notation, practically in universal use today, had virtually displaced all earlier forms of numeration several centuries ago. It is customary to attribute the superiority of this system, especially for purposes of computation, solely to the principle of place value, together with the symbol for zero. This is a somewhat exaggerated idea, for, as we shall soon see, computation is facilitated at least as much, if not more so, by the device of cipherization.[1]

Although various cultures at different times have used 5 and 20 and 60 as a base, among others, by far the most widely used has been the base 10. It was the base used by the Egyptians, the Romans, the Greeks and the Hebrews, and, in part, by the Babylonians. That the base 10 has been used so universally is presumably due to the accidental biological fact that man has ten fingers.

iteration of digits

The first step in creating a system of numeration is to devise marks to indicate the number in question. These might be stylized spears

---

[1] We are indebted to Prof. Carl Boyer for this clarification of ideas concerning numeration in "Fundamental Steps in the Development of Numeration," *Isis* 35 (Part 2), No. 100:153–168; 1944.

or animals, or simply tally marks such as the Egyptian hieroglyphic strokes chiseled in stone, or the Babylonian cuneiform (wedge-shaped) impressions made in clay by their stylus. In any event, they designated a one-to-one correspondence between individual, distinct objects. The second step is the invention of new marks or symbols to represent not individual units (discrete objects), but rather a collection of a specific number of such units. Both these steps are exemplified by the Egyptian numerals. Thus, in Egyptian hieroglyphics, we find:

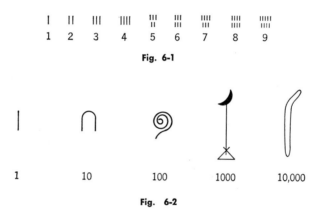

Fig. 6-1

Fig. 6-2

These numerals illustrate the principle of *iteration*, or simple repetition of a digit. When the base (or radix) of the system was reached, a new symbol was introduced; thus the ∩ was used for 10 in lieu of ten separate strokes. Another symbol was invented to represent ten ∩'s, namely, ◎, for 100; and so on. The principle of iteration could be applied to each new symbol. For example (Fig. 6-3):

Fig. 6-3

The Babylonian numerals also exemplify these two steps, as well as the iterative principle (Fig. 6-4).

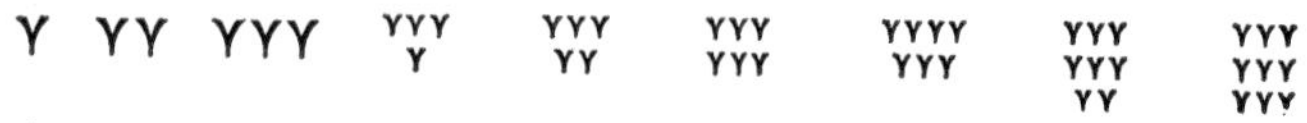

| Y | YY | YYY | YYY
Y | YYY
YY | YYY
YYY | YYYY
YYY | YYY
YYY
YY | YYY
YYY
YYY |
|---|----|-----|-----|------|------|-------|--------|--------|
| 1 | 2 | 3 | 4 | 5 | 6 | 7 | 8 | 9 |

Fig. 6-4

Y   ⟨   Y⟩—   ⟨Y⟩—

1   10   100   1000

YYY⟨Y⟩—   YYY
Y Y⟩—   ⟨⟨ YYY
YYY

3 (1000)   +   4 (100)   +   20 + 6   =   3426

Fig. 6-5

However, a slight modification was introduced; for smaller numbers, simple iteration sufficed, but for larger numbers a multiplicative principle was used, as shown in 6-5. Obviously such systems suffered from two inherent weaknesses: (1) the necessity of repeating, or at least writing, the same symbol as many as nine times, and (2) the need for an indefinite number of new and arbitrary symbols which had to be memorized. The familiar system of Roman numeration was also of this type:

I	II	III	IIII	V	VI	VII	VIII	VIIII
1	2	3	4	5	6	7	8	9

X	XX	L	LX	C	D	M
10	20	50	60	100	500	1000

Fig. 6-6

positional value

The next step in the development and improvement of numeration was the introduction of the idea of place value, together with a zero or some other symbol to mark the "place" if it was "empty." Contrary to popular impression, both the Babylonians and the Mayas used the idea of place value; and the Babylonians, some time before the Christian era, probably introduced a symbol of an empty position, corresponding to our modern use of "zero as a placeholder." [2] In other words, a *cuneus* (Y) might stand for either *one* or *sixty* (the base of their sexagesimal system). The context usually made clear which was intended. But in going beyond 60, the new meaning was distinguished from the old by separating the symbols into "places" or "positions,"— the higher order units were placed to the left. By means of this device of local value, the only symbols needed were the wedge (Y) and bracket (⟨). The real significance of the principle of place value is that it obviates the necessity of introducing more than a very limited number of symbols. This is the only advantage of the place value idea. Even with place value, computation is just as clumsy with Babylonian numerals as with Egyptian numerals, an example of which is given in Fig. 6-7.

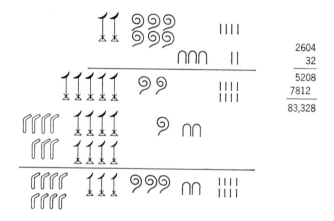

$$
\begin{array}{r}
2604 \\
32 \\
\hline
5208 \\
7812 \\
\hline
83{,}328
\end{array}
$$

Fig. 6-7

the cipherization principle

The fourth step in the development of numeration, and perhaps the most significant and fruitful idea, is the principle of *cipherization*, or what might be called the "cash register" principle. More carefully described, cipherization means the positional *arrangement* into an ordered sequence resembling the manner of writing algebraic polynomials, that is, $x^5 + x^4 + x^3 + x^2 + x^1 + x^0$; the sequence consists of

[2] Boyer, *ibid.*

consecutive powers of the radix of the particular system.[3] Of all the ancient numeration systems, the only ones to make use of the cipherization principle were the later Egyptians in their hieratic and demotic forms (not in their hieroglyphic forms), and the later Ionian Greeks (not the earlier Attic numeration). In Fig. 6-8 the Ionian ciphered

	$(10)^0$	$(10)^1$	$(10)^2$	$(10)^3$	$(10)^4$	$(10)^5$	$(10)^6$
	1	10	100	1000	10,000	100,000	1,000,000
1	α	ι	ρ	$,\alpha$	$\overset{\alpha}{M}$	$\overset{\iota}{M}$	$\overset{\rho}{M}$
2	β	κ	σ	$,\beta$	$\overset{\beta}{M}$	$\overset{\kappa}{M}$	$\overset{\sigma}{M}$
3	γ	λ	τ	$,\gamma$	$\overset{\gamma}{M}$	$\overset{\lambda}{M}$	$\overset{\tau}{M}$
4	δ	μ	υ	$,\delta$	$\overset{\delta}{M}$	$\overset{\mu}{M}$	$\overset{\upsilon}{M}$
5	ϵ	ν	ϕ	$,\epsilon$	$\overset{\epsilon}{M}$	$\overset{\nu}{M}$	etc.
6	ς	ξ	χ	$,\varsigma$	$\overset{\varsigma}{M}$		
7	ζ	o	ψ	$,\zeta$	$\overset{\zeta}{M}$	— etc. —	
8	η	π	ω	$,\eta$	$\overset{\eta}{M}$		
9	ϑ	ϱ	$\lambdabar$	$,\vartheta$	$\overset{\vartheta}{M}$		

Fig. 6-8 Ionian Ciphered Numerals

numerals exemplify a system in which the absence of the place value idea makes for great clumsiness, because without place value there are too many symbols or ciphers to be memorized. On the other hand, the powerful cipherization principle, which replaces the need for iteration, greatly facilitates computation despite the absence of place value. This fact is shown below, where the cipherization is clearly

[3] The reader may recall from his high school mathematics that any number raised to the zero power equals one; thus $(10)^0 = 1$; $(2)^0 = 1$; $a^0 = 1$; $x^0 = 1$; etc. This matter will be discussed in a later chapter.

indicated, in the same multiplication example as was done above in Egyptian numerals; note how much less clumsy the work is (Fig. 6-9).

$$,\beta \quad \chi \quad \delta \qquad\qquad 2604$$
$$\lambda \quad \beta \qquad\qquad\quad 32$$
$$\zeta \quad /\epsilon \quad \sigma \quad \eta \qquad\qquad 5208$$
$$\overset{\eta}{\mathrm{M}} \quad ,\eta \quad \rho \quad \kappa \qquad\qquad 7812$$
$$\overset{\eta}{\mathrm{M}} \quad ,\gamma \quad \tau \quad \kappa \quad \eta \qquad\qquad 83{,}328$$
$$8 \quad 3 \quad 3 \quad 2 \quad 8$$
$$8(10^4)+3(10^3)+3(10^2)+2(10^1)+8(10^0)$$

Fig. 6-9

the Hindu-Arabic system

The culminating step in the improvement of numeration is, of course, combining the Babylonian principle of place value with the

THROUGH HISTORY WITH J. WESLEY SMITH

"So you've invented a zero . . . and what have you got . . . nothing!

Fig. 6-10. By Burr Shafer in *Through History with J. Wesley Smith*, Vanguard Press, New York.

Greco-Egyptian principle of cipherization. The place value device merely reduces the number of ciphers to be memorized to nine, if the base is 10; in general, using place value, the number of ciphers that must be memorized is one less than the base of the system. On the other hand, the cash register cipherization device, through its tabular arrangement, enormously facilitates computation.

In all fairness, it should be pointed out that the historical development of systems of numeration is shrouded in a good deal of obscurity, and may never be fully cleared up. No one knows, for example, just when or where the symbol for zero as we know it today was first introduced, although it is generally attributed to the Arabs; the exact origin of the Hindu numerals themselves is uncertain, and their evolution over the centuries has been a long and complicated process. In view of the above considerations, our modern system of numeration, a ciphered number scale with a radix of ten, using the idea of positional value with a zero, might most aptly be called the Babylonian-Egyptian-Greek-Hindu-Arabic system. Certain it is that this system

$$I \; 2 \; 3 \; 4 \; 5 \; 6 \; 7 \; 8 \; 9$$

Fig. 6-11. Early European Numerals (about A.D. 1000)

has withstood the test of time, and is admirably suited to computation. Of the three distinctive features, the first two are of somewhat less importance for facilitating computations; for this purpose, the base 10 is not ideal. A base of 12 or even 8 would probably be more convenient than 10; a base of 2 would be too small, and a base of 60 is too large. What is more important than the particular base used is the fact that the system is homogeneous and based consistently upon one and only one radix. And more important than place value is the scheme of cipherization—expressing the digits of a number as successive powers of the radix in descending order; that is,

$$57,368 = 5(10^4) + 7(10^3) + 3(10^2) + 6(10^1) + 8(10^0)$$

EXERCISE 6–1

1. State clearly the meaning of each of the following nouns:

(a) *numeral*	(b) *digit*	(c) *number*
(d) *figure*	(e) *integer*	(f) *cipher*

Be as specific and as rigorous as you can; tell, for each term, how it differs from the others; use 397 and CCCXCVII as illustrations.

2. Explain the meaning and significance of (*a*) iteration, (*b*) positional value, and (*c*) cipherization as used in connection with systems of numeration.

3. Explain what is meant by (*a*) "the invention of zero as a digit"; (*b*) "the discovery of zero as a number."

4. Write in modern Hindu-Arabic numerals:

(*a*) XXIX	(*b*) CXCII
(*c*) DCXIII	(*d*) CVII
(*e*) XLIV	(*f*) LXVI
(*g*) CCCLXIX	(*h*) MDCCXI
(*i*) MCMXLIV	(*j*) MDCCCCXXII
(*k*) MCMXXII	(*l*) MCMXC

5. Write in Roman numerals:

(*a*) 308	(*b*) 96	(*c*) 49
(*d*) 750	(*e*) 1906	(*f*) 1960
(*g*) 1492	(*h*) 1942	(*i*) 1958
(*j*) 1895	(*k*) 1861	(*l*) 1619

6. Grant Wood, the well-known American painter, in order to save space, once used MCCMIIC when putting the date on one of his paintings. What year was this? Was he technically correct in the sense that Roman numerals were customarily written in ancient and medieval times? Why, or why not? How would this date usually be written in Roman numerals?

7. (*a*) Add, in Roman notation: XXXI, LXVIII, CXVI, CCIX, and XLVIII.

(*b*) Multiply, in Roman notation, CCXXXII by XXVI.

(*c*) Multiply 123 by 65 in Roman notation.

8. Write in Egyptian hieroglyphic notation and multiply 1426 by 24.

9. Write in Ionic Greek notation and multiply 2315 by 23.

10. Ask a friend to think of a three-digit number whose first and third digit are not alike; then ask him the difference between this number and the number obtained by reversing the digits; finally, ask him to state only the last digit of this difference. With this information only, can you discover the entire difference? Explain.

SCALES OF NOTATION

binary notation

How is it possible for the speed of an automatic digital computer to be from 10,000 to 50,000 times as great as that of a human being equipped with a desk calculator? How is it possible for a machine to perform three or four thousand multiplications in one second? How is it possible for a machine automatically to recall desired numbers in a few millionths of a second?

Among other things, the binary system of notation helps to make these seemingly impossible achievements realities. In this system only two symbols are required to express any number. Since an electric circuit is either "on" or "off," these two symbols can be represented electrically; and since electrical energy moves with the speed of light (approximately 186,000 miles per second), the fantastic speeds of automatic computers become readily believable.

We have seen that in any system of enumeration, no matter what base is used, a number may be expressed as the sum of successive powers of the base. Thus:

$$
\begin{aligned}
527 &= 500 &&+ 20 &&+ 7 \\
&= 5(100) &&+ 2(10) &&+ 7(1) \\
&= 5(10)^2 &&+ 2(10)^1 &&+ 7(10)^0
\end{aligned}
$$

$$
\begin{aligned}
\text{and} \quad 63{,}081 &= 60{,}000 &&+ 3000 &&&&+ 80 &&+ 1 \\
&= 6(10{,}000) &&+ 3(1000) &&&&+ 8(10) &&+ 1(1) \\
&= 6(10)^4 &&+ 3(10)^3 &&+ 0(10)^2 &&+ 8(10)^1 &&+ 1(10)^0.
\end{aligned}
$$

To be sure, other numbers such as 5, 8, 12, or 20, could also be used as a base. Nearly 300 years ago Leibniz, the German philosopher and mathematician, became interested in the possibilities of a system with base 2. He was concerned more with speculative and philosophical considerations rather than practical applications to calculating machines—and in any event, electric circuits were as yet unknown in his time. Today, the system with base 2 is invaluable in electronic computers and automation equipment.[4] Originally used to represent ordinary numbers, the binary system is now used to code English and foreign words as well.

A system with the base 10 requires ten symbols or digits: 1, 2, 3, . . . 8, 9, 0. In counting "by ones," when we have used each symbol once we indicate this by starting a new column to the left of the old one and writing a 1 in it; then we can use the old column to start counting from 1 to 9 over again. For example, the number "35" tells us that we have gone through the entire set of ten digits three times and have

_____

[4] Computers have been designed to use base 8, 10, and 16 instead of base 2; nevertheless they utilize the "yes or no" principle of the binary notation by means of intricate switching devices.

arrived at the digit 5 on the fourth time around. In the binary system (base 2) only two symbols or digits are required: 1 and 0. As before, any number may be expressed as the sum of successive powers of the base. Thus:

$$14 = 8 + 4 + 2$$
$$= 1(2)^3 + 1(2)^2 + 1(2)^1 + 0(2)^0$$
$$= 1110$$

and

$$25 = 16 + 8 + 0 + 0 + 1$$
$$= 1(2)^4 + 1(2)^3 + 0(2)^2 + 0(2)^1 + 1(2)^0$$
$$= 11001.$$

TABLE 1.   Counting in the Binary System

Number in Decimal Digits	Equivalent in Binary Digits	Number in Decimal Digits	Equivalent in Binary Digits
0	0	16	10000
1	1	17	10001
2	10	18	10010
3	11	19	10011
4	100	20	10100
5	101	25	11001
6	110	30	11110
7	111	32	100000
8	1000	35	100011
9	1001	40	101000
10	1010	50	110010
11	1011	60	111100
12	1100	64	1000000
13	1101	80	1010000
14	1110	100	1100100
15	1111	128	10000000

The first two numbers are 0 and 1, the same as in our decimal system. To express *two*, we can't write "2," since this symbol doesn't exist (the "highest" symbol is 1); so we move to the next column to the left and write 10, which means "2" in the decimal system. Now we can use the "old" column again to count one more to "3," which in the binary system is written 11. To get "4," we move to the next column and write 100. And so we can keep right on counting in the binary system. In other words, in the decimal system we move over another "place" after the first 10, the first 100, the first 1000, etc. In the binary system we move over after the first 2, the first 4, the first 8, the first 16, etc.

You can readily see that in a system with only two symbols we need many more columns, or places, to write even "small" numbers; for example, we need *six* places to write the number 43 on the scale of 2. For most purposes this would be a serious disadvantage, but insofar as electronic computers are concerned, the disadvantage is offset by the fact that only two symbols are required.

In using the binary system it would help to memorize the binary multiples, or successive powers of 2, that is, 1, 2, 4, 8, 16, 32, . . . , just as the key values in our decimal system: 1, 10, 100, 1000, etc. As a matter of fact, a pupil when learning the binary system "from scratch" would have to learn only four "addition facts" instead of 100 facts, as in the decimal system, and only four "multiplication facts" instead of 100. Here are the addition and multiplication "tables":

Addition Table	*Multiplication Table*
$0 + 0 = 0$	$0 \times 0 = 0$
$0 + 1 = 1$	$1 \times 0 = 0$
$1 + 0 = 1$	$0 \times 1 = 0$
$1 + 1 = 10$	$1 \times 1 = 1$

Binary numbers are added:

$$
\begin{array}{rr}
111 & 7 \\
101 & 5 \\
1000 & 8 \\
1010 & 10 \\
\underline{11} & \underline{3} \\
100001 = & 33
\end{array}
$$

Binary numbers are multiplied:

$$
\begin{array}{rr}
11011 & \\
\underline{\times\ 1101} & 27 \\
11011 & \underline{\times\ 13} \\
11011 & 81 \\
\underline{11011\quad} & 27 \\
101011111 = & 351
\end{array}
$$

bases other than 10 and 2

Popular opinion has it that we use the decimal system of notation because of some peculiarity of the number ten. The convenience of multiplying and dividing by 10, 100, 1000, etc. is regarded as unique to the base 10. Such is not the case, however. As we have already seen, the distinctive feature of our Hindu–Arabic system is neither the fact of the base ten nor the principle of positional value, but the principle of cipherization, or expressing a number in a sequence of powers of 10, combined with the idea of positional value.[5] Yet these same principles can be applied equally well to a system with any other base—it need not be a decimal system.

The base of a numerative system is often called the *scale of notation*. Whatever base or scale is selected for a system which combines the cipherization principle with the positional value principle, it should be understood that the number of different symbols (numerals or digits) required is equal to the base itself. In the decimal system we need ten digits: 1, 2, . . . , 7, 8, 9, 0; in the binary system we need only two digits: 1, 0. So a scale of six would require six digits; a scale of twelve, or duodecimal system, would require twelve digits; a scale of eight, eight digits; etc.

Here is how numbers are written in the scale of six, which requires six numerals. Let us use 1, 2, 3, 4, 5, 0 as digits in the scale of six. Here each succeeding place, reading from right to left, has a value six times as great as the value of the preceding place. Thus, in the scale of six,

$$43 \text{ means } 4(6)^1 + 3(6)^0,$$
$$\text{or } 4 \times 6 + 3 \times 1, \text{ or } 27, \text{ in the scale of ten.}$$

Similarly:

$$524 = 5(6)^2 + 2(6)^1 + 4(6)^0$$
$$= 5 \times 36 + 2 \times 6 + 4 \times 1, \text{ or } 196 \text{ in the scale of ten}$$
$$5103 = 5(6)^3 + 1(6)^2 + 0(6)^1 + 3(6)^0$$
$$= 5(216) + 1(36) + 0(6) + 3(1), \text{ or, } 1,119 \text{ in the scale of ten.}$$

As a matter of fact, it is always possible to express a number as the sum of powers of any desired base n without using any power more than $(n-1)$ times. For example: (*a*) $123 = 98 + 21 + 4 = 2(7)^2 + 3(7)^1 + 4(7)^0$; here no power of 7 is used more than six times. (*b*) $123 = 64 + 48 + 8 + 3 = 1(4)^3 + 3(4)^2 + 2(4)^1 + 3(4)^0$; here no power of 4 is used more than three times. (*c*) $123 = 64 + 32 + 16 + 8 + 2 + 1 = 1(2)^6 + 1(2)^5 + 1(2)^4 + 1(2)^3 + 0(2)^2 + 1(2)^1 + 1(2)^0$;

[5] Many writers and teachers apparently use the terms "place value" and "positional value" unwittingly to mean the principle of cipherization. This is unfortunate, since the two ideas are not the same; as pointed out earlier, a system of numeration can be positional without being ciphered, or it can be ciphered without being positional.

here no power of 2 is used more than once. This, of course, is in the binary system, where, as we have already seen, only two symbols are used. No more symbols are needed, since any number can be built up by either using or not using each successive power of 2 (the either "yes or no" principle again).

We shall now show how the correct powers can easily be found without resorting to trial and error. If we wish to express 94 as powers of 4, we simply divide 94 by 4; quotient 23, remainder 2. So, 94 is 2 more than a multiple of 4, or

$$94 = 23(4)^1 + 2(4)^0$$

Now if we divide the 23 by 4, we have quotient 5, remainder 3; hence $23 = 5(4)^1 + 3(4)^0$. Substituting this value for 23 above, we get:[6]

$$94 = [5(4)^1 + 3(4)^0] \cdot (4)^1 + 2(4)^0;$$
$$\text{or, } 94 = 5(4)^2 + 3(4)^1 + 2(4)^0.$$

Not only is the above process applicable to any base, but it can be abbreviated into a convenient algorithm. For example, to express 231 in powers of 6, we proceed as follows:

$$
\begin{array}{l}
6)\overline{231} \\
\quad 6)\overline{38} \text{ R3, or, we need three } (6)^0\text{'s} \\
\qquad 6)\overline{6} \text{ R2, or, we need two } (6)^1\text{'s} \\
\qquad\quad 6)\overline{1} \text{ R0, or, we need no } (6)^2\text{'s} \\
\qquad\qquad 0 \text{ R1, or, we need one } (6)^3
\end{array}
$$

So $231 = 1(6)^3 + 0(6)^2 + 2(6)^1 + 3(6)^0$

                $231 = 216 + 0 + 12 + 3$

In short $231_{(\text{base } 10)} = 1023_{(\text{base } 6)}$

Note that the successive digits used to express the number in the scale of 6 are the series of remainders taken in the reverse order from that in which they were obtained. We continue the repeated divisions until we reach a quotient of zero. Note also that each remainder must be less than the base, since we are using the base as the divisor. If a remainder of zero is obtained, the corresponding power is used zero times. That is, it is not used at all.

thinking with other bases

When numbers are written as we ordinarily do, the base 10 is assumed. Thus 24 means 24 in the scale of 10, or $2(10)^1 + 4(10)^0$.

---

[6] Using the law of exponents and recalling that $a^x \cdot a^y = a^{x+y}$, we see that $(4)^1 \cdot (4)^1 = (4)^2$; $(4)^1 (4)^0 = (4)^1$; etc.

But the symbol $24_{(\text{base } 5)}$ means a number with base 5; it cannot be read as "twenty-four," or even as "twenty-four, base five," for the digits 2 and 4 no longer represent coefficients of powers of 10, but rather coefficients of powers of 5. We must read $24_{(\text{base } 5)}$ as "two-four base five"; it means, of course, $2(5)^1 + 4(5)^0$, or $14_{(\text{base } 10)}$. From now on we shall abbreviate $24_{(\text{base } 5)}$ as "24_5"; $14_{(\text{base } 10)}$ as "14_{10}"; etc.

In order to think and operate with numbers written with other bases, we must remember that a unique symbol is required for each number from zero up to but not including the base. The table shows the numbers up to 25 written in base 3, 4, 5, 6, and 12, respectively, next to the corresponding numbers in base 10. Thus, $19_{10} = 201_3 = 103_4 = 34_5 = 31_6 = 17_{12}$. If the base used is greater than 10, we must devise new symbols. Thus in the scale of 12 we might use "X" for 10_{10} and "E" for 11_{10};

then $\qquad 10_{12} = 12_{10}$, that is, 1 twelve and no ones;

$\qquad\qquad 20_{12} = 24_{10}$, that is, 2 twelves and no ones;

$\qquad\qquad 30_{12} = 36_{10}$, that is, 3 twelves and no ones; etc.

It is easy enough to change from any given base to any other given base.

Example 1. Write 247_8 in base 10.

$$247_8 = [2(8)^2 + 4(8)^1 + 7(8)^0]_{10}$$
$$= 128 + 32 + 7 = 167_{10}$$

Check: Change 167_{10} to base 8.

$$8)\overline{167}$$
$$8)\overline{20}\ \text{R7}$$
$$8)\overline{2}\ \text{R4}$$
$$0\ \text{R2}$$
$$\therefore\ 167_{10} = 247_8$$

Example 2. Change 263_{10} to base 12.

$$12)\overline{263}$$
$$12)\overline{21}\ \text{R11}\ \text{(that is, R} = E)\qquad \therefore\ 263_{10} = 19E_{12}$$
$$12)\overline{1}\ \text{R9}$$
$$\overline{)0}\ \text{R1}$$

Check: $\qquad 19E_{12} = [1(12)^2 + 9(12)^1 + 11(12)^0]_{10}$

$\qquad\qquad\qquad = [144 + 108 + 11]_{10} = 263_{10}$

Note that when changing a number to a base greater than 10, a remainder of 10 or more may occur, in which case *the remainder must be written with the new digit notation.*

TABLE 2. Numbers Written in Scales of 3, 4, 5, 6, and 12

10	3	4	5	6	12
0	0	0	0	0	0
1	1	1	1	1	1
2	2	2	2	2	2
3	10	3	3	3	3
4	11	10	4	4	4
5	12	11	10	5	5
6	20	12	11	10	6
7	21	13	12	11	7
8	22	20	13	12	8
9	100	21	14	13	9
10	101	22	20	14	X
11	102	23	21	15	E
12	110	30	22	20	10
13	111	31	23	21	11
14	112	32	24	22	12
15	120	33	30	23	13
16	121	100	31	24	14
17	122	101	32	25	15
18	200	102	33	30	16
19	201	103	34	31	17
20	202	110	40	32	18
21	210	111	41	33	19
22	211	112	42	34	$1X$
23	212	113	43	35	$1E$
24	220	120	44	40	20
25	221	121	100	41	21

Example 3. Change 265_7 to base 4.

$$265_7 = [2(7)^2 + 6(7)^1 + 5(7)^0]_{10}$$
$$= [98 + 42 + 5]_{10} = 145_{10}$$

Changing 145_{10} to base 4, we get:

$$
\begin{array}{l}
4)\overline{145} \\
\quad 4)\overline{36}\text{ R1} \\
\qquad 4)\overline{9}\text{ R0} \qquad \therefore\ 045_{10} = 2101_4 \\
\qquad\quad 4)\overline{2}\text{ R1} \\
\qquad\qquad 0\text{ R2}
\end{array}
$$

Check: $2101_4 = [2(4)^3 + 1(4)^2 + 0(4)^1 + 1(4)^0]_{10}$
                     $= [128 + 16 + 0 + 1]_{10} = 145_{10}$

Therefore, $265_7 = 2101_4$

It is an interesting and illuminating exercise to construct addition tables for numbers in different bases. For example:

Addition Table: Base 3

+	1	2
1	2	10
2	10	11

Addition Table: Base 4

+	1	2	3
1	2	3	10
2	3	10	11
3	10	11	12

Addition Table: Base 6

+	1	2	3	4	5
1	2	3	4	5	10
2	3	4	5	10	11
3	4	5	10	11	12
4	5	10	11	12	13
5	10	11	12	13	14

Addition Table: Base 8

+	1	2	3	4	5	6	7
1	2	3	4	5	6	7	10
2	3	4	5	6	7	10	11
3	4	5	6	7	10	11	12
4	5	6	7	10	11	12	13
5	6	7	10	11	12	13	14
6	7	10	11	12	13	14	15
7	10	11	12	13	14	15	16

Multiplication tables can also be constructed without difficulty: For example:

Multiplication Table: Base 3

×	1	2
1	1	2
2	2	11

Multiplication Table: Base 4

×	1	2	3
1	1	2	3
2	2	10	12
3	3	12	21

Multiplication Table: Base 7

×	1	2	3	4	5	6
1	1	2	3	4	5	6
2	2	4	6	11	13	15
3	3	6	12	15	21	24
4	4	11	15	22	26	33
5	5	13	21	26	34	42
6	6	15	24	33	42	51

Multiplication Table: Base 8

×	1	2	3	4	5	6	7
1	1	2	3	4	5	6	7
2	2	4	6	10	12	14	16
3	3	6	11	14	17	22	25
4	4	10	14	20	24	30	34
5	5	12	17	24	31	36	43
6	6	14	22	30	36	44	52
7	7	16	25	34	43	52	61

EXERCISE 6–2

1. Write the first 25 numbers in the scale of 7; in the scale of 9.

2. Write the first 30 numbers in the scale of 8.

3. Write the numbers from 20 to 40 in the scale of 4; in the scale of 6.

4. Write the numbers from 50 to 75 in the scale of 5.

5. Write the numbers from 90 to 100 in the scale of 8.

6. Write each of the following decimal numbers in the scale indicated:

(a) 49–(five)   (b) 134–(four)
(c) 265–(six)   (d) 318–(eight)
(e) 209–(seven)   (f) 92–(three)
(g) 460–(nine)   (h) 500–(eleven)
(i) 217–(twelve)   (j) 599–(twelve)

7. Write each of the following in the scale of 10:

(a) 158_9 (b) 623_7
(c) 405_6 (d) 340_8
(e) 2104_5 (f) 2220_3
(g) 1020_4 (h) 1100011_2
(i) 66_{12} (j) 1020_{12}

8. Change each of the following as indicated:

(a) 324_6 to base 3   (b) 213_4 to base 5
(c) 1404_5 to base 4   (d) 123_4 to base 8
(e) 302_6 to base 9   (f) 520_8 to base 5

9. Construct an addition table (a) for base 5; (b) for base 7; (c) for base 12.

10. Construct a multiplication table (a) for base 5; (b) for base 6; (c) for base 9.

11. Change the decimal numbers 54, 12, and 27 to base 4 and add them; then verify by changing the sum obtained to base 10.

12. Change the decimal numbers 220, 33, and 12 to base 7 and add them; then verify by changing the sum to base 10.

13. In what scale is $3 \times 3 = 11$? In what scale is $3 \times 3 = 12$?

14. Could 25 represent an even number in some scale? Could 52 represent an odd number in some scale?

15. What advantages might using a scale of 8 have over a scale of 10? What advantages might a scale of 12 have over a scale of 10?

16. Show that $10_b = b_{10}$, where b denotes any natural number on the scale of 10.

EXPONENTS AND LOGARITHMS

exponential notation

The reader may recall from his high school mathematics that when the factors of a product are alike, exponential notation is very convenient. In fact, we have previously used it when we expressed a number as a sum of powers of some base. For example:

4^3 means $4 \times 4 \times 4 = 64$
3^4 means $3 \times 3 \times 3 \times 3 = 81$
a^5 means $a \cdot a \cdot a \cdot a \cdot a$
10^6 means $10 \times 10 \times 10 \times 10 \times 10 \times 10 = 1,000,000$
p^x means $p \cdot p \cdot p \ldots$ to x factors

Such notation did not come into general use until about the middle of the seventeenth century; even as late as about 1750 books still used expressions such as $a^5 + aaaa + aa + 1$. The small number to the upper right (a superscript) is called an *exponent*. By definition, an exponent is a number which shows how many times another number is to be used as a factor. Thus 3^5 is read "three to the fifth power"; the *base* is 3, the *exponent* is 5, and the fifth *power* of 3 is 243.

It was with some difficulty that men finally accepted exponential notation. This is all the more remarkable since logarithms, which *are* exponents, were not invented until 1614, that is, before exponents were fully understood. As has been pointed out:[7]

Men were still feeling for a notation of indices, and the full implications of the Arabic decimal notation had hardly yet been grasped. Napier was looking with the eyes of a Greek-trained mathematician upon this notation as upon a new plaything.

the laws of exponents

Several fundamental laws governing exponents can readily be deduced directly from the definition of an exponent. If $a \neq 0$, then, since $a^3 = a \cdot a \cdot a$, and $a^4 = a \cdot a \cdot a \cdot a$, clearly $a^3 \cdot a^4 = (a \cdot a \cdot a) \cdot (a \cdot a \cdot a \cdot a) = a^7$. In general, when multiplying powers having the same base, we *add* their exponents:

(I) $$a^m \cdot a^n = a^{m+n}$$

Again, by definition:

$$a^6 \div a^4 = \frac{\overset{1}{\not a} \cdot \overset{1}{\not a} \cdot \overset{1}{\not a} \cdot \overset{1}{\not a} \cdot a \cdot a}{\underset{1}{\not a} \cdot \underset{1}{\not a} \cdot \underset{1}{\not a} \cdot \underset{1}{\not a}} = a \cdot a = a^2.$$

In general, when dividing powers having the same base, we subtract their exponents:

(II) $$a^m \div a^n = a^{m-n}.$$

When $m = n$ or $m < n$, the new exponent is either zero or negative, and has no meaning according to the original definition of an exponent, which applies only to positive integers. Hence we extend the definition to include zero and negative integers. Without attempting a rigorous presentation, we suggest intuitively that, since any number divided by itself equals one (excluding division by zero), we have

$$\frac{a^m}{a^m} = 1,$$

and since by law II above we see that

$$\frac{a^m}{a^m} = a^{m-m} = a^0,$$

[7] H. W. Turnbull, *The Great Mathematicians,* London: Methuen (1929), p. 62.

therefore a plausible and consistent meaning for the zero exponent is that given by the definition

(III) $$a^0 = 1,$$

for any value of a different from zero.

The definition of an exponent can similarly be extended, intuitively, to include negative integers. For example, since

$$\frac{a^2}{a^5} = \frac{\overset{1}{\cancel{a}} \cdot \overset{1}{\cancel{a}}}{a \cdot a \cdot \cancel{a} \cdot \cancel{a} \cdot a} = \frac{1}{a \cdot a \cdot a} = \frac{1}{a^3},$$

and since by II

$$\frac{a^2}{a^5} = a^{2-5} = a^{-3},$$

it would seem reasonable and consistent to say that

$$a^{-3} = \frac{1}{a^3}.$$

In general, we take as our definition,

(IV) $$a^{-m} = \frac{1}{a^m}, \quad \text{where} \quad a \neq 0.$$

Another law concerns raising a power to a power. This is evident at once from the original definition of an exponent; since $(a^3)^4$ means $a^3 \cdot a^3 \cdot a^3 \cdot a^3$, we have, by law I:

$$(a^3)^4 = a^{3+3+3+3} = a^{12}.$$

In general, to find a power of a power we *multiply* their exponents:

(V) $$(a^m)^n = a^{mn}.$$

Obviously $$(a^m)^n = (a^n)^m.$$

Finally, we could ask, what meaning might a fractional exponent have? Here again we extend the definition to give a fractional exponent a meaning consistent with previous definitions and laws concerning exponents. For example, let us see what $a^{1/n}$ could mean; call this expression x, so that $x = a^{1/n}$. Raising both quantities to the nth power and applying law V:

$$[(x)]^n = [(a^{1/n})]^n$$
$$\text{or} \quad x^n = a^1;$$

Taking the nth root of each of the equal quantities, we have

$$\sqrt[n]{x^n} = \sqrt[n]{a},$$
$$\text{or} \quad x = \sqrt[n]{a}.$$

But x represented the meaning, or value of $a^{1/n}$; so now we see that it would be logical to assign the meaning of $\sqrt[n]{a}$ to the symbol $a^{1/n}$. For example:

$$p^{1/2} = \sqrt[2]{p^1} \quad \text{or} \quad \sqrt{p};$$
$$k^{1/3} = \sqrt[3]{k^1} \quad \text{or} \quad \sqrt[3]{k};$$
$$10^{1/4} = \sqrt[4]{10^1} \quad \text{or} \quad \sqrt[4]{10}.$$

In general:

(VI) $a^{m/n} = \sqrt[n]{a^m}.$

For example:

$$a^{3/2} = \sqrt{a^3}$$
$$b^{2/3} = \sqrt[3]{b^2}$$
$$k^{4/5} = \sqrt[5]{k^4}$$

It is easily seen that

$$\sqrt[3]{(a^2)} = (\sqrt[3]{a})^2,$$

since $\sqrt[3]{(a^2)} = (a^2)^{1/3}, \quad \text{and} \quad (\sqrt[3]{a})^2 = (a^{1/3})^2;$
so $(a^2)^{1/3} = (a^{1/3})^2,$

and, by law V, $a^{2/3} = a^{2/3}.$

We may summarize these laws of exponents as follows:

I. $a^m \cdot a^n = a^{m+n}$ **II.** $a^m \div a^n = a^{m-n}$

III. $a^0 = 1$ **IV.** $a^{-m} = \dfrac{1}{a^m}$

V. $(a^m)^n = a^{mn}$ **VI.** $a^{m/n} = \sqrt[n]{a^m}$

scientific notation

Astronomers, physicists and other scientists who have occasion to use very large or very small numbers find it convenient to express such numbers in *scientific notation* or *standard form*. This utilizes the fact that when we move the decimal point in a number it merely multiplies the number by some integral power of 10; if the decimal point is

moved to the right, we are multiplying by a *positive* power of 10, and
if to the left, by a *negative* power of 10. For example:

1. $43.26 \times 1000 = 43,260$;   2. $93,000,000 = 93 \times 10^6$;
   $43,260 = 43.26 \times 10^3$. $93,000,000 = 9.3 \times 10^7$.
3. $0.000257 \times 10,000 = 2.57$;   4. $348,200 = 3.482 \times 10^5$
   $2.57 \times 10^{-4} = 0.000257$;   5. $0.000000695 = 69.5 \times 10^{-8}$
   $257 \times 10^{-6} = 0.000257$.

When a measured number in this notation is so written that the factor
which is multiplied by a power of 10 is less than 10 but greater than 1
and contains only significant figures,[8] then the measurement is expressed in standard form. Thus a and b below are in standard scientific
notation, whereas c and d are not:

(a) $186,000 = 1.86 \times 10^5$ (b) $348,200 = 3.482 \times 10^5$
(c) $0.00073 = 0.73 \times 10^{-3}$ (d) $0.00625 = 62.5 \times 10^{-4}$

EXERCISE 6–3

1. Simplify each of the following:

(a) $2^4 \cdot 2^5$ (b) $3^p \cdot 3^q$ (c) $a^{2k} \div a$
(d) $(\frac{1}{2}r)^3$ (e) $(-3y^2)^4$ (f) $b^{3x} \div b^x$
(g) $a^4 \cdot a^0$ (h) $a^3 b^2 \cdot a^{-2}$ (i) $y^2 \div y^6$
(j) $p^{2n+3} \div p^2$

2. Find the value of:

(a) $10^4 \cdot 10^2$ (b) $a^{-3} \div a^0$ (c) $(10^{-1})^2$
(d) $3^2 \cdot 2^3$ (e) $2^5 \times 2^{-2} - 2^0$ (f) $4^2 \cdot 8^{-2}$
(g) $3^{2x} \cdot 3^{-2x}$ (h) $(8^{-\frac{1}{3}})(2^0)$ (i) $3^{-2} + 3^0 + 9^{\frac{1}{2}}$
(j) $(3^{-4})^{-\frac{1}{2}}$

3. Express as a power of 2:

(a) 8^2 (b) 4^n (c) $\frac{1}{2}$ (d) 80 (e) 96

4. Express as a power of 3:

(a) 9^4 (b) 27^n (c) $81^{x/2}$ (d) 54 (e) $\frac{4}{9}$

5. Express as a power of 5:

(a) $(\sqrt[3]{125})^2$ (b) 25^{3n} (c) 1 (d) 250 (e) $\frac{1}{625}$

6. Express as a power of 10:

(a) $10,000,000$ (b) $(100)^{30}$ (c) 0.001 (d) 0.0000001

7. Why is it incorrect to say that 2^5 means "2 multiplied by itself five
times"? What is a correct way to state the meaning of 2^5 verbally?

[8] See Chapter 7.

8. Which of the five numbers below is represented by the sum of the following four terms:

$$2(10)^3 + 3(10)^2 + 4(10)^0 + 5(10)^{-2}$$

(a) 234.5   (b) 230.45   (c) 230.405
(d) 2304.05   (e) 2300.405

9. What exponent must 10 have to give:

(a) 10   (b) 1000   (c) 1   (d) $\frac{1}{10}$ (e) 0.01

10. Change each of the following to ordinary notation:

(a) 6×10^8 (b) 6.00×10^8 (c) 4.75×10^3
(d) 3.28×10^{-4} (e) 3.286×10^6 (f) 2.1×10^{-9}
       (g) 2.690×10^{19} (h) 1.60×10^{-12}

11. Write each of the following in scientific notation:

(a) 29.41   (b) 0.00208   (c) 20.8
(d) 0.208   (e) 1728   (f) 6,030,000
       (g) 0.003284   (h) 0.0000000816

12. Express in ordinary notation:

(a) The speed of light, 2.9979×10^{10} centimeters per second.
(b) The mass of the electron at rest, 9.106×10^{-28} grams.
(c) The electron charge, 4.8024×10^{-10} electrostatic units.
(d) One electrostatic unit, 2.08×10^9 electron charges.

13. In number 12, show that d can be derived from c, or vice versa.

14. To avoid long decimal fractions, the physicist uses the following units of length: (a) the mu ($\mu = 0.001$ millimeter), (b) the mu-mu ($\mu\mu = 0.000001$ millimeter), (c) the angstrom ($A = 10^{-8}$ centimeter).

(1) Show that 1 angstrom equals 0.1 $\mu\mu$.
(2) An X-ray unit of length is a thousandth part of the A; show that 1 X-ray unit $= 10^{-11}$ centimeter.

15. The time required for light to travel the diameter of the nucleus of an atom is that fraction of a second described by a decimal point followed by 22 zeros and a one. Express this fraction in scientific notation.

16. Comparing the numbers 10^{-39} and $2 \cdot 10^{-40}$, which is correct?

(a) the first exceeds the second by 5
(b) the first is 5 times the second
(c) the second is 5 times the first
(d) the first exceeds the second by $2 \cdot 10^{-1}$

tables of powers

Using the tables below, which are partial lists of powers of **2**, **3**, and **10**, study the following illustrative examples.

TABLE 3.   Table of Powers

Powers of 2

$2^0 = 1$	$2^{11} = 2048$
$2^1 = 2$	$2^{12} = 4096$
$2^2 = 4$	$2^{13} = 8192$
$2^3 = 8$	$2^{14} = 16{,}384$
$2^4 = 16$	$2^{15} = 32{,}768$
$2^5 = 32$	$2^{16} = 65{,}536$
$2^6 = 64$	$2^{17} = 131{,}072$
$2^7 = 128$	$2^{18} = 262{,}144$
$2^8 = 256$	$2^{19} = 524{,}288$
$2^9 = 512$	$2^{20} = 1{,}048{,}576$
$2^{10} = 1024$	$2^{21} = 2{,}097{,}152$

Powers of 3   *Powers of 10*

$3^0 = 1$	$10^0 = 1$
$3^1 = 3$	$10^1 = 10$
$3^2 = 9$	$10^2 = 100$
$3^3 = 27$	$10^3 = 1000$
$3^4 = 81$	$10^4 = 10{,}000$
$3^5 = 243$	$10^5 = 100{,}000$
$3^6 = 729$	$10^6 = 1{,}000{,}000$
$3^7 = 2187$	$10^7 = 10{,}000{,}000$
$3^8 = 6561$	$10^8 = 100{,}000{,}000$
$3^9 = 19{,}683$	$10^9 = 1{,}000{,}000{,}000$
$3^{10} = 59{,}049$	$10^{10} = 10{,}000{,}000{,}000$

Example 1. Find 128×1024. From the table: $128 = 2^7$, and $1024 = 2^{10}$; and from the law of exponents, $2^7 \times 2^{10} = 2^{17}$. But the table shows us that $2^{17} = 131{,}072$; hence $128 \times 1024 = 131{,}072$.

Example 2. Find the value of $(64)^3$. From the table: $64 = 2^6$; hence $(64)^3 = (2^6)^3 = 2^{18}$. But, from the table: $2^{18} = 262{,}144$; so $(64)^3 = 262{,}144$.

Example 3. Divide $59{,}049$ by 729. From the table: $59{,}049 = 3^{10}$, and $729 = 3^6$. Hence, $59{,}049 \div 729 = 3^{10} \div 3^6 = 3^4$, or 81.

Example 4. Find $\sqrt[3]{32{,}768}$. From the table: $32{,}768 = 2^{15}$. From the law of exponents: $\sqrt[3]{2^{15}} = 2^{\frac{15}{3}} = 2^5 = 32$. Hence, $\sqrt[3]{32{,}768} = 32$.

In these examples, certain numbers are seen to be integral powers of 2, or of 3, or of 10. A moment's reflection will suggest that if $2^4 = 16$ and $2^5 = 32$, then the exponent in $2^x = 20$ must lie between 4 and 5, say about $4.3+$; so that $2^{4.3+} = 20$. Similarly, to represent the number 20 as a power of 3, the exponent would have to lie between 2 and 3, since $3^2 = 9$ and $3^3 = 27$; actually, $3^{2.7+} = 20$, where "$2.7+$" is an approximate value of the required exponent. To express 20 as a power of 10, the exponent would obviously have to lie between 1 and 2; actually, it is about 1.301, so that $10^{1.301} = 20$.

Thus we see that any positive number can be expressed as a power of any positive integral base; in some of these cases the exponent would also be an integer, but in many, many other cases the exponent would be an approximate number, usually written as a mixed decimal (that is, an integer plus a decimal fraction such as 1.5 or 3.2578).

logarithms are exponents

The exponents of the powers of **2**, **3**, and **10**, in the preceding paragraph are called *logarithms*. By definition, then:

If b is any positive number not equal to 1, and $b^x = N$, then the exponent x is called the logarithm of the number N to the base b.

In symbols:

$$x = \log_b N.$$

Thus

$$\log_2 8 \quad = 3, \text{ because } 2^3 = 8$$
$$\log_5 125 \quad = 3, \text{ because } 5^3 = 125$$
$$\log_3 343 \quad = 5, \text{ because } 3^5 = 343$$
$$\log_5 625 \quad = 4, \text{ because } 5^4 = 625$$
$$\log_4 1024 = 5, \text{ because } 4^5 = 1024$$

So you see that a logarithm is nothing more than an exponent; $\log_b N$ simply means the exponent x to which the base must be raised to obtain the number N, that is,

$$b^x = N, \text{ or } b^{(\log_b N)} = N.$$

It can be proved that every positive real number N can be expressed as b^x, where x is a real number, rational or irrational. We shall limit our discussion, however, to logarithms of positive numbers with positive bases.

Theoretically, we could choose any number for a base, but only two bases are in general use: the base 10, which is the base of *common* logarithms, and the irrational number e, which is the base of *natural* logarithms. The constant e is defined as the limit which the expression $(1 + 1/k)^k$ approaches as k increases without limit. The approximate value of e is 2.718. This number is of great significance in advanced mathematics, but for practical purposes such as computation, the base 10 is very convenient. If we customarily wrote numbers on the scale of 2, or 5, etc., then logarithms to the base 2, or 5, etc., would be most convenient for computation. In this book, when no other base is explicitly stated, then the base 10 is understood; thus "log 29" means "$\log_{10} 29$"; "log A" means "$\log_{10} A$"; etc.

laws of logarithms

There are three fundamental laws of logarithms which hold true for all bases:

$$\log_b (PQ) = \log_b P + \log_b Q \tag{1}$$

$$\log_b \left(\frac{P}{Q}\right) = \log_b P - \log_b Q \tag{2}$$

$$\log_b (P^k) = k \cdot \log_b P \tag{3}$$

These laws are easily derived from the basic theorems on exponents (page 186). Thus we shall derive equation 1, leaving the proofs of 2 and 3 to the reader.

Let $\qquad\qquad P = b^x$, and $Q = b^y$;

$\qquad\qquad$ then $x = \log_b P$, and $y = \log_b Q$.

From I, page 184, we may say:

$$P \cdot Q = b^x \cdot b^y = b^{(x+y)};$$

hence $\quad \log_b (PQ) = x + y,$

and, by substitution, $\log_b (PQ) = \log_b P + \log_b Q.$

EXERCISE 6–4

1. Determine each of the following logarithms, using the table on page 189 if necessary:

(a) $\log_2 128$
(c) $\log_{10} 100,000$
(e) $\log_3 81$
(g) $\log_2 1024$

(b) $\log_3 729$
(d) $\log_2 4096$
(f) $\log_{10} 1,000,000,000$
(h) $\log_{10} 1$

2. Write each of the following in exponential form:

(a) $\log_2 32 = 5$
(c) $\log_{10} 10,000 = 4$
(e) $\log_a R = y$
(g) $\log_y x = z$

(b) $\log_5 25 = 2$
(d) $\log_{10} 10 = 1$
(f) $\log_n M = x$
(h) $\log_{17} 1 = 0$

3. Complete each of the following:

(a) $\log_{10} 1000 = ?$
(c) $\log_5 125 = ?$
(e) $\log_{10} (\frac{1}{10}) = ?$
(g) $\log_9 3 = ?$

(b) $\log_3 9 = ?$
(d) $\log_2 64 = ?$
(f) $\log_b b = ?$
(h) $\log_a (a^n) = ?$

TABLE 4.   Table of Logarithms

COMMON LOGARITHMS

	0	1	2	3	4	5	6	7	8	9
10	0000	0043	0086	0128	0170	0212	0253	0294	0334	0374
11	0414	0453	0492	0531	0569	0607	0645	0682	0719	0755
12	0792	0828	0864	0899	0934	0969	1004	1038	1072	1106
13	1139	1173	1206	1239	1271	1303	1335	1367	1399	1430
14	1461	1492	1523	1553	1584	1614	1644	1673	1703	1732
15	1761	1790	1818	1847	1875	1903	1931	1959	1987	2014
16	2041	2068	2095	2122	2148	2175	2201	2227	2253	2279
17	2304	2330	2355	2380	2405	2430	2455	2480	2504	2529
18	2553	2577	2601	2625	2648	2672	2695	2718	2742	2765
19	2788	2810	2833	2856	2878	2900	2923	2945	2967	2989
20	3010	3032	3054	3075	3096	3118	3139	3160	3181	3201
21	3222	3243	3263	3284	3304	3324	3345	3365	3385	3404
22	3424	3444	3464	3483	3502	3522	3541	3560	3579	3598
23	3617	3636	3655	3674	3692	3711	3729	3747	3766	3784
24	3802	3820	3838	3856	3874	3892	3909	3927	3945	3962
25	3979	3997	4014	4031	4048	4065	4082	4099	4116	4133
26	4150	4166	4183	4200	4216	4232	4249	4265	4281	4298
27	4314	4330	4346	4362	4378	4393	4409	4425	4440	4456
28	4472	4487	4502	4518	4533	4548	4564	4579	4594	4609
29	4624	4639	4654	4669	4683	4698	4713	4728	4742	4757
30	4771	4786	4800	4814	4829	4843	4857	4871	4886	4900
31	4914	4928	4942	4955	4969	4983	4997	5011	5024	5038
32	5051	5065	5079	5092	5105	5119	5132	5145	5159	5172
33	5185	5198	5211	5224	5237	5250	5263	5276	5289	5302
34	5315	5328	5340	5353	5366	5378	5391	5403	5416	5428
35	5441	5453	5465	5478	5490	5502	5514	5527	5539	5551
36	5563	5575	5587	5599	5611	5623	5635	5647	5658	5670
37	5682	5694	5705	5717	5729	5740	5752	5763	5775	5786
38	5798	5809	5821	5832	5843	5855	5866	5877	5888	5899
39	5911	5922	5933	5944	5955	5966	5977	5988	5999	6010
40	6021	6031	6042	6053	6064	6075	6085	6096	6107	6117
41	6128	6138	6149	6160	6170	6180	6191	6201	6212	6222
42	6232	6243	6253	6263	6274	6284	6294	6304	6314	6325
43	6335	6345	6355	6365	6375	6385	6395	6405	6415	6425
44	6435	6444	6454	6464	6474	6484	6493	6503	6513	6522
45	6532	6542	6551	6561	6571	6580	6590	6599	6609	6618
46	6628	6637	6646	6656	6665	6675	6684	6693	6702	6712
47	6721	6730	6739	6749	6758	6767	6776	6785	6794	6803
48	6812	6821	6830	6839	6848	6857	6866	6875	6884	6893
49	6902	6911	6920	6928	6937	6946	6955	6964	6972	6981
50	6990	6998	7007	7016	7024	7033	7042	7050	7059	7067
51	7076	7084	7093	7101	7110	7118	7126	7135	7143	7152
52	7160	7168	7177	7185	7193	7202	7210	7218	7226	7235
53	7243	7251	7259	7267	7275	7284	7292	7300	7308	7316
54	7324	7332	7340	7348	7356	7364	7372	7380	7388	7396

TABLE 4.   Table of Logarithms—(*Continued*)

COMMON LOGARITHMS (*Continued*)

	0	1	2	3	4	5	6	7	8	9
55	7404	7412	7419	7427	7435	7443	7451	7459	7466	7474
56	7482	7490	7497	7505	7513	7520	7528	7536	7543	7551
57	7559	7566	7574	7582	7589	7597	7604	7612	7619	7627
58	7634	7642	7649	7657	7664	7672	7679	7686	7694	7701
59	7709	7716	7723	7731	7738	7745	7752	7760	7767	7774
60	7782	7789	7796	7803	7810	7818	7825	7832	7839	7846
61	7853	7860	7868	7875	7882	7889	7896	7903	7910	7917
62	7924	7931	7938	7945	7952	7959	7966	7973	7980	7987
63	7993	8000	8007	8014	8021	8028	8035	8041	8048	8055
64	8062	8069	8075	8082	8089	8096	8102	8109	8116	8122
65	8129	8136	8142	8149	8156	8162	8169	8176	8182	8189
66	8195	8202	8209	8215	8222	8228	8235	8241	8248	8254
67	8261	8267	8274	8280	8287	8293	8299	8306	8312	8319
68	8325	8331	8338	8344	8351	8357	8363	8370	8376	8382
69	8388	8395	8401	8407	8414	8420	8426	8432	8439	8445
70	8451	8457	8463	8470	8476	8482	8488	8494	8500	8506
71	8513	8519	8525	8531	8537	8543	8549	8555	8561	8567
72	8573	8579	8585	8591	8597	8603	8609	8615	8621	8627
73	8633	8639	8645	8651	8657	8663	8669	8675	8681	8686
74	8692	8698	8704	8710	8716	8722	8727	8733	8739	8745
75	8751	8756	8762	8768	8774	8779	8785	8791	8797	8802
76	8808	8814	8820	8825	8831	8837	8842	8848	8854	8859
77	8865	8871	8876	8882	8887	8893	8899	8904	8910	8915
78	8921	8927	8932	8938	8943	8949	8954	8960	8965	8971
79	8976	8982	8987	8993	8998	9004	9009	9015	9020	9025
80	9031	9036	9042	9047	9053	9058	9063	9069	9074	9079
81	9085	9090	9096	9101	9106	9112	9117	9122	9128	9133
82	9138	9143	9149	9154	9159	9165	9170	9175	9180	9186
83	9191	9196	9201	9206	9212	9217	9222	9227	9232	9238
84	9243	9248	9253	9258	9263	9269	9274	9279	9284	9289
85	9294	9299	9304	9309	9315	9320	9325	9330	9335	9340
86	9345	9350	9355	9360	9365	9370	9375	9380	9385	9390
87	9395	9400	9405	9410	9415	9420	9425	9430	9435	9440
88	9445	9450	9455	9460	9465	9469	9474	9479	9484	9489
89	9494	9499	9504	9509	9513	9518	9523	9528	9533	9538
90	9542	9547	9552	9557	9562	9566	9571	9576	9581	9586
91	9590	9595	9600	9605	9609	9614	9619	9624	9628	9633
92	9638	9643	9647	9652	9657	9661	9666	9671	9675	9680
93	9685	9689	9694	9699	9703	9708	9713	9717	9722	9727
94	9731	9736	9741	9745	9750	9754	9759	9763	9768	9773
95	9777	9782	9786	9791	9795	9800	9805	9809	9814	9818
96	9823	9827	9832	9836	9841	9845	9850	9854	9859	9863
97	9868	9872	9877	9881	9886	9890	9894	9899	9903	9908
98	9912	9917	9921	9926	9930	9934	9939	9943	9948	9952
99	9956	9961	9965	9969	9974	9978	9983	9987	9991	9996

4. Write each of the following in logarithmic form:

(a) $3^5 = 243$ (b) $10^2 = 100$

(c) $A^m = x$ (d) $10^0 = 1$

(e) $10^{1.6263} = 42.3$ (f) $8.67 = 10^{0.9380}$

(g) $2^0 = 1$ (h) $x = e^k$

5. Complete:

(a) $\log_? 49 = 2$ (b) $\log_? 8 = 3$

(c) $\log_{10} 10 = ?$ (d) $\log_{10} 1 = ?$

(e) $\log_A A = ?$ (f) $\log_A 1 = ?$

6. Explain why 1 cannot be used as a base in a system of logarithms. (*Hint:* $\log_1 1 = ?$ $\log_1 2 = ?$ etc.)

7. What difficulty would you encounter if a negative number were used as a base in a system of logarithms?

8. Explain why the logarithm of 1 equals 0, no matter what base is used.

9. Explain why the logarithm of the base equals 1, no matter what base is used.

10. State the three fundamental laws of logarithms in words: Log $(PQ) =$ log $P +$ log Q; Log $(P/Q) = ?$ Log $(P^k) = ?$

11. Show how the second and third laws of logarithms can be derived from the basic theorems on exponents.

12. Explain the difference in meaning between log (P/Q) and $\dfrac{\log P}{\log Q}$.

13. Given that $\log_b 2 = 0.693$ and $\log_b 3 = 1.099$, find $\log_b 12$.

14. Which of the following expressions is identical with the expression log $(x/y)^n$:

(a) $\dfrac{\log x}{\log y}$ (b) $\dfrac{\log nx}{\log ny}$ (c) $\log nx - \log ny$

(d) $n(\log x - \log y)$ (e) $1/n(\log x - \log y)$

15. Find the value of x if $x = 10^{\log 7}$.

16. Show that $b^{\log_b N} = N$ is an identity.

17. State whether the following are true or false: If log $a = x$ and log $b = y$, then

(a) log $(a + b) = x + y$ (b) $\log \left(\dfrac{a}{b^2}\right) = x - 2y$

(c) $\dfrac{\log a}{\log b} = x - y$ (d) $\log \sqrt[3]{ab} = \dfrac{x + y}{3}$ (e) $\log \left(\dfrac{a}{b}\right) = \dfrac{x}{y}$

18. Find the value of

$$\frac{1}{16a^0} + \left(\frac{1}{16a}\right)^0 - (64^{-\frac{1}{2}}) - (-32)^{-\frac{4}{5}}$$

19. If $P = \dfrac{S}{(1 + k)^n}$, then n equals:

(a) $\dfrac{\log S}{\log P(1 + k)}$ (b) $\log \dfrac{S}{P(1 + k)}$

(c) $\dfrac{\log \left(\dfrac{S}{P}\right)}{\log (1 + k)}$ (d) $\log \left(\dfrac{S - P}{1 + k}\right)$

logarithms of numbers between 1 and 10

Study this list of logarithms (base 10) of the numbers from 1 to 10:

N	$\log N$	N	$\log N$
1	0.0000	6	0.7782
2	0.3010	7	0.8451
3	0.4771	8	0.9031
4	0.6021	9	0.9542
5	0.6990	10	1.0000

Since $\log 1 = 0$ and $\log 10 = 1$, we conclude that the logarithms of numbers between 1 and 10 are numbers greater than zero but less than one, as in fact they are. These numbers are expressed as decimal fractions in the above table. If we make use of the principle of scientific notation, it will be realized that the logarithm of any number consists of an integer (which is the exponent of the integral power of 10), plus a fraction (which is the exponent of the power of 10 corresponding to the number between 1 and 10.

Examples:

1. $8000 = 8 \times 10^3$.
Since
$$8 = 10^{0.9031},$$
$$\text{therefore } 8000 = 10^{0.9031} \times 10^3 = 10^{3.9031},$$
$$\text{or } \log 8000 = 3 + 0.9031 = 3.9031.$$

2.
$$50,000,000 = 5 \times 10^7.$$
Since
$$5 = 10^{0.6990},$$
$$\text{therefore } 50,000,000 = 10^{0.6990} \times 10^7 = 10^{7.6990},$$
$$\text{or } \log 50,000,000 = 7 + 0.6990 = 7.6990.$$

Hence, if we know the logarithms of numbers between 1 and 10, we can find the logarithm of any number simply by using scientific notation. The table on pages 192–193 gives us the logarithms of such numbers to four decimal places. All decimal points have been omitted from the table. The numbers between 1 and 10 appear in the column headed "N"; a decimal point is understood between the two digits in these numbers. Thus, reading down, under "N," we really think: "1.0, 1.1, 1.2, 1.3," etc. The third figure of the number "N" is found at the top of the table heading, running horizontally across. For example, the logarithm of 1.7 is 0.2304 (decimal points are understood before each four-place logarithm). Similarly, the logarithms of the following numbers are as shown:

$$\log 5.4 = 0.7324 \qquad \log 7.06 = 0.8488$$
$$\log 8.0 = 0.9031 \qquad \log 9.90 = 0.9956$$
$$\log 3.14 = 0.4969 \qquad \log 9.98 = 0.9991$$

finding a logarithm from a table

To find the logarithm of a number having three significant figures, we proceed as suggested above, using the idea of scientific notation. (If the number has more than three significant figures, we either round the number first, or use interpolation as described later.) We wish to find the logarithm of 49,300. From the table, we find

$$\log 4.93 = 0.6928.$$

By scientific notation,

$$49,300 = 10^4 \times 4.93.$$

So,
$$\log 49,300 = 4 \log 10 + \log 4.93$$
$$= 4 + 0.6928, \text{ or } 4.6928.$$

For similar reasons:

$$\log 49.3 = 1.6928$$
$$\log 493 = 2.6928$$
$$\log 4,930 = 3.6928$$
$$\log 4,930,000 = 6.6928$$

In every case, the fractional or decimal part of the logarithm, taken from the table, is known as the *mantissa*. The integral part of the logarithm, supplied "by inspection," is known as the *characteristic*.

The procedure applies equally when finding the logarithm of a decimal, let us say 0.493. We note that

$$0.493 = 10^{-1} \times 4.93;$$
$$\text{so, } \log 0.493 = (-1)(\log 10) + \log 4.93,$$
$$\text{or } \log 0.493 = -1 + 0.6928.$$

Now the negative integer (-1) and the positive decimal fraction (0.6928) could be combined and written as a mixed decimal, namely,

-0.3072. But since all mantissas in a table are positive, it is convenient to preserve the positive fractional part of logarithms; if we did not, the negative fraction obtained could not be identified in the table. Hence it is customary to write

log 0.493	$= 9.6928 - 10.$
Similarly, log 0.0493	$= 8.6928 - 10,$
log 0.00493	$= 7.6928 - 10,$
log 0.00000493	$= 4.6928 - 10.$

The procedure for finding the characteristic of a logarithm by inspection may be summarized, for convenience, into the following rules:

Rule 1. *The characteristic of the logarithm of a number greater than 1 is one less than the number of digits to the left of the decimal point.*

Examples:

log 6 = 0.778	log 317 = 2.501
log 8.34 = 0.921	log 42,500 = 4.628
log 52 = 1.716	log 834,000 = 5.921

Rule 2. *The characteristic of the logarithm of a number less than 1 is negative and is numerically one more than the number of zeros between the decimal point and the first significant digit.*

Examples:

log 0.346	$= 9.5391 - 10$
log 0.0723	$= 8.8591 - 10$
log 0.000624	$= 6.7952 - 10$
log 0.009	$= 7.9542 - 10$

linear interpolation

If we wish to find the logarithm of a number consisting of a sequence of four or more significant digits, we have recourse to interpolation. Careful study of the table reveals that as a number increases, its logarithm also increases. But they do not increase at the same rate; for example, log 4 = 0.6021 and log 2 = 0.3010, which might suggest that doubling the number would double its logarithm. This is not true, however; for example, log 25 = 1.3979, whereas log 50 = 1.6990, which is far from double the former logarithm. However, further examination of the table shows that there is approximately a constant difference between consecutive entries in the table. In other words, although a number and its logarithm do not change at the same rate, the differences of the logarithms of consecutive numbers is approximately constant. This fact permits us to make linear interpolations, or interpolations by proportional parts.

Example 1. Find log 2724. From the table, we find log 2720 and log 2730:

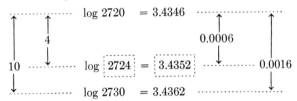

$$\begin{array}{ll} \log 2720 & = 3.4346 \\ \log 2724 & = 3.4352 \\ \log 2730 & = 3.4362 \end{array}$$

Since the number 2724 is $\frac{4}{10}$ of the interval from 2720 to 2730, we assume that the logarithm of 2724 is also $\frac{4}{10}$ of the difference between log 2720 and log 2730. This difference is $3.4362 - 3.4346 = 0.0016$; $\frac{4}{10} \times 0.0016 = 0.00064 \approx 0.0006$.[9] Hence log 2724 = 3.4346 + 0.0006 = 3.4352.

Example 2. Find log 54.36.

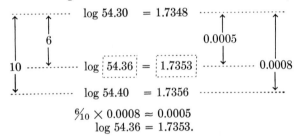

$$\begin{array}{ll} \log 54.30 & = 1.7348 \\ \log 54.36 & = 1.7353 \\ \log 54.40 & = 1.7356 \end{array}$$

$$\frac{6}{10} \times 0.0008 \approx 0.0005$$
$$\log 54.36 = 1.7353.$$

finding an antilogarithm

The number which corresponds to a given logarithm is called the *antilogarithm*. It is found from the table by a reverse process.

Example 1. Find the antilog 1.5775. Disregarding the characteristic 1, we "hunt" for the mantissa "0.5775" in the body of the table. When located, the corresponding number "N" is 378; hence the desired antilog 1.5775 is 37.8.

Example 2. Find antilog 2.3922.
Searching for the mantissa "0.3922" in the table, we find that it lies between "0.7520" and "0.7528."

⎯⎯⎯⎯⎯⎯⎯⎯⎯⎯⎯⎯

[9] The symbol "≈" means "is approximately equal to."

$$
\begin{array}{ll}
0.3927 & 0.3922 \\
0.3909 & 0.3909 \\
\hline
0.0018 & 0.0013
\end{array}
\qquad
\frac{0.0013}{0.0018} \approx 0.7
$$

So, antilog 0.3922 lies $\frac{7}{10}$ the way between 2.460 and 2.470, or at 2.467. So, antilog 2.3922 = 246.7.

Example 3. Find antilog $8.7522 - 10$. Mantissa "0.7522" lies between "0.7520" and "0.7528."

$$0.7528 = \log 5.66$$
$$0.7520 = \log 5.65$$
$$\frac{0.0002}{0.0008} = 0.25 \approx 0.3$$
$$0.7522 = \log \boxed{5.65} + (0.3)(0.01) = 5.653$$

So, antilog $8.7522 - 10 = 0.05653$.

EXERCISE 6–5

1. Express each of the following in exponential form:

(a) log 26.4 = 1.4216 $\qquad$ (b) log 7500 = 3.8751
(c) log 100,000 = 5 $\qquad$ (d) log 0.18 = 9.2553 $-$ 10
(e) log 5.21 = 0.7168 $\qquad$ (f) log 0.00001 = -5
(g) log 0.00388 = 7.5888 $-$ 10 $\qquad$ (h) log 9,560,000 = 6.9805

2. Find the following:

(a) log 274 $\qquad$ (b) log 3.95 $\qquad$ (c) log 61.8
(d) log 0.7 $\qquad$ (e) log 327,000 $\qquad$ (f) log 0.445
(g) log 0.051 $\qquad$ (h) log 0.00742 $\qquad$ (i) log 8,040 $\qquad$ (j) log 0.65

3. Find the number whose logarithm is:

(a) 1.0492 $\qquad$ (b) 3.4742 $\qquad$ (c) 0.9410
(d) 9.5717 $-$ 10 $\qquad$ (e) 2.6721 $\qquad$ (f) 8.7789 $-$ 10
(g) .8500 $\qquad$ (h) 6.3243 $-$ 10 $\qquad$ (i) 5.8035

4. Find by interpolation:

(a) log 125.4 $\qquad$ (b) log 67.58 $\qquad$ (c) log 0.08533
(d) log 3.142 $\qquad$ (e) log 0.5316 $\qquad$ (f) log 0.007591
(g) log 856,500 $\qquad$ (h) log 0.0002147

5. Find by interpolation:

(a) antilog 2.6842 $\qquad$ (b) antilog 0.9564
(c) antilog 8.4876 $-$ 10 $\qquad$ (d) antilog 1.8782
(e) antilog 9.8009 $-$ 10 $\qquad$ (f) antilog 0.8741
(g) antilog 3.5767 $\qquad$ (h) antilog 7.3370 $-$ 10

computing with logarithms

These properties are helpful when using logarithms to carry out computations, as suggested below.

Example 1.

$$\text{Find } \frac{0.512 \times 24.9}{88.3 \times 0.0345}.$$

$$
\begin{aligned}
\log 0.512 &= 9.7093 - 10 \\
\log 24.9 &= 1.3962 \\
\hline
&\quad 11.1055 - 10
\end{aligned}
\qquad
\begin{aligned}
&\text{Subtracting:} \\
&11.1055 - 10 \\
&10.4838 - 10 \\
\hline
&0.6217
\end{aligned}
$$

$$
\begin{aligned}
\log 88.3 &= 1.9460 \\
\log 0.0345 &= 8.5378 - 10 \\
\hline
&10.4838 - 10
\end{aligned}
\qquad
\text{antilog } 0.6217 = 4.185
$$

Answer: 4.19, approximately.

Example 2.

$$
\begin{aligned}
&\text{Find } \sqrt[5]{138} \\
&\log (138)^{\frac{1}{5}} = \tfrac{1}{5}(\log 138) \\
&\qquad\qquad\; = (0.2)(2.1399) = 0.4280 \\
&\text{antilog } 0.4280 = 2.589
\end{aligned}
$$

Answer: $\sqrt[5]{138} = 2.59$, approximately.

Example 3.

$$\text{Find } \sqrt[3]{4\pi R^2} \text{ when } R = 28.6.$$

$$
\begin{aligned}
\log 4 &= 0.6021 \\
\log 3.14 &= 0.4969 \\
2 \log 28.6 &= 2.9128 \\
\hline
3)&\,4.0118 \\
&\,1.3373
\end{aligned}
$$

$$\text{antilog } 1.3373 = 21.74$$

Answer: $\sqrt[3]{(4)(3.14)(28.6)^2} = 21.7$, approximately.

EXERCISE 6–6

1. Find the value of each of the following by means of logarithms:

(a) $(1.74)(24.6)(0.38)$ (b) $(256.4)(0.0085)(67.04)$

(c) $\dfrac{7.52 \times 8.918}{4.82}$ (d) $\dfrac{8.6 \times 5.426}{\dfrac{22}{7} \times 0.321}$ (e) $\dfrac{4.016}{0.0675}$

2. Find:

(a) $(1.05)^8$ (b) $\sqrt[3]{2.64}$ (c) $\sqrt[4]{1850}$

(d) $(1500)(1.04)^{20}$ (e) $\sqrt[5]{0.0976}$ (f) $(3.72)^{\frac{3}{2}}$

3. Evaluate by means of logarithms:

(a) $(356)(1.06)^{12}$ (b) $\dfrac{(75.2)^2 \, (3.08)^5}{(0.0084)^3}$

(c) $\dfrac{(7.68)(624.8)}{(14.6)(2.93)}$ (d) $\dfrac{0.43 \times \sqrt[5]{66.2}}{(0.051)^2}$

4. State the value of each of the following:

(a) $\log_5 125$;   (b) $\log_5 5$;   (c) $\log_5 1$.

5. Given $\log 3 = 0.47712$, how many digits are there in the expansion of 3^{48}?

6. Given $\log 3 = 0.47712$ and $\log 7 = 0.84510$, express $\dfrac{7}{3}$ as a power of 10.

7. Given $\log 2 = 0.30103$ and $\log 3 = 0.47712$, find without using the table the value of $\log \sqrt[5]{6}$.

8. The volume of a right circular cylinder is $V = \pi R^2 H$. Find by means of logarithms the value of R when $V = 906.0$, $H = 14.60$, and $\pi = 3.142$.

9. (a) If $\log \sqrt{x} = 0.7211$, what is the value of $\log x^2$?

(b) If $\log n = 1.7487$, what is $\log \sqrt[3]{n}$?

10. In the formula $A = P(1 + r)^n$, find A when $P = 2000$, $r = 0.05$, and $n = 12$.

11. If $R = \sqrt[3]{\dfrac{3V}{4\pi}}$, find R when $\pi = 3.14$ and $V = 56.3$.

12. (a) If $\log_a N = E$, then the power to which a must be raised to equal N is ?.

(b) If $y = 2^a$, then when a is increased by 3, the value of y becomes ? times as great.

13. If $0.3^x = 6$, $\log 2 = 0.301$, and $\log 3 = 0.477$, find the value of x.

14. (a) What is the relation between $\log 5$ and $\log 125$?

(b) Complete: $\log 83.42 - \log 0.8342 = ?$

15. Prove that $(\log_b a) \cdot (\log_a b) = 1$.

FOR FURTHER READING AND STUDY

Systems of Numeration

1. Dantzig, Tobias. *Number: The Language of Science.* New York: Macmillan, 1939. Pp. 1–17: "Fingerprints."
2. Eves, Howard. *An Introduction to the History of Mathematics.* New York: Rinehart and Company, 1953. Chapter 1: "Number Systems."
3. Larsen, Harold. *Arithmetic for Colleges.* New York: Macmillan, 1958. Chapter 1: "Number."
4. Smeltzer, Donald. *Man and Number.* New York: Emerson Books Inc., 1958.

Scales of Notation

5. Jones, Phillip S. "Binary System." *The Mathematics Teacher* 46:575–577; 1953.
6. McKay, Herbert. *Odd Numbers, or Arithmetic Revisited.* New York: Cambridge University Press, 1940. Pp. 210–215: "Scales of Notation."

7. Swain, Robert. *Understanding Arithmetic.* New York: Rinehart and Company, 1957. Chapter 6: "Twelves and Twos."

8. Tingley, E. M. "Base Eight Arithmetic and Money." *School Science and Mathematics* 40:503–508; 1940.

Exponents and Logarithms

9. Bakst, A. *Mathematics: Its Magic and Mastery.* New York: Van Nostrand, 1941. Chapters 17, 18: "Logarithms."

10. De Bray, M. E. J. G. *Exponentials Made Easy.* New York: Macmillan, 1928.

11. Hogben, L. *Mathematics for the Million.* New York: W. W. Norton, 1937. Chapter 10: "How Logarithms Were Discovered."

12. McKay, Herbert. *Odd Numbers.* Cambridge University Press, 1940. Pp. 22–36: "How We Got Logarithms."

CHAPTER 7

Measurement

Things do not, in general, run around
with their measures stamped on them
like the capacity of a freight car; it
requires a certain amount of investigation to discover what their measures
are.

—Norbert Wiener

THE NATURE OF MEASUREMENT

the concept of measurement

More than half a century ago the eminent physicist Lord Kelvin in-
sisted that "when you can measure what you are speaking about and
express it in numbers, you know something about it; but when you
cannot express it in numbers, your knowledge is of a meager and un-
satisfactory kind; it may be the beginning of knowledge, but you have
scarcely in your thoughts advanced to the stage of science." The
implications of these remarks are as cogent today as they have been
since the beginnings of modern science.

At the outset, let us recognize that there are (1) physical measurements, such as length, mass, volume, weight, wave length of light,

electrical conductivity, and so on, and (2) measurements in the social and behavioral sciences, such as intelligence, achievement, aptitudes, socio-economic status, thrift, motivation, social attitudes, and the like. For the time being, we shall confine our attention to physical measurements, which, in general, are what we mean by "quantitative measurements."

When considering physical measurements we must distinguish clearly between *things* and their *properties*.[1] "Things" are not only material objects such as nails, boards, boxes, chairs, rugs, windows, etc., but also include molecules, light waves, electrical charges, cell nuclei, and so on. "Properties" of things refer to observable characteristics; for example color, texture, length, width, area, density, temperature. In this connection we do not think of a property in the abstract, but rather as a property *of something*. We always measure properties of things, never the things themselves. Thus we do not measure a metal curtain rod; we measure its *length*, or its *diameter*, or its *weight*. Since measurement refers to properties of things, or relations among properties, measurement is one way of defining a property. Thus *density* is defined as the ratio of mass to volume; *pressure* is defined as force per unit of area.

Not all properties, of course, admit of measurement. For example, color, hardness, and turbidity are sometimes "measured" according to an arbitrary numerical scale, on which various shades of color are designated, or on which the relative hardness of various materials is specified. But these are quasi-measurements, not true measurements.

number and magnitude

For our present purpose, magnitude may be informally defined as an amount of a particular property—"how muchness" rather than "how manyness." A quantity may be defined as an instance of a particular property. To measure a magnitude[2] means, in essence, to find some sort of correspondence between magnitudes of the same kind, on the one hand, and numbers, whether integers, rational, or real. In other words, measuring implies the assignment of numbers to represent properties of material things. Numbers are admirably suited for this purpose. If two sets have different cardinal numbers, then one set has a greater number of elements than the other, which permits of arranging the sets in order. Being able to arrange things according to their numerosity is a necessary, but not a sufficient condition for

[1] W. S. Torgerson, *Theory and Methods of Scaling,* John Wiley, 1958; p. 9 ff.
[2] W. S. Torgerson, *ibid.,* p. 13.

measuring. Indeed, we utilize the isomorphism of the properties of real numbers and the relations of quantities to describe a given property. Basically, all physical measurements are comparisons, involving (1) the assignment of numbers and (2) the act of counting. But we hasten to point out that measuring is more than assigning numbers or merely counting. For example, counting the seats in a theater or the rooms in a hotel does not constitute measuring.

Numbering the units on a measuring scale utilizes the ordinal properties of numbers, but it is only a part of the making of a measurement. Although counting is a necessary part of measuring, of itself it, too, is only a part of the measuring process. In effect, when we count, we assign cardinal numbers to sets of objects; when we measure, we assign a ratio to represent a property of an object. We count discrete objects; the number of things counted is specific and unambiguous; we do not have to handle the objects or manipulate them in any way in order to count or add. On the other hand, the act of measuring involves the use of a scale and the manipulation of objects. We compare two things with respect to some property. To measure length, for example, we compare one object with another of a similar kind, called a *standard*. By repeated appropriate applications of the standard to the other object, we find how many times greater the object is than the standard. In this process, two crucial considerations should be emphasized. One is that the number assigned to the resulting measurement is not absolute, but depends upon the particular standard that happens to have been used. The other is that the number assigned is not sharply defined, but is stated as lying between two limits. The latter gives rise to the *error* of the measurement, which is inherent in the very act of measuring. Furthermore, as we have already anticipated in an earlier chapter, neither the integers nor the rational numbers are sufficient to assign a number to a measurement. The real numbers are required for incommensurable quantities such as the diagonal of a square, or other irrational quantities. (However, when the measurement is stated, no matter with how many figures, it is always expressed as a mixed number or as a terminating decimal and is therefore a rational number.)

quantitative measurement

Quantities which admit of direct measurement are called fundamental magnitudes, as, for example, length, mass, weight, time intervals. A property thus becomes a fundamental magnitude. As a matter of fact, since the things subjected to physical measurement exist in space and time, geometric properties, together with time, become the fundamental magnitudes of science: *distance, angle,* and *time.*

Every fundamental magnitude is measured in terms of a particular property of its own kind. This is the unit, or *step,* of the measuring instrument, as, for example, the length of the interval on a scale (inch, foot, centimeter, etc.). When we say that the length of a given object is 6 inches, we are saying, in effect, that the length of the object, when compared with an inch-scale, is the number 6. Now if we regard "an inch" as something that can be multiplied by a real number, then "length" can no longer be regarded as a property of the object, but must be *postulated* as a quantity.[3]

Let us summarize. The process of measurement implies the existence and recognition of a standard unit of measure, which must be familiar from previous direct perception, and which is independent of the thing to be measured. No knowledge of the thing to be measured is necessary for the understanding of the standard unit. Thus the picturing of an individual thing as three thirds of itself is not measurement. The act of measuring an extensive object consists essentially of using another extensive object (a standard unit), thinking of the first object as equivalent to a set of such equal units and a negligible residue, and counting the standard units in this set.

Hence counting is essentially prior to measuring. Furthermore, measuring consists of more than merely counting. And finally, it should be clear why all measurements are, of necessity, inexact. No "final" or "perfect" measurement is ever possible. Since there can be no exact measurement, no theorem of arithmetic, algebra, or geometry can ever be "proved" by measurement.

To measure, we must make certain assumptions which are not necessary for counting. Spatial measurement rests upon the assumption that there is available a standard object which may be transferred from place to place without undergoing any other change. This involves further assumptions not only about the nature of space itself, but also about the nature of space-occupying bodies. Analogous assumptions are required for measuring mass and time. In reality, these assumptions are not literally fulfilled. Then there is the further assumption that the order in which the standard unit is "laid off" or "marked out" is unessential to the cardinal number and does not affect the final residue.

---

[3] The reader who wishes to pursue these ideas still further may consult Harold Jeffreys, *Scientific Inference,* Cambridge University Press, 1957, Chapter 6.

WEIGHTS AND MEASURES

man the measurer

In every culture the art of measurement is highly significant. Contemporary Western civilization is utterly dependent upon measurement, the more so, since it is pre-eminently a culture based largely upon science and technology. Our high standard of living is a function of our ability to measure accurately everything from the weight of an ocean liner or a cyclotron to the rulings on a diffraction grating or the diameter of a submicroscopic particle. Everyday countless industrial operations and commercial activities are made possible through the use of a uniform and improved system of weights and measures. Without accurate measurements, there could be no cameras or watches, no computing machines, no jet engines or hydro-electric turbines, no radio, television, or radar, no telescopes or microscopes, no tunnels or bridges, no rockets or missiles.

The early history and development of weights and measures, shrouded in obscurity, can be traced back to prehistoric times. Length units were probably first conceived. In early times man was prone to use parts of the human body as crude units: the *digit*, the width of the *palm*, the length of the *foot*, the length of the *forearm* (cubit), the out-stretched *arm* (yard). Sometimes he used common experiences as measures, for example, a stone's throw or a day's journey; sometimes he used common objects, such as the weight of a kernel of grain or of a shell. Obviously, such units lacked uniformity and were poorly defined. Through many centuries of evolution units of measure became highly refined and standardized.

Since inexactness in measurement is intrinsic to the operation, we recognize varying degrees of inexactness (or exactness). As man's understanding of the process increased and his technological needs varied, he strove to increase the accuracy of his measurements—that is, to diminish the residual error. One of the earliest devices to this end was the creation of smaller standard units, or sub-units; for example, from the yard to the foot, then to the inch; or from the hour to the minute, then to the second. However, there inevitably comes a time when the creation of still smaller sub-units is no longer feasible, owing to the limitations of our instruments or of human perception. We then resort to fractions. A mass of about 3 pounds may be more accurately described as $3\frac{1}{4}$ pounds (or 3.25 pounds), although this measurement is no more precise than 3 pounds 4 ounces. It is true that when fractions, common or decimal, are used with the smallest recognized sub-units, a greater degree of accuracy is achieved. We shall have more to say shortly about precision measurements, such as millionths of an inch. Despite the fact that no measurement can be "absolutely" accurate, it is usually possible to achieve a degree of accuracy which is adequate for most purposes.

Machinists, toolmakers, gage makers, scientists, and others who are engaged in precision measurements of relatively small distances, even though concerned with measurements of length only, find it convenient to use the inch, instead of the tenth of a foot; however, they divide the inch decimally into tenths, hundredths, thousandths, etc., even down to millionths of an inch. Verniers, micrometers, and other precision measuring instruments are usually graduated in this manner. Machinist's scales are commonly graduated decimally along one edge, and along another edge in binary fractions as small as $\frac{1}{128}$ inch.

units and standards

The distinction between the terms "unit" and "standard" is extremely important. A unit is a value, quantity, or magnitude in terms of which other values, quantities, or magnitudes are expressed. In general, a unit is fixed by definition and is independent of such physical conditions as temperature; for example, the yard, the pound, the gallon, the meter, the liter, the gram. A *standard* is a physical embodiment of a unit. In general it is not independent of physical conditions, and it is a true embodiment of the unit only under specified conditions. Thus a standard yard has a length of one yard when at some definite temperature and supported in a certain manner; if supported in a different manner, it might have to be at a different temperature in order to have a length of 1 yard.

the metric system

The metric system is the international decimal system of weights and measures based on two fundamental units—the *meter* and the *kilogram*. The other units of length and mass, as well as all units of area, volume, and capacity, together with compound units such as pressure, work, energy, power, etc., are derived from these two fundamental units. Although the metric system is a decimal system, the words "metric" and "decimal" are not synonymous, and should not be confounded. By itself, the metric system is not a complete system covering all physical measurements. A complete system requires certain additional units such as units of temperature, of time, and of electrical resistance. The metric system is now either obligatory or permissive in every civilized country in the world.

In the metric system the fundamental units are the *meter* and the *kilogram*. Originally, about 1790, the meter was intended to be 1 ten-millionth part of a meridional quadrant of the earth. Due, however, to certain errors of triangulation, this was not successful; instead, a platinum bar of approximately this length was accepted as the standard meter. This was superseded in 1889 by the present *International Prototype Meter,* which is defined as the distance, at the temperature of melting ice, between the centers of two lines traced on the platinum-iridium bar deposited at the International Bureau of Weights and Measures in Sèvres, near Paris, France.

The *kilogram* was originally intended to be the mass of one cubic decimeter of water at its maximum density, but it is now defined as the mass of the *International Prototype Kilogram* without reference to the mass of a cubic decimeter of water.

The *liter* is a unit of capacity based on the mass standard and is defined as the volume occupied, under standard conditions, by a quantity of pure water having a mass of 1 kilogram. This volume is very nearly equal to 1 000 cubic centimeters, or 1 cubic decimeter; the actual metric equivalent is, 1 liter = 1 000.028 cubic centimeters. Thus the milliliter and the liter are larger than the cubic centimeter and the cubic decimeter, respectively, by 28 parts in 1 000 000; except for determinations of high precision, this difference is so small as to be of no consequence.

standards of length and mass

There is in the United States no primary standard either of length or mass in the ordinary system. The yard is defined in terms of the meter, and the pound in terms of the kilogram. The primary standard of length in the United States is the United States Prototype Meter 27, a platinum-iridium (90 per cent platinum, 10 per cent iridium) line standard having an X-shaped cross section. The length of this bar, which is deposited at the National Bureau of Standards in Washington, is known in terms of the *International Prototype Meter* at the International Bureau of Weights and Measures.

The United States yard is defined as follows:

$$1 \text{ U.S. yard} = \frac{3\ 600}{3\ 937} \text{ meter.}$$

The relation 1 U.S. yard = 3 600/3 937 meter, derived from the Law of 1866 that made the use of the metric system legal in the United States, was confirmed by later comparisons of copies of the British yard with the United States national copies of the meter. Since then it has been used as an exact relation. From this it follows that 1 U.S. inch is slightly larger than 0.025 400 05 meter, or 25.400 05 millimeters.

For industrial purposes a relation between the yard and the meter was adopted (1933) by the American Standards Association and by similar organizations in 15 other countries. This relation is 1 inch = 25.4 millimeters (exactly), that is, 0.025 4 meters (exactly), from which 1 yard = 0.914 4 meter (exactly), or 914.4 millimeters (exactly).

the search for a natural standard

In modern times, scientists have been seeking a "natural standard" of length, one which is invariant in nature and independent of man's devices. In 1887, A. A. Michelson and E. W. Morley arrived at a method of making the wavelength of sodium light the actual and practical standard of length. They measured the wavelength by means of an optical interferometer, counting the number of interference fringes. About 1905–1907, American and French scientists succeeded in determining accurately the relation between the meter and the wavelength of cadmium red radiation. Accordingly, in 1927, it was agreed upon that the wavelength of red radiation of cadmium under specified conditions of temperature, pressure, and humidity was 0.000 643 846 96 millimeters. This corresponds to

$$1 \text{ meter} = 1\ 553\ 164.13 \text{ wavelengths.}$$

Since an angstrom is defined as 0.000 000 1, or 10^{-7} millimeters, the angstrom is defined basically in terms of the wavelength of cadmium red radiation under standard conditions by the relation

$$1 \text{ wavelength} = 6\ 438.469\ 6 \text{ angstroms.}$$

An angstrom unit is a little less than 4 billionths of an inch.

The meter is a convenient and useful unit of measure, and will not be supplanted by a wavelength unit. However, for great precision, and for scientific purposes, it is a rather crude and arbitrary procedure to define the primary standard of length as the distance between two relatively coarse, irregular lines scratched on a metal-alloy bar, the permanence and durability of which, to say nothing of its exact reproducibility, are rather dubious. Modern industry and technology, as well as science, demand far greater accuracy than this; the meter is not adequate. Johansson metric gage blocks (1896) were a significant improvement. But the most precise measurements of lengths in recent years have been made with light waves. Fearing that the International Prototype meter might accidentally be destroyed during World War II, and with the goal of ever greater accuracy, the search for an indestructible but accurately and easily reproducible wavelength continues. In the near future, scientists will probably adopt as the ultimate standard of length the wavelength of green light from mercury 198 (= 5 461 A). Thus with optical instruments man has achieved a degree of precision many hundreds of times finer than can be obtained by using standard prototype bars. Even if these national and international standards were destroyed overnight, measurements to within less than a billionth of an inch could still be made with confidence, and a far more precise standard could be duplicated at will with comparative ease.

THE RELIABILITY OF A MEASUREMENT

the nature of errors

Physical measurements are always subject to several kinds of errors: (1) instrumental errors, (2) personal errors, (3) theoretical errors, (4) accidental errors.

Instrumental errors may be caused by imperfections in the instrument, such as faulty graduation marks, warping of a wooden yardstick due to moisture, or some other defect of construction. Such instrumental errors are usually constant errors, and their magnitude can be determined. Similarly, constant errors may be caused by a personal bias of the observer. He may use an instrument ineptly or incorrectly. Some observers don't look "squarely" at a scale when they read it (parallax); or they do not use good judgment when estimating half of the smallest subdivision; or there may be a time lag in recording the occurrence of an event. Constant errors may also be caused by theoretical considerations, that is, errors of method. These arise when properly adjusted instruments are used under conditions other than those for which the instrument is designed or calibrated—for example, when a steel tape that is graduated for use at 0° C is used when the temperature is 20° C. The slightest expansion of the metal will change the size of the graduated divisions. A series of measurements made under such conditions might agree closely among themselves, but would all be too small.

It is clear, then, that the mere agreement of a series of measurements made under similar conditions is of itself no guarantee of the absence of constant errors, whether instrumental, personal, or theoretical. Constant errors can generally be detected by the use of different instruments, different methods, or different observers. The magnitude of constant errors can usually be determined, and appropriate corrections applied.

Accidental errors, on the other hand, are due to causes over which the observer has no control: for example, the instrument may slip imperceptibly; the ends of the object and the scale don't coincide "perfectly"; slight vibrations may occur; the barometric pressure may fluctuate; the hand isn't as steady as it might be; the eyes are fatigued; and so on. Accidental errors follow the law of probability, which implies (1) the mean value of the accidental errors is zero, that is, they tend to counterbalance each other, and (2) that the probability of occurrence of an accidental error decreases as the magnitude of the error increases. The occurrence of accidental errors is shown by the curve of error, or *probability curve,* whose equation is of the form $y = ae^{-kx^2}$, where y is the frequency of occurrence of an error of magnitude x, and a, e, and k are appropriate known constants. From the general shape of the curve, it will be seen that small errors occur more frequently than large ones and that very large errors are rela-

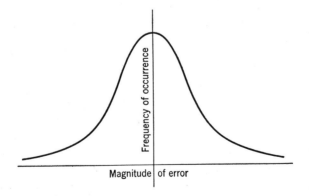

Fig. 7-1

tively unlikely to occur; whereas, from the symmetry of the curve we can see that positive and negative errors of the same numerical magnitude are equally likely to occur. It must be remembered, of course, that this law represents a limiting case, which implies an infinite number of observations. A finite, small number of observations will not conform perfectly to this ideal. Even in such a simple operation as finding the length of a metal rod, a series of several measurements may differ in at least the last decimal place.

the arithmetic mean

A measurement isn't worth much if we can't say how "good" it is. How much can it be depended upon? For example, which of these six measurements is the "best" value: 4.09? 4.15? 4.13? To answer these questions, we find the arithmetical average of the six observations. Rounding the average to three significant figures, we obtain 4.12 inches.

$$
\begin{array}{r}
4.15 \\
4.14 \\
4.09 \\
4.10 \\
4.13 \\
4.09 \\
\hline
6 \overline{)24.70}
\end{array}
$$

mean = 4.117, or 4.12

If the measuring instrument is used to its full precision, that is, to the "nearest" fraction of the smallest division of the scale, and if all the observations are made with equal care and are equally probable, then the arithmetic average gives the most convenient probable value of the measured quantity.

The arithmetical average is also called the *arithmetic mean*, or the *mean*. In symbols, if n observations are taken, $a_1, a_2, a_3, \ldots . a_n$, then

$$ m = \frac{a_1 + a_2 + a_3 + \cdots + a_n}{n}; $$

or $$ m = \frac{\sum (a)}{n}. $$

The odd-looking symbol "Σ" is simply a short way of saying "the sum of all the a's."

the average deviation

We shall see later how the accuracy and precision of a single measurement may be described. But with a series of measurements, we generally use the following procedure to indicate the degree of accuracy or reliability of the mean of the series. First we find the amount by which each measurement differs from the arithmetic mean. The difference between any observation and the mean is called the *deviation* from the mean. Measurements greater than the mean have a positive (+) deviation; measurements smaller than the mean have a negative (−) deviation.

Measurement	Mean	Deviation	
4.15	4.12	+0.03	
4.14	4.12	+0.02	
4.09	4.12		−0.03
4.10	4.12		−0.02
4.13	4.12	+0.01	
4.09	4.12		−0.03
		+0.06	−0.08

Notice that the sum of the positive deviations is +0.06; the sum of the negative deviations is −0.08. The sum of the positive and negative deviations is always approximately zero. In other words, the number of accidental errors that is too large is about the same as the number that is too small. When finding the deviations, remember always to subtract the mean from the measurement, regardless of which is larger. In symbols: $d_1 = a_1 - m$; $d_2 = a_2 - m$; etc. We are not interested in whether the deviations are positive or negative. We are chiefly concerned with the actual amount of the deviations. When we disregard the + and − signs of numbers, we are using their *absolute values*.

Just as we found the average of the six measurements, so we can find the average of the six deviations; this is called the *average deviation,* or "a.d."

$$
\begin{array}{r}
+0.03 \\
+0.02 \\
-0.03 \\
-0.02 \\
+0.01 \\
-0.03 \\
\hline
6)\overline{0.14} \\
\end{array}
$$

$$a.d. = \overline{0.023} \text{ inch}$$

The average deviation, *a.d.*, is the arithmetic average of all the deviations (regardless of sign, + or −); or

$$a.d. = \frac{\sum (d)}{n}.$$

The average deviation of a set of observations may be regarded as the amount by which a new observation would most likely differ from the mean.

the deviation of the mean

We come now to a more sensitive measure of trustworthiness. We have just learned that the average deviation, or a.d., indicates the reliability of a single observation. Since the mean of the series of observations is more accurate than any single observation, then it would require an even smaller number than the a.d. to tell how reliable the mean is. It can be shown by the mathematical theory of probability that an arithmetical mean computed from n equally probable observations is $\sqrt{n}$ times as reliable as any one observation. Hence to find the reliability of the mean of a series of measurements, we divide the average deviation of the set of measurements by the square root of the number of measurements. This ratio is called the "deviation of the mean," or A.D. In symbols: A.D. $= \frac{a.d.}{\sqrt{n}}$. In our illustration, there are six measurements, or $n = 6$; so $\sqrt{n} = \sqrt{6} = 2.45$. Therefore:

$$\text{A.D.} = \frac{a.d.}{\sqrt{n}} = \frac{0.023}{\sqrt{6}} = \frac{0.023}{2.45} = 0.009.$$

We have reached our goal. We can say with confidence how dependable our measurement of the length of the rod is. The most probable value to be obtained from these six observations is 4.117 inches, which is reliable, or accurate, to 0.009 inch, either way. The result is usually written:

length = 4.117 ± 0.009 inches.

The chance that the true length is more than 4.126 inches or less than 4.108 inches is very slight indeed.[4]

[4] The reader is cautioned that the deviation measure 0.009 is not the same as the "probable error" of the measurement; the probable error is quite another concept.

This deviation test of reliability applies only when the errors are accidental or chance errors. Every one of the observations could have been in error by the same amount, for example, if the instrument had been imperfect. In such a situation, the deviation measure would not be an indication of reliability or accuracy.

Example. The diameter of a brass cylinder was measured nine times, as shown below. Find the best value of the diameter and tell how reliable it is.

Measurement	Deviations
6.28 centimeters	0.03
6.26	0.01
6.24	0.01
6.28	0.03
6.23	0.02
6.25	0.00
6.27	0.02
6.23	0.02
6.25	0.00
9)56.29	9)0.14
mean = 6.254 centimeters	a.d. = 0.016

$$\text{A.D.} = \frac{0.016}{\sqrt{9}} = 0.005 \text{ centimeter}$$

Best value = 6.254 ± 0.005 centimeters

EXERCISE 7–1

1. Distinguish between a *unit* of measure and a *standard* of measure.

2. What is meant by a *natural standard* of measure?

3. What is the difference between an *error* and a *mistake?*

4. In Fig. 7–2, the figures given are basic dimensions; find the acceptable limits if the tolerance is ±0.002."

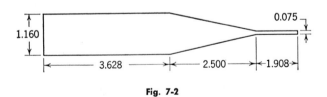

Fig. 7-2

5. The basic dimension of a piece of work is 2 inches, with a tolerance of $\pm\frac{1}{16}$ inch. Which of the finished jobs is acceptable?

(a) $2\frac{1}{32}$ inches   (b) $2\frac{1}{4}$ inches   (c) $1\frac{7}{8}$ inches
(d) $2\frac{1}{64}$ inches   (e) $1\frac{63}{64}$ inches   (f) $1\frac{31}{32}$ inches

6. A blueprint calls for a basic size of $3\frac{5}{8}$ inch; the tolerance is $\pm\frac{1}{32}$ inch. Which of these pieces should be rejected?

(a) $3\frac{19}{32}$ (b) $3\frac{37}{64}$ (c) $3\frac{11}{16}$ (d) $3\frac{41}{64}$

In each of the following sets of measurements, find the best value, the average deviation (a.d.), and the deviation of the mean (A.D.); state the final result to show how reliable it is. (For your convenience, $\sqrt{5} = 2.24$; $\sqrt{6} = 2.45$.)

7. 12.32 inches
12.38
12.36
12.35

8. 8.54 centimeters
8.50
8.54
8.53
8.55
8.56

9. 5.43 centimeters
5.40
5.44
5.41
5.44
5.42
5.46
5.45
5.43

10. 10.312 grams
10.309
10.313
10.311
10.313

PRECISION AND ACCURACY

approximate numbers

Counting discrete objects, as we have seen, leads to exact numbers. Approximate numbers may arise from measurements, from estimates, from rounding exact numbers, or from computations with exact numbers. If we count the number of persons living in a given town and give the population as 25,394, that is an exact number, insofar as it represents an enumeration as of a given time. If we round the number to 25,400, or to 25,000, we are using an approximate number. If we estimate the number of apples in a basket to be about 40, this again is an approximate number. If we say that a man weighs 160 pounds we do not mean that he weighs exactly 160 pounds; this is an approximate number which suggests that his weight is closer to 160 than it is to 165 or 155 pounds. When we read that a particular government expenditure was $6\frac{1}{2}$ million dollars, that, too, is an approximate number; it tells us that the expenditure was somewhere between \$6,450,000 and \$6,550,000, or, to the nearest hundred thousand, \$6,500,000.

All measurements are approximations, but not all approximations arise from measurements. For example: the product 19 × 42 is about 800; or the square root of 45 is approximately 6.71; and so on. Any kind of number may be used as an exact number or as an approximate number, depending upon the context. The integer 4 in a price of \$4 is exact, but in 4 pounds of butter the integer 4 is an approximate number. The rational numbers ⅚ and 0.83⅓ are both exact, but the rational number 0.83 is an approximation of the former. The irrational number $\sqrt{10}$ is an exact number, but the rational number 3.16 is an approximation of the irrational number $\sqrt{10}$.

Since an approximate number implies the existence of an exact number or ideal to which the approximate number is related, we naturally wish to know how "good" or how "close" the approximation is. This question may be answered by giving either the precision or the accuracy of the approximation; these are by no means the same.

precision of a measurement

Taking into consideration how a measuring scale is used, in any measurement, the amount of the error can never be greater than one-half of the smallest unit on the scale. This is called the greatest possible error. For example, in a measurement of 16.4 inches, the smallest unit is ⅒ of an inch; so, the greatest possible error is ½ of 0.1, or 0.05 inch. Similarly, in a measurement of 9.78 centimeters, the smallest unit is 0.01 centimeter, and the greatest possible error is therefore ½ of 0.01, or 0.005 centimeter.

The precision of a measurement is an index of the maximum amount it can vary from the exact number or ideal quantity which it approximates. In short, the greatest possible error, or maximum error, is the degree of precision of the measurement.

How precise a given measurement is can be expressed in several ways:

1. The maximum error may be stated as a plus or minus correction. For example, the boiling point of a liquid might be 108° ± 2°. This means that the error of measurement may be as great as 2 degrees "either way," that is, the "true" boiling point lies somewhere between 106° and 110°.

2. The maximum possible variation may be stated explicitly in

terms of appropriate units. Thus: the length of the metal rod is 65 centimeters, correct to the nearest centimeter. This means that the true length of the rod may be anywhere from 64.5 and 65.5 centimeters.

3. The maximum error may be shown by the position of the last significant figure; for example, 32.7 feet, or 238 feet, where the maximum errors are 0.05 foot and 0.5 foot, respectively. For example, a weight of "26.3 ± 0.05 ounces," or "26.3 ounces correct to the nearest 0.1 ounce," or "26.3 ounces," all express the same degree of precision, indicated by the fact that the largest possible error is 0.05 ounce.

Expressing the size of the error in this way enables us to tell how refined or how sensitive the measuring instrument is. The smaller the possible error, the finer the instrument. This is called the *precision* of the instrument or of the measurement. A measurement to 0.01 inch is more precise than a measurement to 0.1 inch. A measurement to 0.001 inch is more precise than one to 0.01 inch.

In other words:

1. The smaller the unit of measure used, the more precise the measurement will be.

2. The smaller the maximum error, the more precise the measurement will be.

EXERCISE 7–2

1. Tell which of the following are exact numbers and which are approximate numbers, giving your reason:

(a) A class of 31 pupils.
(b) 200,000 acres of timber land destroyed by fire.
(c) Yesterday's rainfall was 1.3 inches.
(d) $2.9 million allocated to slum clearance.
(e) 190 miles by rail between two cities.
(f) The barometer reading is 29.39 inches.
(g) An elevation of 2150 feet above sea level.
(h) The first prize of $1000.
(i) The ceiling was 2000 feet.
(j) A tax rate of 18.4 mills.

2. Is $\sqrt{16}$ an exact number or an approximate number? What about $\sqrt{3}$? What about 1.732 . . . ? What about 1.732?

3. Is π an exact number or an approximate number? What about the number $3\frac{1}{7}$? The number 3.14159. . . ?

4. Explain the meaning of each of these approximate numbers representing measurements: $6\frac{1}{4}$; 6.25; 6.250.

5. Give an example of:

(*a*) An exact number that does not result from counting.

(*b*) An approximate number not obtained by counting or measuring.

(*c*) An approximate number resulting from a computation with exact numbers.

6. What is the greatest possible error in each of these measurements? Of each pair of measurements, which is the more precise? (*a*) 2.3 feet; 6.73 feet; (*b*) 14 inches; 13.6 inches; (*c*) 25.9 centimeters; 28.84 centimeters; (*d*) 8.004 inches; 8.04 inches; (*e*) 135.8 feet; 136 feet.

accuracy of a measurement

If an error of 1 foot is made in measuring a distance of 100 feet, the error is $\frac{1}{100}$ of the distance measured. But if an error of 1 foot is made in measuring a mile, the error is only $\frac{1}{5280}$ of the total distance measured. In the second case the error is a smaller part of the total measurement; we say that the second measurement is more accurate than the first. The ratio of the error in a measurement to the measurement itself is called the relative error of the measurement. In other words, the relative error is the actual error divided by the measurement. But the actual error can never be determined, since the true value can never be determined. So, instead of finding the ratio of the actual error to the true value, we use the ratio of the greatest possible error to the measured value. The relative error of a measurement is the ratio of the greatest possible error of the measurement to the measurement itself. Of any two measurements, the one having the smaller relative error is the more accurate measurement.

Example 1. The diameter of a cylinder is measured by a machinist as 1.8 inches. The greatest possible error is $\frac{1}{2}$ of 0.1 inch, or 0.05 inch; therefore,

relative error $= \dfrac{0.05}{1.8} = 0.03$.

Example 2. The length of a metal rod when measured is found to be 2.36 centimeters. The greatest possible error is $\frac{1}{2}$ of 0.01 centimeter, or 0.005 centimeter. Therefore, relative error $= \dfrac{0.005}{2.36} = 0.002$, or about 2 parts in 1000.

The relative-error ratio can obviously be expressed as a per cent, in which case it is referred to as the "percentage error." For example:

(*a*) a relative error of 0.028 = a 2.8 per cent error

(*b*) a relative error of $\frac{2}{25}$ = an 8 per cent error

(*c*) a relative error of 0.0003 = an error of 0.03 per cent

(d) a relative error of 3 parts in 500 is a percentage error of 0.6 per cent.

EXERCISE 7–3

1. Explain why it is impossible ever to determine the actual error of a measurement.

2. Between what two values do the following measurements approximate?

(a) 2 miles   (b) 98.6°F
(c) 3¼ pounds   (d) 246 yards
(e) 4.12 centimeters   (f) 6⁵⁄₁₆ inches

3. What is the relative error of each of these measurements?

(a) 5 inches   (b) 25 inches   (c) 3.8 inches
(d) 50.2 centimeters (e) 258 feet   (f) 5.24 yards
(g) 12 ounces   (h) 0.2 mile   (i) 0.02 mile
(j) 0.26 mile

4. Complete the following table:

Measurement	Greatest Possible Error	Relative Error	Per Cent of Error
(a) 22 inches	?	?	?
(b) 124 feet	?	?	?
(c) 1.6 yards	?	?	?
(d) 70.4 centimeters	?	?	?

5. Find the per cent of error in each of the following measurements:

(a) 18 inches   (b) 152 yards   (c) 2.3 centimeters
(d) 29.4 inches   (e) 12.31 centimeters (f) 1.62 inches

significant figures

Consider the following situations:

1. A man says it is 14 miles from one place to some other place. He is measuring to the nearest whole mile. The measurement 14 miles has *two* significant figures.

2. If the distance is "clocked" by the odometer, it is 14.7 miles. Now it has been measured to the nearest tenth of a mile; "the unit" is really 0.1 mile, and there are 147 tenths. This measurement has *three* significant figures.

3. A machinist measures the length of a bolt and says it is 2.38 inches. The unit is hundredths of an inch, and there are 238 such hundredths. There are *three* significant figures.

4. Another machinist measures the thickness of a metal plate; it is 0.026 inches thick. The unit is 0.001 inch, and there are 26 such thousandths. The measurement has only *two* significant figures.

5. If it had measured 1.026 inches, the unit is still 0.001 inch, but there are 1026 such units; then there are *four* significant figures in the measurement.

The following are important principles in connection with significant figures.

1. *All non-zero figures are always significant wherever used.* In each of these numbers, all figures are significant:

$$24; \quad 48.3; \quad 519; \quad 6.38.$$

2. *Zeros occurring between non-zero figures are always significant.* In each of these numbers, all the zeros are significant:

$$207; \quad 3024; \quad 1.502; \quad 46.05; \quad 5009.$$

For example, if we know the number of units and the number of hundreds in a number, we obviously also know the number of tens (for example, in 207, none).

3. *Terminal zeros following the decimal point are always significant.*

(a) The odometer of a car shows that it has traveled 6.0 miles. We know that the tenth's place has been measured. The unit is 0.1 mile, and there are 60 tenths of a mile, not 59 tenths of a mile (5.9 mile), nor 61 tenths of a mile (6.1 mile). The measurement is correct to the nearest tenth of a mile, and the zero means something. There are two significant figures in 6.0 miles.

(b) If a metal disc is 0.20 inch thick, the terminal zero is significant, for it shows that the hundredth's place as well as the tenths' place has been measured. The unit measure is one-hundredth of an inch, and there are two significant figures.

4. *In a number less than 1, zeros immediately following the decimal point are not significant.*

(a) If a sample weighs 0.086 gram, the zero following the decimal point is used only as a place holder; it is not a significant figure, since it is not needed to show that there are no tenths. There are two significant figures in 0.086.

(b) If a spark gap measures 0.002 inch, the two zeros following the decimal point are not significant. They are not measured; they simply tell us where to place the decimal point. The unit of measure is one-thousandth of an inch, and there is only one significant figure.

5. *Terminal zeros in an integer should not be considered significant unless so indicated.* Suppose, for example, that the speed of sound is given as 1100 feet per second, and the units' and tens' places have not been measured (or the number has been rounded). Under these circumstances the implied unit of measure is not feet, but hundred feet. Since there are 11 hundred feet, the approximate number "1100 feet per second" has only two significant figures; in this case the two terminal zeros are not significant.

The application of these principles is further illustrated by the following examples:

Measurement	Unit of Measure Assumed	Total Number of Units	Number of Significant Figures
(a) 136 miles	1 mile	136	3
(b) 170 miles	10 miles	17	2
(c) 3200 miles	100 miles	32	2
(d) 8.6 miles	0.1 mile	86	2
(e) 24.0 pounds	0.1 pound	240	3
(f) 3.008 grams	0.001 gram	3008	4
(g) 205.02 feet	0.01 foot	20,502	5
(h) 3294.6 feet	0.1 foot	32,946	5
(i) 4360 cubic feet	10 cubic feet	436	3
(j) 0.0040 millimeter	0.0001 millimeter	40	2

A number such as 480 yards or 2600 feet is ambiguous unless something is said about the terminal zeros; we are entitled to know whether the zeros have been measured, or whether the number has been rounded. Or again, if the distance between two cities is given as "3000 miles," is the implied unit of measure 100 or 1000 miles? There are two ways in which such ambiguities can be avoided.

First Method. Doubtful or non-significant zeros to the right of the last significant figure are sometimes printed in smaller type; this method is not too common in actual practice.

Examples:

(a) 48$_0$ has only 2 significant figures; 480 has 3 significant figures.
(b) 238,0$_{00}$ has 4 significant figures; 238,000 has 6 significant figures.

Second Method. Using "scientific notation," all the significant figures are included in the first part of the product.

Examples:

(*a*) 24,000, correct to the nearest hundred, or 24,0₀₀, could be written in scientific notation as 2.40×10^4 (three significant figures).

(*b*) If 93,000,000 miles is correct to the nearest million miles, we can write 93,₀₀₀,₀₀₀, or 9.3×10^7 (two significant figures).

(*c*) Similarly: 48₀ means 4.8×10^2 (two significant figures); 238,0₀₀ means 2.380×10^5 (four significant figures).

When using scientific notation in this way, the standard practice is to place the decimal point between the first and second significant figures, no matter how many significant figures there are.

rounding off numbers

Rounding off measurements to a desired degree of accuracy sometimes causes confusion. The following points should be borne in mind. If the measurement number is an integer, any digits dropped when rounding must always be replaced by zeros. For example, rounding 317 miles to the nearest 10 miles becomes 320 miles; rounding $235,-643 to the nearest 100 dollars becomes $235,600. If the number is a fraction, however, the dropped digits are never replaced with zeros. For example: 12.423 grams becomes 12.4 grams when rounded to the nearest tenth of a gram.

If the last digit dropped is 5, 6, 7, 8, or 9, the first digit retained is increased by one; if the last digit dropped is 0, 1, 2, 3, or 4, the remaining digits are unchanged. (In a whole number, if the first digit retained is zero, it may be underscored to show that it is a significant figure.) For example:

1. $4872 = 4870$ to *three* significant figures, or 4.87×10^3.
2. $4872 = 4900$ to *two* significant figures, or 4.9×10^3.
3. $4872 = 5000$ to *one* significant figure, or 5×10^3.
4. $4972 = 5000$ to *two* significant figures, or 5.0×10^3.
5. $4648 = 4\underline{6}50$ to *three* significant figures, or 4.65×10^3.
6. $4648 = 4600$ to *two* significant figures, or 4.6×10^3.
7. $4652 = 4700$ to *two* significant figures, or 4.7×10^3.

Examples 6 and 7 show that rounding is done in one step, not one digit at a time. Thus

28.7648 = 28.765 to 5 significant figures
28.7648 = 28.76 to 4 significant figures
28.7648 = 28.8 to 3 significant figures
28.7648 = 29 to 2 significant figures

If the only non-zero digit dropped is 5 and it occupies the highest position of the dropped digits, it is customary to round to the nearest *even* digit. For example, 406.5 rounded to three significant figures becomes 406, and 409.50 rounded to three significant figures becomes 410.

precision versus accuracy

These terms are often confounded, or worse still, used interchangeably. The precision of a measurement states the *absolute* size of the maximum error; the accuracy states the *relative* size of the maximum error (relative to the measurement). In symbols:

If v = true value (unobtainable),
M = measured value,
e = actual error (unobtainable),
E = maximum possible error;
then $e = v - M$,
$E \geq e$,
precision = E,
and accuracy = E/M.

Measurements having equal possible errors have the same degree of precision. For example, in each of the following instances, the two measures have the same degree of precision:

(a) 115 and 79 (to the nearest whole number).
(b) 15.2 and 8.4 (nearest tenth).
(c) 9_{00} and 14_{00} (nearest hundred).
(d) 0.0029 and 16.8537 (nearest ten-thousandth).

The smaller the unit of measure used, the more precise the measurement; the smaller the relative error, the more accurate the measurement. Consider the following:

Measurement	Possible Error	Per Cent of Error
10 inches	0.5	5%
10.0 inches	0.05	0.5%
10.00 inches	0.005	0.05%

Notice that as the number of significant figures in the measurement increases, the per cent of error becomes smaller. As the number of significant figures increases, therefore, the more accurate the measurement becomes.

Precision is an approximation of the difference between the true value and the measured value. Accuracy is the ratio of this difference to the measured value. It is clear that they are two entirely different things. Given any two measurements, the more precise may or may not be the more accurate, and the more accurate may or may not be the more precise.

Example 1.   Compare the two measurements 1.25 centimeters and 12.5 centimeters.

(a) 1.25 is *more precise* than 12.5; possible error of 1.25 = 0.005, possible error of 12.5 = 0.05.

(b) But, 1.25 and 12.5 are *equally accurate*; relative error $\frac{0.005}{1.25} = 0.004 = 0.4$ per cent, relative error $\frac{0.05}{12.5} = 0.004 = 0.4$ per cent.

Example 2.   Compare the two measurements 48.3 in. and 4.8 inch.

(a) They are *equally precise*, since the possible error of each is 0.05 inch.

(b) But, 48.3 is *more accurate* than 4.8; for relative error $\frac{0.05}{48.3} = 0.001 = \frac{1}{10}$ of 1 per cent, and relative error $\frac{0.05}{4.8} = 0.01 = 1$ per cent.

Example 3.   The diameter of the earth is often taken as 8000 miles, which is obviously precise to the nearest thousand miles. The diameter of a half dollar is 1 inch, precise to the nearest inch. The measured diameter of the coin is far more precise than the diameter of the earth. But 8000 miles is more accurate, since its relative error is $\frac{500}{8000} = 0.0625$, whereas the relative error of the diameter of the coin is $\frac{0.5}{1} = 0.5$.

Another observation: it is impossible to compare the precision of two measurements involving different kinds of units. A temperature of 78.6° C is precise to the *nearest tenth* of a degree; a mass of 78.6 grams is precise to the *nearest tenth* of a gram; and a volume of 78.6 gallons is precise to the *nearest tenth* of a gallon. It is meaningless to try to compare the precision of these three measurements, since temperature, mass, and volume are entirely different kinds of magnitudes. On the other hand, we can say that 78.6 grams is more precise than 78.6 kilograms, since the maximum error is only $\frac{1}{1000}$ as great; similarly, 78.6 gallons is less precise than 78.6 quarts, since the maximum error is 4 times as great in the former case.

Since accuracy is a ratio, it is independent of the units used. Thus it is possible to compare in two measurements with respect to their accuracy, no matter what kind of measurements they may be. For example: 24.8 inches, 24.8 amperes, and 24.8 tons all have the same degree of accuracy, with a relative error in each case of very nearly 0.002, or about 1 part in 500.

Both precision and accuracy are very important. Which is more appropriate or more useful in any given instance depends upon the circumstances. The desired degree of precision or accuracy to be realized depends very largely upon the purpose for which the measurement is to be made. An error of a few hundred pounds in a shipment of 30 carloads of coal may be negligible, but an error of a few tenths of a gram in weighing diamonds is far from negligible! An error of an ounce or two in 100 pounds of milk is unimportant, but the same error in administering a drug might well prove fatal.

EXERCISE 7–4

In Examples 1–4 below, assume that all measurements are properly expressed; that is, terminal zeros are significant except in 1(c).

1. State the number of significant figures in each case:

(a) 0.002 inch   0.20 inch   0.020 inch   0.012 inch
    0.21 inch   0.201 inch   0.210 inch   0.0030 inch

(b) 65 miles   43.8 pounds   20.04 grams
    9.006 centimeters   27.3 miles   10.24 centimeters
    20.0 miles   106.04 grams   3.060 inches   0.003025 inch

(c) 4520 tons; 1300 miles; 19,400 cubic yards; 186,000 miles; 93,000,-000.

2. Arrange the numbers in each of the following sets in order of precision, putting the least precise first:

(a) 32   0.04   5.8   230
(b) 26.3   852   0.005   125.36
(c) 0.1   0.001   0.10   1.0001
(d) 1.23   0.123   0.0123   123   12.3

3. Explain the difference between:

(a) 76.8 centimeters and 76.80 centimeters;   (b) 0.54 inch and 0.540 inch.

4. In each of the following pairs, which measurement has the greater precision? which measurement has the greater accuracy?

(a) 8.0 millimeters; 0.0080 millimeters   (b) 8.0 meter; 0.0080 millimeters
(c) $2\frac{1}{2}$ miles; 430 yards   (d) 8 inches; 8 quarts
(e) 12.9 pounds; 12.90 pounds.
(f) Height of a man, 6 feet; distance from New York to San Francisco, 3000 miles.
(g) Height of a man, 6 feet 0 inches; height of his wife, 5 feet 8 inches.

5. Indicate the number of significant figures in each of the following numbers:

(a) 82; 509; 8.00   (b) 60; 60.0; 6_0
(c) 290; 45_{00}; 0.030   (d) 9.0; 0.0004; 76_0
(e) 2350_{00}; 600; 208_0 (f) 5000; 50_{00}; $7{,}23_{0,000}$

6. If two measurements have the same degree of precision, do they necessarily have the same number of significant figures? Illustrate.

7. If two measurements have the same number of significant figures, do they necessarily have the same degree of accuracy? Illustrate.

8. Write the following in another form; in each case, tell how many significant figures there are, assuming that they are properly expressed:

(a) 8.5×10^2 (b) 3.4×10^3 (c) 6.29×10^6 (d) 9.3×10^7
(e) 6.30×10^4 (f) 2.80×10^5 (g) 2.37×10^8 (h) 1.86×10^5

9. Write the following numbers in scientific notation:

(a) 58_{00} (b) $362{,}0_{00}$ (c) $40{,}0_{00}$
(d) $200{,}_{000}$ (e) $75{,}0_{00}$ (f) $3{,}690{,}_{000}$

10. (a) At one time the total crop land in the United States was estimated at approximately 1.2×10^9 acres. The farm population at that time was 3.2×10^6. This is equivalent to how many acres per capita? (b) The wavelength of red cadmium light is 0.000064384696 centimeters. How many significant figures is this?

COMPUTING WITH APPROXIMATE NUMBERS

adding approximate numbers

What is the sum of these two measurements?

$$
\begin{array}{r}
4.56 \text{ inches} \\
5.2 \ \text{ inches} \\
\hline
9.76 \text{ inches}
\end{array}
$$

Is it 9.76? Not necessarily. Notice that in 5.2 inches, the hundredth's place has not been measured. If it had been, this measure might have been as little as 5.15 or as large as 5.24. The sum, therefore, might be as little as 9.71 or as great as 9.80. What should we do in such cases?

$$4.6$$
$$\underline{5.2}$$
$$9.8 \text{ (approximately)}$$

We round the other measurement to the same degree of precision as the 5.2, that is, to the nearest tenth, and then add; answer: **9.8**.

If numbers to be added are of different degrees of precision, as in *a* below, they should all be rounded to the same degree of precision as that of the least precise number, as in *b*. The sum, 24.8, is labeled "approximate," since it may or may not be correct; it is, however, the most "sensible" sum that can be obtained from the data as given.

Example.

(a)	(b)
8.46	8.5
5.944	5.9
9.8	9.8
.480	.5
.075	.1
24.759	24.8 (approximately)

To find the sum of measured numbers, they should all be expressed to the same degree of precision. This implies that they are all measured in the same unit of measure. *The sum of approximate numbers cannot be more precise than the least precise number among those to be added.*

subtracting approximate numbers

We must follow the same procedure when subtracting approximate numbers having different degrees of precision. Round the more precise number to the same precision as the least precise number. Then subtract, and label the remainder "approximate," since it is only a reasonable answer.

Example. Subtract 8.47 from 12.5083.

Do	12.51	*not*	12.5083
this →	8.47	*this* →	8.47
	4.04 (approximate),		4.0383.

EXERCISE 7–5

1. Find the most reasonable sums of these approximate numbers:

(a) 21.83	(b) 8.3927	(c) 18.5
6.294	5.01	6.0
25.736	6.8	12.67
	3.546	

(d) 16.32	(e) 1,300	(f) $35.
8.6	22,000	6.75
21.05	4,000	12.45
14.	1,900	
	2,000	

2. Find the greatest possible sum of $32.8 + 124.6$; the least possible sum.

3. Find the greatest possible sum of $26.32 + 17.08$; the least possible sum.

4. Subtract the following approximate numbers:

(a) 12.3	(b) 25.8	(c) 6.08
9.0	6.34	2.752

(d) 8.569	(e) 18.007	(f) 54,000
3.2	10.48	2,800

5. What is the greatest possible remainder in number 4a? In number 4b?

6. What is the least possible remainder in number 4a? In number 4b?

multiplying approximate numbers

Suppose you wish to find the area of a rectangle 7.5 inches $\times$ 4.3 inches. Multiplying the length by the width, we obtain 32.25.

$$
\begin{array}{r}
7.5 \\
4.3 \\
\hline
225 \\
300 \\
\hline
32.25
\end{array}
$$

How "exact" are the figures to the right of the decimal point? Since the greatest possible error in each of the given numbers is 0.05, the greatest possible product would be (a), and the least possible product would be (b):

$$
\begin{array}{rr}
(a) \quad 7.54 & (b) \quad 7.45 \\
4.34 & 4.25 \\
\hline
3016 & 3725 \\
2262 & 1490 \\
3016 & 2980 \\
\hline
32.7236 & 31.6625
\end{array}
$$

Notice that our first answer above, 32.25, is approximately half-way between the greatest and least possible values (*a*) and (*b*). Therefore, we might just as well use the value 32.25, and round it to two significant figures (since the original numbers each had only two significant figures). So, the best reasonable answer is **32** square inches. This illustrates the following principle: *The product of approximate numbers may contain no more significant figures than in the least accurate of the numbers.*

Example 1. Find the product of the two approximate numbers 8.64 and 4.53.

$$
\begin{array}{r}
8.64 \leftarrow \text{3 significant figures} \\
4.53 \leftarrow \text{3 significant figures} \\
\hline
2592 \\
4320 \\
3456 \\
\hline
39.1392 \qquad \textit{Answer: } 39.1 \text{ (3 significant figures)}
\end{array}
$$

Example 2. Find the product of 47.3 and 14.35.

$$
\begin{array}{r}
14.35 \leftarrow \text{4 significant figures} \\
47.3 \leftarrow \text{3 significant figures} \\
\hline
4305 \\
10045 \\
5740 \\
\hline
678.755 \qquad \textit{Answer: } 679 \text{ (3 significant figures)}
\end{array}
$$

multiplying with π (pi)

The value of π correct to 5 decimal places is 3.14159. It may be rounded to 3.1416, 3.142, or 3.14, depending upon whether we need 5, 4, or 3 significant figures.

Although π is an approximate number, it differs from other approximate numbers. When we use a rounded value of π, we know what the dropped figures were; this means we know what the error is. For example: what is the best value for the product of $5.62 \times \pi$? The measurement 5.62, having a possible error of 0.005, lies between 5.615 and 5.625. If we use $\pi = 3.14$, the known error is $3.1416 - 3.14$, or 0.0016; if we use $\pi = 3.142$, the known error is $3.142 - 3.1416$, or only 0.0004. Now study these results:

(*a*) $3.142 \times 5.615 = 17.642$ (nearest thousandth)
(*b*) $3.142 \times 5.62 = 17.658$ (nearest thousandth)
(*c*) $3.142 \times 5.625 = 17.674$ (nearest thousandth)

But, $3.14 \times 5.62 = 17.647$, which is less than **17.658**. So, we have the following rule: *When using a rounded value of π, the most reasonable result is obtained by using a value for π which contains one more significant figure than the approximate number with which it is to be multiplied (or divided).*

In other words:

To multiply 39 or 3.9 by π, use 3.14.
To multiply 392, 39.2 or 3.92 by π, use 3.142.
To multiply 392.7, 39.27, or 3.927 by π, use 3.1416.

In every case, the product should be given to the same number of significant figures as in the approximate number which was multiplied (or divided) by π.

dividing with approximate numbers

As in multiplication, when dividing two approximate numbers, the quotient should contain no more significant figures than in the number which contains the fewer significant figures.

Example. Divide 83.5 by 24. The dividend has three significant figures; the divisor has only two. The quotient should therefore be rounded to two significant figures.

$$
\begin{array}{ll}
3.4 & 3.47 \\
(a)\ 24\overline{)83.5} & (b)\ 24\overline{)83.50} \\
\underline{72} & \underline{72} \\
11\ 5 & 11\ 5 \\
\underline{9\ 6} & \underline{9\ 6} \\
1\ 9 & 1\ 90 \\
& \underline{1\ 68}
\end{array}
$$

Answer: 3.5.

Since the remainder in *a* is more than half the divisor, we increase the last figure in the quotient by 1; answer, 3.5. We could have carried the division to one more significant figure than necessary, as in *b*, and then rounded the quotient 3.47 to two significant figures; answer, 3.5.

EXERCISE 7–6

1. Find the products of the following approximate numbers:

(a) 17.5×324.6 (b) 6.7×8.92
(c) 31×432 (d) 15.25×6.24 (e) $2.15 \times 24{,}560$

2. Find the product of $2 \times 3.14 \times 4.8$, where "2" is an exact number; that is, $2 = 2.0000. . .$

3. Find the greatest possible area of a rectangular plot of ground measuring 62.8 yards by 20.4 yards.

4. What is the least possible area of a square field whose side is correctly measured as 82 feet?

5. Since we multiply to find an area, should the dimensions of a rectangle be given with the same number of significant figures? If the length of a rectangle is correctly given as 168 feet, to what degree of accuracy should the width be measured if the width is less than 100 feet?

6. Find the circumference of a circle whose diameter measured to the nearest foot is 15.

7. Find the circumference of each of the following circles:

(a) $d = 6.4$ feet   (b) $d = 24.3$ inches
(c) $d = 8.21$ centimeters (d) $d = 12.32$ inches
(e) radius $= 3.24$ inches

8. What is the area of a circle whose radius is 4.2 inches?

9. The surface of a sphere equals $\pi \times D^2$; find the surface when $D = 6.4$ inches.

10. The area of an ellipse is the product of $a \times b \times \pi$. Find the area when $a = 4.2$ inches and $b = 6.1$ inches (Fig. 7–3).

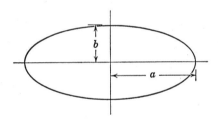

Fig. 7-3

11. Find the following:

(a) $14.8 \div 12$.   (b) $253 \div 21$.
(c) $78.15 \div 3.6$.   (d) $264.58 \div 3.26$.
(e) $39.37 \div 12.5$.   (f) $7.89 \div 0.52$.

12. Find the diameter of a circle whose circumference is 32.4 feet.

13. The volume of a rectangular box is 448 cubic inches. Its height is 3.8 inches. Find the area of the base.

14. A 75-watt lamp operates on a 112-volt circuit. If amperes = watts ÷ volts, find the number of amperes of current used by this lamp to the correct number of significant figures.

15. If sound travels at a speed of 1100 feet per second, how long will it take to travel a distance of 5280 feet?

16. In each of the following, the numbers to the left of the equality sign represent approximate numbers (measurements) correctly expressed; which products and quotients are correctly expressed?

(a) $140.8 \times 0.024 = 3.4$ (b) $14.08 \times 0.024 = 0.3379$
(c) $0.148 \div 0.02 = 7$ (d) $1.480 \div 0.20 = 7.4$

FOR FURTHER READING AND STUDY

1. Banks, J. Houston. *Elements of Mathematics.* Boston: Allyn and Bacon, 1956. Chap. 9: "Measurement Computation."
2. Buckingham, B. R. *Elementary Arithmetic: It's Meaning and Practice.* Boston: Ginn and Company, 1947. Chapter 13: "Measurement, An Application of Real Numbers to Continuous Magnitudes."
3. Edwards, William H. *Precision Shop Mathematics.* Boston: D. C. Heath, 1947. Chapter I: "Precision Shop Arithmetic."
4. Gager, William. "Approximate Data—Terminology and Computation." *National Council of Teachers of Mathematics, Twenty-second Yearbook,* 1954. Pp. 323–338.
5. General Motors Corporation. *Precision: A Measure of Progress.* Detroit: General Motors Corporation, Department of Public Relations, 1952. Free pamphlet.
6. Helmholtz, Hermann von. *Counting and Measuring.* (Trans. by C. L. Bryan.) New York: Van Nostrand, 1930.
7. Larsen, H. D. *Arithmetic for Colleges.* New York: Macmillan, 1958. Chapter 10: "Units of Measure and Dimensional Relations." Chapter 11: "Approximate Numbers and Computation."
8. Shuster, C. N. "Working with Approximate Data." *National Council of Teachers of Mathematics, Twenty-second Yearbook,* 1954. Pp. 310–323.
9. Stevens, S. S. "Measurement and Man." *Science* 127:383–389; February, 1958.
10. Swain, Robert L. *Understanding Arithmetic.* New York: Rinehart and Company, 1957. Chapter 12: "Computational Topics."

CHAPTER 8

Mensuration

They (the Alexandrians) were eventually able to measure by indirect means the radius of the Earth, the diameters of the sun and moon, and the distances to the moon, the sun, the planets, and the stars. That we can measure such physically inaccessible lengths and do so, moreover, with an accuracy as great as we wish, seems, at first blush, incredible.

—**Morris Kline:** *Mathematics in Western Culture*

AREAS AND VOLUMES

the concept of length

To ask how long a particular thing is seems an innocent enough question. Just what do we mean by length? We could say that a length is the *distance* between two particular points on a line. But this obviously begs the question: the "distance" between the points *is* the length of that segment. We have gotten exactly nowhere. Try again. The magnitude of a line can be determined by appropriately applying a unit of measure especially designed to measure length. Clearly this attempt is no better than our first one.

The idea of length, and indeed of all measures, rests upon two fundamental concepts: (1) the notion of the *relative magnitude* of two quantities of the same sort, and (2) the notion of a *continuum*.

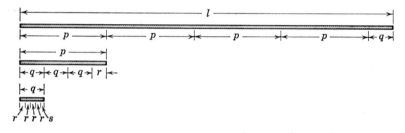

Fig. 8-1

Relative magnitude arises from the concept of similitude and proportion. The only difference between a relative magnitude and a measurement is that in the measurement one of the two quantities is presumably a permanent standard, or conventional unit. The thinking follows the pattern of Euclid's algorithm. In Fig. 8-1, l and p are two given segments ($p < l$). Lay off, in thought, the smaller segment p along the larger segment l. If by chance it can be "laid off" an exact number of times (say k times), then the relative magnitude of the two segments is k, since $l/p = k$, or $l = kp$. If, however, after having laid off segment p a certain number of times, there remains a residual segment q, which is smaller than p, we may repeat the process, laying off q on p. If q is contained an exact number of times in p, then it is said to be the common measure of l and p; if q is contained m times in l and n times in p, then the relative magnitude of the segments l and q is the fraction m/n. For example: if $m = 13$ and $n = 3$, we have $l = 13q$ and $p = 3q$, or

$$\frac{l}{p} = \frac{13q}{3q} = \frac{13}{3} = 4\frac{1}{3}.$$

Should p represent an inch, the length of l is $4\frac{1}{3}$ inches. If, when q

is applied to p, there is a residual segment r, the same process may be repeated (to q and r). This process is continued until there is no longer a remainder.

It is assumed that a finite number of repetitions will bring us to the place where there is no remainder. This is not always possible. For example, if an arbitrary segment is applied to the diagonal of a square and to the side of the square, there would always be a remainder in the case of the diagonal, even with an infinite number of repetitions. In practical measurements, however, the same principle is used, with this modification: when the residual segment is less than the permissible error of observation, inherent in the instrument used, we simply disregard the last residue.

The concept of a continuum is born of intuition. We think of all the points on a line as a linear continuum. What does this mean? It means that if any two points on the line are selected at random, however close together, there is an infinitude of points between them. This concept may not be easy to visualize; but if the points on a line are regarded as a model of the real numbers, we need only recall the properties of an infinite set. In short, our intuition suggests the notion of "density" along a line, or of continuity.

When we measure a length, we use a scale. However the scale may be calibrated, the numbers which designate the divisions of the scale are integers, and those designating the subdivisions of the standard unit are fractions of the unit. As far as the measuring instrument is concerned, therefore, we use only rational numbers and finite processes. But we also tacitly assume that what is being measured is a continuum. By so doing, we are assuming that to any possible measure of a quantity there corresponds a real number, whether rational or irrational. This makes it possible to apply other mathematical processes to the measurements. Without this, science would be quite helpless.

In brief, quantities that can be counted are called *discrete* quantities; quantities that are measured are *continuous* quantities. When we measure a length we are not counting (even though it may seem so). We are finding the ratio between the measured length and a standard length—or at least finding the approximate value of that ratio. The value so found is a rational number. Areas, volumes, masses, weights, time, electrical resistances are also, like length, examples of continuous quantities, subject to measuring, but not to counting.

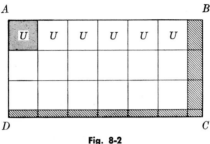

Fig. 8-2

the concept of area

The idea of an area measurement is again the relative magnitude of two surfaces, one of which is a conventional unit or standard, such as a square inch, a square foot, a square yard, a square centimeter, or a square mile. The same principle of Euclid's algorithm is applied again. The area of rectangle $ABCD$ is the relative measure of the rectangle to the unit square U, with suitably small residues which are eventually disregarded. If U can be laid off exactly m times along AB, and n times along AD, we have m rows each containing n units, or a total of mn such units in the rectangle $ABCD$. This is the basis for postulating the area of a rectangle as equal to the product of its length and its width.

mensuration formulas

Mensuration formulas for some common plane and solid figures are summarized below for convenience. The reader who is unfamiliar with them can easily find their explanation in any standard textbook on plane or solid geometry.

Plane Figures

P = perimeter d_1, d_2 = diagonals
A = area b, b_1, b_2 = bases
l = length s = semiperimeter
w = width a = side of equilateral triangle
h = altitude m = median

Certain commonly used formulas related to the circle are summarized below.

D = diameter A = area
R = radius l = length of arc
C = circumference a = central angle (in degrees)

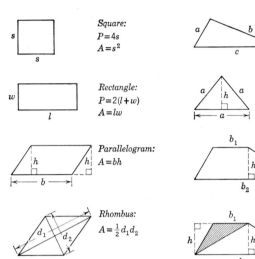

Square:
$P=4s$
$A=s^2$

Triangle:
$s=\frac{1}{2}(a+b+c)$
$A=\sqrt{s(s-a)(s-b)(s-c)}$

Rectangle:
$P=2(l+w)$
$A=lw$

Equilateral Triangle:
$h=\frac{a}{2}\sqrt{3}$
$A=\frac{a^2}{4}\sqrt{3}$

Parallelogram:
$A=bh$

Trapezoid:
$A=\frac{h}{2}(b_1+b_2)$

Rhombus:
$A=\frac{1}{2}d_1d_2$

Trapezoid:
$A=\frac{1}{2}b_1h+\frac{1}{2}b_2h$

Triangle:
$A=\frac{1}{2}bh$

Trapezoid:
$m=\frac{1}{2}(b_1+b_2)$
$A=mh$

Fig. 8-3

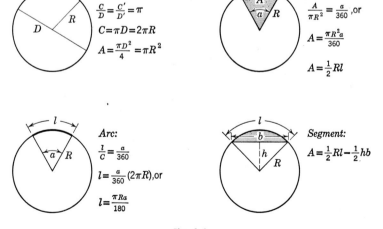

Circle:
$\frac{C}{D}=\frac{C'}{D'}=\pi$
$C=\pi D=2\pi R$
$A=\frac{\pi D^2}{4}=\pi R^2$

Sector:
$\frac{A}{\pi R^2}=\frac{a}{360}$,or
$A=\frac{\pi R^2 a}{360}$
$A=\frac{1}{2}Rl$

Arc:
$\frac{l}{C}=\frac{a}{360}$
$l=\frac{a}{360}(2\pi R)$,or
$l=\frac{\pi Ra}{180}$

Segment:
$A=\frac{1}{2}Rl-\frac{1}{2}hb$

Fig. 8-4

The ratio of any circumference to the diameter of the circle is called π (pi). It can be shown that the value of π is a little more than 3; more precisely, it is 3.14159+. For most ordinary purposes it is sufficiently accurate to use one of the two approximate values, $3\frac{1}{7}$ or 3.14; actually, as we have already seen, the number π is irrational, and therefore cannot be expressed as a terminating decimal or as a repeating decimal.

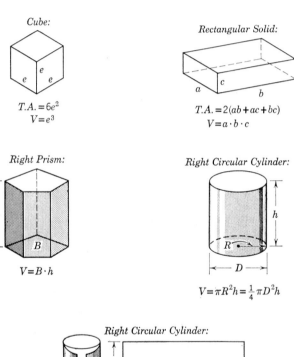

Cube:

$T.A. = 6e^2$
$V = e^3$

Rectangular Solid:

$T.A. = 2(ab + ac + bc)$
$V = a \cdot b \cdot c$

Right Prism:

$V = B \cdot h$

Right Circular Cylinder:

$V = \pi R^2 h = \frac{1}{4}\pi D^2 h$

Right Circular Cylinder:

$L.A. = 2\pi Rh$
$T.A. = 2\pi R^2 + 2\pi Rh$
$\quad = 2\pi R(R + h)$

Fig. 8-5

Right Circular Cone:

$$L.A. = \pi Rs$$
$$T.A. = \pi Rs + \pi R^2$$
$$= \pi R(s+R)$$
$$V = \frac{1}{3}\pi R^2 h$$

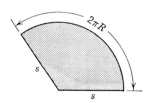

Sphere:

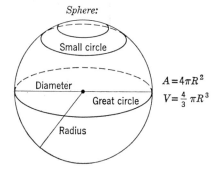

$$A = 4\pi R^2$$
$$V = \frac{4}{3}\pi R^3$$

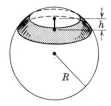

Zone:

$$A = 2\pi Rh$$

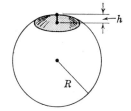

Fig. 8-5 (continued)

Solid Figures

A = area
$L.A.$ = lateral area
$T.A.$ = total area
V = volume
B = base area
p,P = perimeter(s)

e = edge
h = altitude
s = slant height
R,r = radius
D = diameter
C,c = circumference(s)

EXERCISE 8–1

1. Find the area of a regular hexagon inscribed in a circle of radius 12 inches (Fig. 8–6).

2. A fillet is a structural piece, the cross section of which is bounded by two adjacent sides of a square and a quadrant whose center is the opposite vertex of the square. Find the area of the shaded fillet, if the radius $R = 8$ inches (Fig. 8–7).

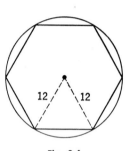

Fig. 8-6

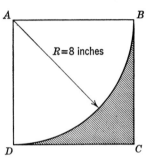

Fig. 8-7

3. The area of an equilateral triangle equals $12\sqrt{3}$; find its altitude; its perimeter.

4. Find the area of a triangle whose sides are 14, 18, and 28.

5. Find the ratio of the area of the shaded portion to the area of the entire circle (Fig. 8–8).

6. A sphere "justs fits" into, or is inscribed in a right circular cylinder whose altitude is twice the radius of the sphere. Find the ratio of their volumes (Fig. 8–9).

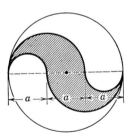

Fig. 8-8

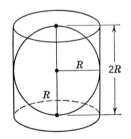

Fig. 8-9

7. A lampshade is to be made from a piece of material cut as shown in the Fig. 8–10; find the area of the material required.

8. Find the area of the cross section of the steel channel beam shown in Fig. 8–11.

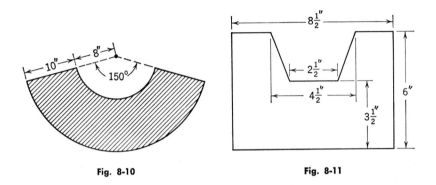

Fig. 8-10   Fig. 8-11

9. An irregularly shaped mineral specimen is placed in a cylindrical vessel $3\frac{1}{2}$ inches in diameter and partly filled with water. If the water rises 4 inches, what is the volume of the specimen? (See Fig. 8–12.)

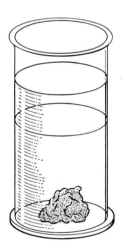

Fig. 8-12

10. Find the volume of the solid generated (1) when a right triangle of base b and altitude h revolves about its side h; (2) when the triangle revolves about its side b (Fig. 8–13). Would you expect these two volumes to be equivalent? Under what conditions would they be equivalent?

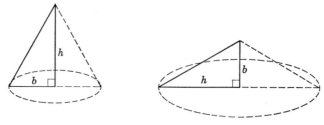

Fig. 8-13

11. A right circular cone and a right circular cylinder have the same base and altitude; find the ratio of the volume of the cone to the volume of the cylinder.

12. Using the formula for the area of a zone, $A = 2\pi Rh$, verify the total area of the sphere as $4\pi R^2$. (*Hint:* Consider the sphere as consisting of two zones of one base.)

13. If the area of a circle is doubled when its radius r is increased by n, find (*a*) the value of r in terms of n; (*b*) the value of n in terms of r.

14. Suppose the earth were a perfect sphere and a belt were fitted snugly around the equator. Now suppose that the belt were cut and a piece 8 inches long were inserted, thus making the belt 8 inches longer than the equator. (*a*) How much would the new belt stand away from the earth, that is, by how much is the original radius of the belt increased? (*b*) Prove that the increase in the radius is independent of the length of the original radius. (*c*) What possible implications or applications are suggested by (*b*) above?

SCALE DRAWINGS

ratio and proportion

A ratio is used to compare two quantities of the same sort—two distances, two weights, two areas, etc. A ratio always tells us either (1) how many times as great one quantity is as the other, or (2) what part one quantity is of the other. When using a ratio, both quantities must be expressed in the same unit of measure. For example: to compare 3 pints and 2 quarts, we cannot say that the ratio is 3:2 or 2:3. We must first change the 2 quarts to 4 pints, and then compare them; the ratio is 3:4, or 4:3.

This tree is 18 feet tall; its shadow is 36 feet long. The man is 6 feet tall, and his shadow is 12 feet long. The ratio of the tree's height to its shadow equals 18:36. The ratio of the man's height to his

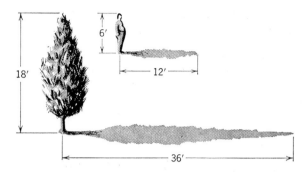

Fig. 8-14

shadow is 6:12. Notice that $\dfrac{18}{36} = \dfrac{6}{12}$. The ratio sign (:) is really nothing but an abbreviated symbol for division (÷); so we may write

$$18{:}36 = 18 \div 36 = \frac{18}{36}.$$

The tree's height has the same relation (ratio) to the length of its shadow that the man's height has to the length of his shadow. In other words:

$$\frac{\text{tree's height}}{\text{tree's shadow}} = \frac{\text{man's height}}{\text{man's shadow}},$$

$$\text{or} \quad \frac{18}{36} = \frac{6}{12}$$

$$\frac{1}{2} = \frac{1}{2}$$

We could also make a comparison in this manner:

$$\frac{\text{man's height}}{\text{tree's height}} = \frac{\text{man's shadow}}{\text{tree's shadow}},$$

$$\text{or} \quad \frac{6}{18} = \frac{12}{36}$$

$$\frac{1}{3} = \frac{1}{3}$$

Any statement which shows that two ratios are equal is called a *proportion*. A proportion is therefore simply an equation stating that two fractions are equal. But by a previously discussed principle, if two fractions are equal, that is, if $a/b = c/d$, then $ad = bc$. This suggests an easy method for finding any one of the four quantities of a proportion if the other three are known.

Example. A snapshot measuring $2\frac{1}{4}$ inches $\times$ $3\frac{1}{4}$ inches is enlarged so that its width is 12 inches. How long is the enlargement.

$$\frac{2\frac{1}{4}}{3\frac{1}{4}} = \frac{12}{x}$$

$$\frac{9}{4}x = \left(\frac{13}{4}\right)(12)$$

$$x = \left(\frac{4}{9}\right)\left(\frac{13}{4}\right)(12) = 17\frac{1}{3} \text{ inches}$$

EXERCISE 8–2

1. Compare the first quantity with the second:

   (a) 2 pounds; 8 ounces   (b) 3 gallons; 2 quarts
   (c) 25¢; $1.75   (d) $1\frac{1}{2}$ feet; $\frac{3}{4}$ yard

2. Find the ratio of the second quantity to the first:

   (a) 20 inches; 2 feet   (b) $\frac{1}{4}$ ton; 200 pounds
   (c) $1\frac{1}{2}$ quarts; 2 pints   (d) 1 yard; 28 inches

3. A picture frame measures $4\frac{1}{2}$ inches $\times$ $7\frac{1}{2}$ inches. What is the ratio of the width to the length?

4. Three cups of olive oil are mixed with four cups of vinegar. What is the ratio of oil to vinegar? What part of the mixture is vinegar? What part of the mixture is oil?

5. Find the missing term in each of these proportions:

   (a) $\dfrac{3}{13} = \dfrac{x}{52}$ (b) $\dfrac{6}{11} = \dfrac{15}{y}$

   (c) $\dfrac{45}{n} = \dfrac{3}{7}$ (d) $\dfrac{h}{12} = \dfrac{12}{5}$

6. A picture $5\frac{1}{4}$ inches wide and $8\frac{1}{4}$ inches long is reduced in size so that it is now only $3\frac{1}{2}$ inches wide. What is its new length?

7. A certain stamping machine can punch out 84 parts in the same time that another machine punches out 105 parts. How many parts will the first machine make in the time that the second machine makes 630 parts?

8. If 9 parts of tin are melted with 38 parts of copper to form a certain alloy, how many pounds of copper should be used with 150 pounds of tin to form a similar alloy?

9. If the cost of living index is 113 one year and 121 the next year, how much more will a housewife need the second year if she spent $1250 in the first year?

10. A house valued at $12,500 is taxed $215. At this rate, what is the tax on a house valued at $17,500?

scale drawing

All maps, as well as plans and blueprints of houses, machines and the like, are examples of scale drawings. Such a drawing shows the exact shape of the original object, but the size of the object has been reduced or enlarged. In Fig. 8-15 are shown scale drawings of two

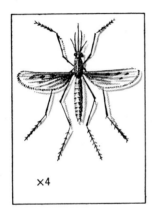 

Fig. 8-15

animals. The picture of the mosquito is labeled "×4." This means that every line in the picture is 4 times as long as the corresponding line in the actual animal. Similarly, the picture of the giraffe is labeled "$\frac{1}{300}$." This means that each line in the drawing is only $\frac{1}{300}$ as long as the corresponding line in the actual animal. Notice carefully that we did not say that the picture mosquito is 4 times as large as the real mosquito, nor that the real giraffe is 300 times as large as the picture giraffe. It is the heights and widths and other *lengths* whose ratios are compared in a scale drawing.

A scale drawing preserves the shape of the original object, but reduces or enlarges every line in it according to some fixed relation or ratio. This fixed ratio is called the *scale*. For example, the scale of this floor plan is 1 inch = 8 feet. Every $\frac{1}{8}$ of an inch on the plan represents 1 foot in the actual house. A room that is actually 14 feet ×

20 feet would appear on the drawing as $1\frac{3}{4}$ inches wide and $2\frac{1}{2}$ inches long, since $14 \times \frac{1}{8} = 1\frac{3}{4}$, and $20 \times \frac{1}{8} = 2\frac{1}{2}$.

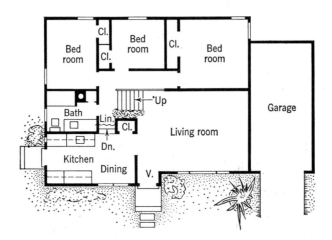

Fig. 8-16

the use of scales

The scale of a map or a drawing is extremely important. The scale shows what distance on the drawing or on the map represents some actual distance in the object or on the ground. On some maps, an inch may represent several hundred miles. On other drawings, an inch may represent only a few feet. The scale used may be shown in several ways.

Method I. This is the method that is commonly used in mechanical drawings, floor plans, etc. For example:

   (a) 1 inch = 10 feet
   (b) $\frac{1}{8}$ inch = 1 foot
   (c) 1 inch = 40 miles

These mean, respectively:

   (a) 1 inch on the map represents 10 feet of the object.
   (b) 1 inch on the map represents 8 feet of the object.
   (c) 1 inch on the map represents 40 miles on the ground.

This method does not always show clearly the actual ratio between drawing and object. For example:

1 inch = 10 feet, or 1 inch = 120 inches; ratio, 1:120
¼ inch = 1 foot, or 1 inch = 48 inches; ratio, 1:48
1 inch = 100 yards, or 1 inch = 3600 inches; ratio, 1:3600

Method II. A very common device used on maps is a small line, or bar, drawn right on the map, usually in one corner, such as those shown in Fig. 8-17.

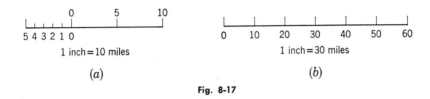

(a) 1 inch = 10 miles

(b) 1 inch = 30 miles

Fig. 8-17

In Fig. 8-17a, the segment from 0 to 10 is 1 inch long and represents 10 miles of actual distance. Sometimes the scale is drawn as shown in Fig. 8-17b, where 1 inch = 30 miles. Check this with your ruler.

Method III. Another way of indicating the scale of a map is by giving the ratio simply as a fraction, as for example,

$$\text{Scale: } \frac{1}{63,360}.$$

This fraction is called the *representative fraction*. It is abbreviated, RF. The numerator of the RF is a distance on the map or drawing; the denominator is the corresponding distance on the ground. In this case, 1 unit on the map stands for 63,360 of the same units on the ground. Since 63,360 = 5280 × 12, or the number of inches in a mile, this RF (1/63,360) is another way of saying "1 inch on the map equals 1 mile on the ground."

The RF used varies for different purposes. On aviation maps the RF might be 1/500,000, or 1:500,000, which makes 1 inch represent approximately 8 miles. On artillery maps, the RF is often 1/20,000; here 1 inch equals about ⅓ of a mile.

Example 1. The scale on a local map reads 1 inch = 5 miles. What is the ratio, or representative fraction?

$$1 \text{ mile} = 12 \times 5280 = 63,360 \text{ inches}$$
$$5 \text{ miles} = 5 \times 63,360 = 318,150 \text{ inches}$$

$$\text{So, RF} = \frac{1}{318,150}$$

Example 2. The RF on a United States Sectional Chart is 1:500,000. On this chart, 1 inch represents about how many miles (nearest mile)?

> 1 mile = 12 × 5280 = 63,360 inches
> 500,000 miles ÷ 63,360 = 7.89 miles, or about 8 miles
> So, 1 inch = 8 miles (approximately)

Example 3. Two markers on an aerial photograph are 3.4 inches apart on the photograph. How far apart are they really, if the RF is 1/10,000? One inch represents 10,000 inches of object; so, 3.4 inches represents 3.4 × 10,-000 = 34,000 inches. Changing 34,000 inches to miles, we get

$$34,000 \div 63,360 = 0.54 \text{ miles.}$$

So, the markers are a little more than ½ mile apart.

EXERCISE 8–3

1. On a blueprint, 1 inch = 12 feet. What is the actual length represented by a line 2¾ inches long? A distance of 27 feet should be how many inches on the plan?

2. A chart is drawn to a scale of $\frac{1}{10}$ inch = 1 foot. A distance of 65 feet should be how long on the chart? A length of 3¾ inches on the chart represents a distance of how many feet?

3. With a scale of 40 feet to the inch, a length of 14½ inches represents an actual distance of how many feet? A fence 128 feet long would be represented by a line how many inches long?

4. If a line 4½ inches long on a plan represents an actual distance of 9 feet, the scale used is 1 inch = ? feet, or ? inches = 1 foot. Using this scale, what are the dimensions of a room that measures 2¼ inches by 4½ inches on the plan?

5. On a certain map, the scale is given as 1 inch = 40 miles. This means that a line 2¼ inches long represents ? miles; a ground distance of 140 miles would be represented on the map by a line ? inches long.

6. If 1 inch represents ¼ mile on a map, how many inches on the map represent a ground distance of 220 yards?

7. A map is drawn to the scale of 1 inch = 100 miles. How long should a line be on the map to represent 50 miles? 75 miles? 350 miles?

8. Many automobile road maps are drawn to the scale of 1 inch = 20 miles. What is the RF on such a map?

9. Maps used by the United States Forest Service are drawn to three scales: ¼ inch = 1 mile; ½ inch = 1 mile; 1 inch = 1 mile. Express each of these scales as a ratio, that is, find the RF in each case.

10. Draw lines to represent the following:

(*a*) The width of a gymnasium, 38 feet, if the scale is 1 inch = 16 feet.

(*b*) A straight road between two towns, 70 miles, if the scale is 1 inch = 40 miles.

11. The RF on an aerial photograph is 1:18,000. Two places are marked

4.8 inches apart on the photograph. How far apart on the ground are these two places? (nearest tenth of a mile).

12. A certain military map is drawn to the scale of 1 to 400,000. On this map, one inch represents about how many miles? (nearest tenth of a mile).

measuring inaccessible distances

Scale drawings furnish a convenient way of measuring inaccessible heights and distances.

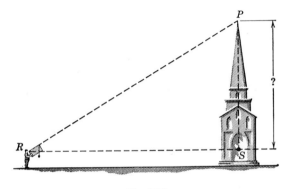

Fig. 8-18

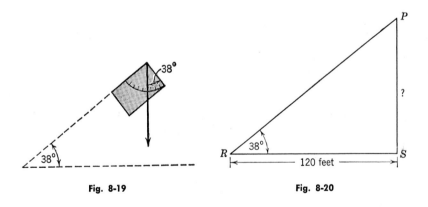

Fig. 8-19   Fig. 8-20

Example 1. Suppose we wish to find the height of the top of the church steeple. We simply measure a distance RS (Fig. 8-18) from the foot of the steeple to the observer at R. Say that this distance is 120 feet. With a suitable instrument (Fig. 8-19) carrying an angle-scale and a plumb line mounted on a board, the angle PRS is measured and found to be 38°. With the aid of your protractor (Fig. 8-20), draw right triangle *PRS* to scale, using a scale of 1 inch equals 20 feet. How long is *RS* on your drawing? How long is *PS*? Then how high is the steeple? (To be accurate, you should add to *PS* the height of the man's eyes above the ground; why?)

Example 2. To determine the inaccessible distance from *P* to *Q*, the measurements shown in the figure below were taken. Copy triangle *PTQ*, using a scale of 1 inch = 40 yards. How long should you make *TP*? *TQ*? How long is side *PQ* of the triangle? Then how far is it actually from *P* to *Q*?

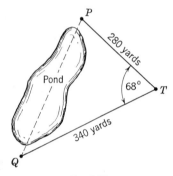

Fig. 8-21

vectors; forces and velocities

Everyone knows that when you swim or row a boat against the current as here shown, the actual path of the swimmer or the boat will not be *OA*, but some oblique path such as *OR*. To find the actual path and speed, we use vectors. A *vector* is simply a line which shows both the amount and the direction of a force, or of motion. For example: A ship starting at *O* proceeds at 15 miles per hour heading due east. If there were no current, the ship would be at *A* at the end of 1 hour. The line segment *OA* is a vector. It represents the actual direction of the motion ($\angle NOA = 90°$), and it represents the speed by using a length of 15 units (drawn to scale). Notice how the vector *OA* is drawn in Fig. 8-22:

1. The vector has a specific starting point and a definite sense (push or pull, up or down, left or right, etc.).

2. The vector is drawn to scale to show the amount of force (or the rate of motion).

3. The vector makes a definite angle with a line of reference which shows the direction of the force or motion.

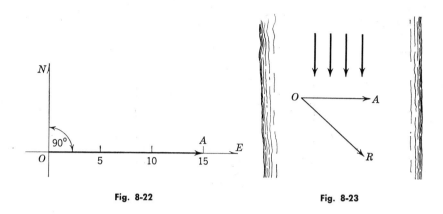

Fig. 8-22   Fig. 8-23

Now suppose that our ship (in Fig. 8-23) encounters a current running due south at 6 miles per hour. What happens? If the ship were to cut off its power and just drift with the current, it would be at point B at the end of one hour. (Fig. 8-24a). But, both forces propel

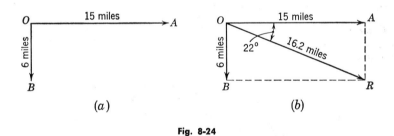

(a)   (b)

Fig. 8-24

the ship at the same time (its engines and the current), and each force achieves its own full effect, just as if the other weren't acting. The only place which is both 15 miles east of point O and 6 miles south of O is point R, the end of the diagonal OR of the rectangle $OARB$. (Fig. 8-24b). The directed line OR is the vector which represents the actual path of the ship when subjected to both forces simultaneously. If the ship starts at O, its direction of motion will be given by $\angle AOR$ (approx. 22°), and the rate of speed will be about 16.2 miles per hour along this path. The angle AOR can be measured from the scale drawing by using your protractor; the length of OR gives the rate (or distance) when changed to miles per hour (or miles) according to the scale used.

Example 1. A man rows a boat across a stream at the rate of 4 miles per hour. The current down stream runs at 2 miles per hour. Using a scale drawing, find the actual path and the actual speed of the boat.

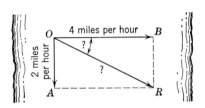

Fig. 8-25

Make a scale drawing, preferably on graph paper for convenience. If graph paper is not at hand, draw a right angle with your protractor; then lay off OA and OB, using a scale of 1 inch = 1 mile. Complete the rectangle $OARB$, and draw diagonal OR. Measure the length of OR, and, with your protractor, measure angle BOR. If the work is done carefully, OR should be almost 4.5 inches, that is, 4.5 miles per hour; angle BOR should be approximately 27°.

Example 2. Two forces, OP and OS, act at an angle of 60°. Find the amount and direction of the resulting single force to which they are equivalent (OR, the resultant).

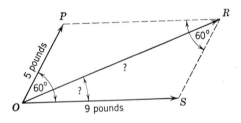

Fig. 8-26

Using graph paper (to get PR parallel to OS), draw the parallelogram $OPRS$, making $\angle POS$ equal to 60°, and $\angle PRS$ equal to 60° (Why?). Use a scale of 1 inch = 2 pounds. From the scale drawing, find OR and $\angle SOR$. If the work has been done carefully, OR = 12.3 pounds, and $\angle SOR$ equals about 21°.

Example 3. A man pushes on the handle of a lawn mower, at the angle shown, with a force of 80 pounds. How much is he pushing vertically downward, in effect, and how much horizontally forward?

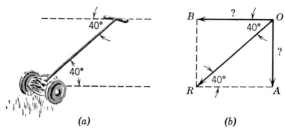

Fig. 8-27

Use a scale of 1 inch = 20 pounds; make a scale drawing as in Fig. 8-27b. Measure *OA* and *OB*. A careful drawing will show that the vertical downward push (*OA*) is about 51 pounds and the horizontal forward thrust (*OB*) is about 61 pounds.

EXERCISE 8–4

Solve the following problems by using a protractor and making appropriate scale drawings.

1. The mast *HK* is supported by a cable *HM* which reaches from a point 3 feet from the top of the mast to a fastening in the ground 18 feet from the base of the mast. The angle *HMK* is 70°. Copy the triangle, using a scale of 1 inch = 8 feet. How long should you make *MK*? How long is *HK*? How high is the mast? (See Fig. 8–28.)

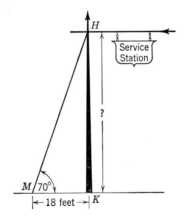

Fig. 8-28

2. Using an instrument at eye level, 5½ feet above the ground at point *C*, a man sights the top of the tree at *A* as 26°. If he is standing 80 feet from the base of the tree at D, how high is the tree? Use a scale 1 inch = 16 feet. (See Fig. 8–29.)

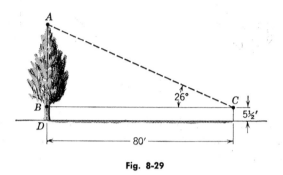

Fig. 8-29

3. When a ship is at S, the lighthouse L makes an angle of 40° with the ship's course. When the ship has sailed 2500 yards to point T, the angle is 65°. Using a scale of 1 inch = 500 yards, find the distance from S to L, and also from T to L. (See Fig. 8–30.)

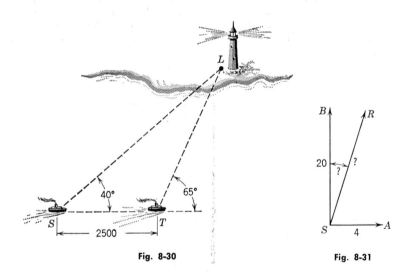

Fig. 8-30   Fig. 8-31

4. A ship starting at S sails due north at 20 miles per hour, while a current is moving due east at 4 miles per hour. Find the actual speed and direction of the ship SR. (Scale: 1 inch = 4 miles.) See Fig. 8–31.

5. A boy pulls his wagon with a force of 40 pounds, holding the handle at an angle of 35° with the horizontal. Find (*a*) the vertical upward thrust

(*OA*), and (*b*) the effective forward horizontal pull (*OB*). (Scale: 1 inch = 8 pounds.) See Fig. 8–32.

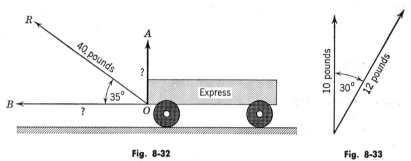

Fig. 8-32   Fig. 8-33

6. Find the resultant of a force of 12 pounds to the right and a force of 6 pounds straight down. (Scale: 1 inch = 3 pounds.)

7. Find the resultant of a force of 10 pounds vertically upward, and a force of 12 pounds at an angle of 30° to the right and upward. (Scale: 1 inch = 4 pounds.) See Fig. 8–33.

8. Find the resultant of forces 6 pounds and 10 pounds, making an angle of 60° with each other. (Scale: 1 inch = 4 pounds.)

9. A ship sets its course at N35°E, moving at 20 miles per hour. The wind is from the west at 4 miles per hour. Find the ship's actual speed and direction. (Scale: 1 inch = 4 miles.) See Fig. 8–34.

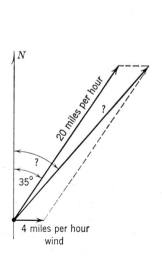

Fig. 8-34

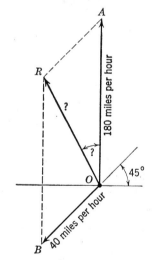

Fig. 8-35

10. A plane is headed due north at 180 miles per hour. The wind is from the northeast at 40 miles per hour. Find the plane's track (OR), and the angle of drift, $\measuredangle$ AOR. (Scale: 1 inch $=$ 40 miles.) See Fig. 8-35, previous page.

SIMILAR FIGURES

same shape, different size

Geometric figures that can coincide in all respects (angles and lengths) are said to be *congruent*. They are the same in shape and in size. Figures that have the same shape but differ in size are said to be *similar* figures. Their corresponding angles are respectively equal, but their corresponding sides are proportional—that is, any pair of corresponding sides has the same ratio as any other corresponding pair of sides.

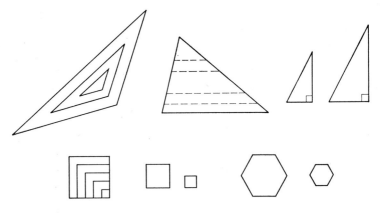

Fig. 8-36. Regular Polygons

Observe that congruent figures may be regarded as a special case of similar figures in which the ratio of the corresponding sides is 1:1. Note also that all regular polygons of the same number of sides are necessarily similar figures, since by definition a regular polygon is one which is both equiangular and equilateral. Thus all squares are similar in shape; also similar are all equilateral triangles, all regular hexagons, etc. In fact, if a circle is loosely defined as a regular polygon with an infinite number of sides, we may regard all circles as similar figures. But it should be remembered that a figure may be equiangular without being equilateral, and vice versa (Fig. 8-37).

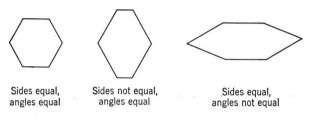

Sides equal,   Sides not equal,   Sides equal,
angles equal   angles equal   angles not equal

Fig. 8-37

It will be seen, therefore, that size and shape, or magnitude and form, are independent of each other. To specify the angles of a triangle is not sufficient to determine a specific triangle, for there are infinitely many triangles having definite given angles. This indeterminacy is a significant peculiarity of plane surfaces only; it does not hold true on a spherical surface. A spherical triangle is completely determined by its angles. That is, given the angles, there is only one such triangle on the sphere. On the surface of a sphere similar triangles are impossible. This fact accounts for important differences in plane and spherical geometry and trigonometry.

Indeed, we may regard the property of congruence as the hallmark of freedom of motion on a plane—both translation and rotation—without destroying either the magnitude or the form of a figure. We may regard the property of similarity as the hallmark of freedom of growth, that is, a change in magnitude—expansion or contraction—without change of form. On the surface of a sphere, free change of position is always possible, but free change of magnitude is not possible. In a plane, freedom of motion and freedom of growth are both possible.

The fact that in a plane free change of position (motion) is always possible means that there can be neither absolute position nor absolute direction. Position can be described only relative to some other position; direction can be described only relatively with respect to some other direction. What is true of position and direction in the plane is also true on the sphere. When it comes to magnitude, the sphere provides its own natural unit of length, namely, the circumference of a great circle. All other distances on the sphere can be expressed (measured) in relation to the great circle as an absolute unit of length.

But in the plane we are still limited to relativistic devices. There is no absolute unit of length, intrinsic to some geometric property. In the plane, length can be described or measured only in terms of a comparison (ratio) between two segments, one of which, the standard unit, is arbitrarily selected by man without reference to any geometric property, as we have already seen.

indirect measurement with similar triangles

The fact that the corresponding sides of similar triangles are in proportion can be used in practical situations to make indirect measurements without the aid of a scale drawing. One method of doing this is by using a proportion derived from two similar triangles, as shown below; the other is by means of trigonometric ratios. Both methods are based on essentially the same principles of similarity and proportionality.

EXERCISE 8–5

1. Find the missing dimensions in these similar triangles (Figs. 8–38, 8–39):

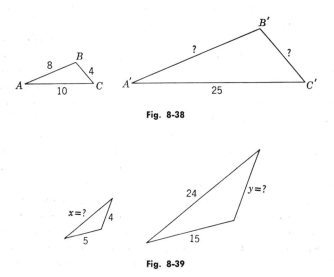

Fig. 8-38

Fig. 8-39

2. Find the height of a flagpole if its shadow (RS) equals 27 feet at the same time a boy 5 feet 4 inches tall throws a shadow 4 feet long (Fig. 8–40).

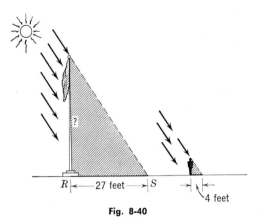

Fig. 8-40

3. An electric light pole throws a shadow 22 feet long at the same time that a fire plug 3 feet high casts a shadow 4 feet long. How high is the pole?

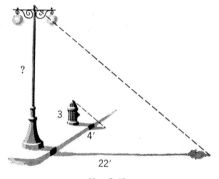

Fig. 8-41

4. The distance from A to B is 40 yards, from A to R is 240 yards, and from B to C is 25 yards. How wide is the river from R to S?

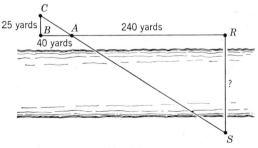

Fig. 8-42

5. Find the distance PQ across an inaccessible marsh by using the dimensions staked out as shown in Fig. 8–43.

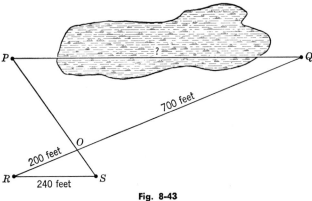

Fig. 8-43

6. Find the height of the telegraph pole if the observer at A can see the top of the pole (C) reflected in a shallow pan of water at B. Why does angle m equal angle n?

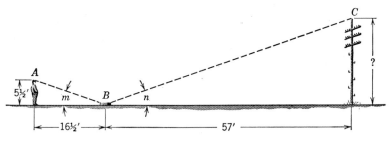

Fig. 8-44

7. The diameters of two pulleys are in the ratio of 4:9. If the diameter of the larger pulley is 11.25 inches, find the diameter of the smaller pulley.

8. The circumferences of two circles are to each other as 18:37. If the radius of the first circle is $4\frac{1}{2}$ inches, what is the radius of the second circle?

9. The radii of two circles are in the ratio of 5 to 8. If the circumference of the second circle is 36 centimeters, what is the circumference of the first circle?

areas and volumes of similar figures

It is easy to see why the areas of two similar triangles are to each other as the squares of any two corresponding linear dimensions.

Thus, in Fig. 8-45,

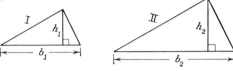

Fig. 8-45

$$\frac{\text{Area of } \Delta \text{I}}{\text{Area of } \Delta \text{II}} = \frac{\frac{1}{2}b_1h_1}{\frac{1}{2}b_2h_2} = \left(\frac{b_1}{b_2}\right)\left(\frac{h_1}{h_2}\right);$$

$$\text{but } \frac{b_1}{b_2} = \frac{h_1}{h_2};$$

$$\text{so } \frac{\Delta \text{I}}{\Delta \text{II}} = \frac{b_1^2}{b_2^2} = \frac{h_1^2}{h_2^2}.$$

Generalizing: the areas of any two similar plane figures are to each other as the *squares* of any two corresponding linear dimensions, that is, sides, altitudes, medians, etc. In the same way, the areas of two circles are to each other as the squares of their radii or their diameters. For example, doubling the radius (or the diameter) of a circle makes the new area four times as great. A circle 9 times as large in area as another circle, has a diameter (or radius) 3 times as great.

In the same way it will be seen that the volumes of similar solids are to each other as the *cubes* of their corresponding linear dimensions (Fig. 8-46).

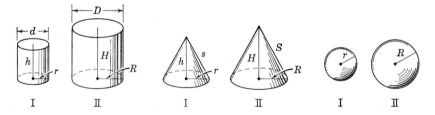

Fig. 8-46

Similar cylinders:

$$\frac{V_{\text{I}}}{V_{\text{II}}} = \frac{h^3}{H^3} = \frac{r^3}{R^3} = \frac{d^3}{D^3}.$$

Similar cones:

$$\frac{V_I}{V_{II}} = \frac{h^3}{H^3} = \frac{r^3}{R^3} = \frac{d^3}{D^3} = \frac{s^3}{S^3}.$$

Spheres:

$$\frac{V_I}{V_{II}} = \frac{r^3}{R^3} = \frac{d^3}{D^3}.$$

Thus, for example, if both the altitude and diameter of a right circular cylinder are doubled, the volume will become $(2)^3$, or **8** times as great, and the new cylinder will be similar to the original. If the altitude is doubled while the base remains the same, the volume is doubled; if the diameter is doubled while the altitude remains the same, the volume becomes four times as great. In neither of these cases is the new cylinder similar to the original one.

The areas and volumes of similar solids sometimes unwittingly play a role in connection with certain types of pictographs, not infrequently a deceptive role. For example: if the petroleum production in one period was 2,000,000 barrels and in some other comparable period 3,000,000 barrels, this increase might be represented by a "realistic" pictograph showing two petroleum drums with their linear dimensions in the ratio of 2:3. The "barrels" are similar cylinders, in perspective. If Fig. 8-47 is shaded to create the illusion of three-

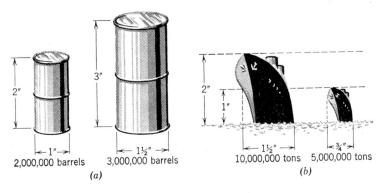

Fig. 8-47

dimensional depth, the reader may visualize the pictograph as *solid* cylinders, whose volumes are in the ratio of $\frac{2^3}{3^3}$, or $\frac{8}{27}$. This ratio would indicate that the production during the second period had been nearly 3½ times as great as during the earlier period, instead of only half again as great. In short, for this pictograph in three dimensions or in perspective, the linear dimensions should be in the ratio of $\sqrt[3]{2}:\sqrt[3]{3}$ or 1.26:1.44, or very nearly 7:8. In the same way, the "bulks" of the ships in Fig. 8-47b, as drawn, suggest volumes in the ratio 8:1, since the linear dimensions are in the ratio 2:1. Actually, such graphs leave much to be desired by way of accuracy and unambiguity; better practice would be to use simple bar graphs, of equal (and arbitrary) widths, so that the eye can concentrate on comparing *lengths* instead of areas or suggested volumes.

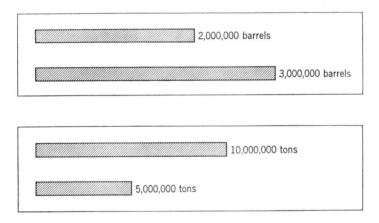

Fig. 8-48

EXERCISE 8–6

1. If the edge of a cube is doubled, how is its total surface changed? Its volume?

2. If the edge of a cube is increased by 10 per cent, by what per cent is the volume increased?

3. The areas of two circles are as 4:9. If the diameter of the smaller circle is 12 inches, what is the diameter of the larger?

4. The radii of two circles are 6 feet and 8 feet respectively. Find (a) the ratio of their circumferences; (b) the ratio of their areas.

5. The circumference of a circle is 10 centimeters. What is the circumference of a circle whose area is four times that of the given circle?

6. (a) If the height of a cylinder is twice that of another cylinder, but the diameters of the bases are the same, how do their volumes compare? (b) If the diameter of a cylinder is twice that of another, but their heights are the same, how do their volumes compare? (See Fig. 8-49.)

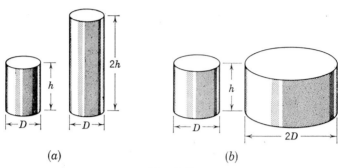

(a)   (b)

Fig. 8-49

7. If the height of a cylindrical container is cut in half, and the diameter is doubled, how is the volume changed?

8. A rectangular zinc cut used for photoengraving is reduced "four-fifths." What is the ratio of the areas involved?

9. If a cylindrical metal drum used for transporting liquids has each dimension increased by 33⅓ per cent, by what per cent is its capacity increased?

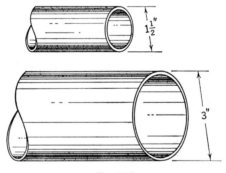

Fig. 8-50

10. How much water will flow through a pipe depends upon (a) the speed with which it flows and (b) the area of the open end (or cross-section). If the speed of flow is the same for both, how many times as much water will be delivered by a 3-inch pipe than by a pipe 1½ inches in diameter?

TRIGONOMETRY OF THE RIGHT TRIANGLE

the tangent ratio

We shall assume that it is a necessary and sufficient condition for two plane triangles to be similar that two angles of one triangle are equal respectively to two angles of the other triangle. Since the right triangles below have a common acute angle, x, the triangles are similar to one another, and hence their corresponding sides are in proportion.

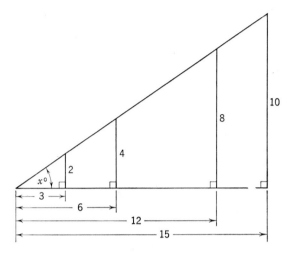

Fig. 8-51

Thus, $\frac{2}{3} = \frac{4}{6}$; or $\frac{2}{3} = \frac{8}{12}$; or $\frac{2}{3} = \frac{10}{15}$. In each of these right triangles, then, the ratio of the vertical side to the horizontal side is always the same:

$$\frac{2}{3} = \frac{4}{6} = \frac{8}{12} = \frac{10}{15} = \text{a constant value.}$$

We might also say:

$$\frac{\text{``vertical side''}}{\text{``horizontal side''}} = \frac{2}{3} = 0.6667, \text{ for this particular angle of } x \text{ degrees.}$$

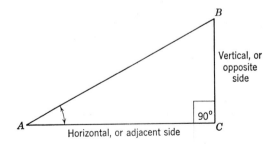

Fig. 8-52

Since the triangle may not always be placed in this position, the ratio in question for this particular acute angle A in Fig. 8-52, namely,

$$\frac{\text{vertical side}}{\text{horizontal side}}$$

is better described as the ratio:

$$\frac{\text{side opposite the angle}}{\text{side adjacent to the angle}}.$$

This ratio is called the tangent ratio, or the *tangent of the angle* A. It is written

$$\text{tangent of } A = \frac{\text{length of } BC}{\text{length of } AC},$$

or simply

$$\tan A = \frac{BC}{AC}.$$

From Fig. 8-53 you can see that

$$\tan A = \frac{B_1C_1}{AC_1} = \frac{B_2C_2}{AC_2} = \frac{B_3C_3}{AC_3} = \frac{B_4C_4}{AC_4} = \text{etc.}$$

Now try the following experiment. On a sheet of graph paper, use a base line AC of 10 convenient units. (See Fig. 8-54.) With your protractor, draw angles as follows:

$$\angle CAB_1 = 10° \quad \angle CAB_2 = 20° \quad \angle CAB_3 = 30°$$
$$\angle CAB_4 = 40° \quad \angle CAB_5 = 50° \quad \angle CAB_6 = 60° \quad \angle CAB_7 = 65°$$

Then measure the lengths B_1C, B_2C, B_3C, B_4C, etc., and draw up a table like the one shown below:

Angle	Degrees	Opposite side (BC)	Adjacent side (AC)	$\dfrac{BC}{AC}$	Tan A
CAB_1	10°	1.8 units	10 units	0.18	$\tan 10° = 0.18$
CAB_2	20°	3.6 units	10 units	0.36	$\tan 20° = 0.36$
CAB_3	30°	5.8 units	10 units	0.58	$\tan 30° = 0.58$
CAB_4	40°	8.4 units	10 units	0.84	$\tan 40° = 0.84$
CAB_5	50°	11.9 units	10 units	1.19	$\tan 50° = 1.19$
CAB_6	60°	17.3 units	10 units	1.73	$\tan 60° = 1.73$
CAB_7	65°	21.4 units	10 units	2.14	$\tan 65° = 2.14$

These measurements show that as an angle increases or decreases, the tangent ratio also increases or decreases. The tangents of all angles from 0° to 89° are listed in the table on page 270. These values are correct to four decimal places. Notice that as the angle becomes smaller and smaller, the tangent ratio also becomes smaller and smaller. The nearer the angle approaches to zero degrees, the nearer

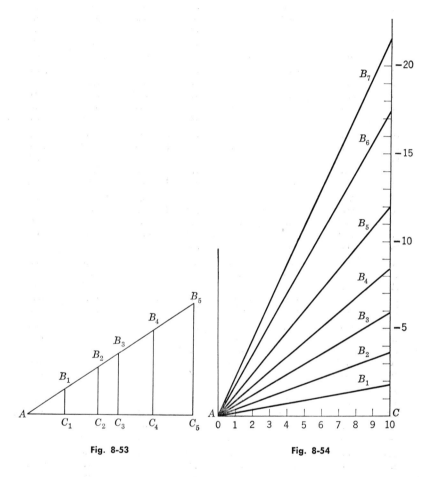

Fig. 8-53   Fig. 8-54

the value of the tangent approaches zero. When the angle is 0°, there is no triangle, for the "opposite side" has vanished; hence

$$\tan 0° = \frac{\text{opposite side}}{\text{adjacent side}} = \frac{0}{\text{adjacent side}} = 0,$$

since zero divided by any number is zero. Notice also that as the angle becomes larger and larger, the tangent ratio also becomes larger

TABLE 5.   Table of Tangents, Cosines, and Sines

Angle	Tangent $\left(\dfrac{opp.}{adj.}\right)$	Cosine $\left(\dfrac{adj.}{hyp.}\right)$	Sine $\left(\dfrac{opp.}{hyp.}\right)$	Angle	Tangent $\left(\dfrac{opp.}{adj.}\right)$	Cosine $\left(\dfrac{adj.}{hyp.}\right)$	Sine $\left(\dfrac{opp.}{hyp.}\right)$
0°	.0000	1.0000	.0000	45°	1.0000	.7071	.7071
1°	.0175	.9998	.0175	46°	1.0355	.6947	.7193
2°	.0349	.9994	.0349	47°	1.0724	.6820	.7314
3°	.0524	.9986	.0523	48°	1.1106	.6691	.7431
4°	.0699	.9976	.0698	49°	1.1504	.6561	.7547
5°	.0875	.9962	.0872	50°	1.1918	.6428	.7660
6°	.1051	.9945	.1045	51°	1.2349	.6293	.7771
7°	.1228	.9925	.1219	52°	1.2799	.6157	.7880
8°	.1405	.9903	.1392	53°	1.3270	.6018	.7986
9°	.1584	.9877	.1564	54°	1.3764	.5878	.8090
10°	.1763	.9848	.1736	55°	1.4281	.5736	.8192
11°	.1944	.9816	.1908	56°	1.4826	.5592	.8290
12°	.2126	.9781	.2079	57°	1.5399	.5446	.8387
13°	.2309	.9744	.2250	58°	1.6003	.5299	.8480
14°	.2493	.9703	.2419	59°	1.6643	.5150	.8572
15°	.2679	.9659	.2588	60°	1.7321	.5000	.8660
16°	.2867	.9613	.2756	61°	1.8040	.4848	.8746
17°	.3057	.9563	.2924	62°	1.8807	.4695	.8829
18°	.3249	.9511	.3090	63°	1.9626	.4540	.8910
19°	.3443	.9455	.3256	64°	2.0503	.4384	.8988
20°	.3640	.9397	.3420	65°	2.1445	.4226	.9063
21°	.3839	.9336	.3584	66°	2.2460	.4067	.9135
22°	.4040	.9272	.3746	67°	2.3559	.3907	.9205
23°	.4245	.9205	.3907	68°	2.4751	.3746	.9272
24°	.4452	.9135	.4067	69°	2.6051	.3584	.9336
25°	.4663	.9063	.4226	70°	2.7475	.3420	.9397
26°	.4877	.8988	.4384	71°	2.9042	.3256	.9455
27°	.5095	.8910	.4540	72°	3.0777	.3090	.9511
28°	.5317	.8829	.4695	73°	3.2709	.2924	.9563
29°	.5543	.8746	.4848	74°	3.4874	.2756	.9613
30°	.5774	.8660	.5000	75°	3.7321	.2588	.9659
31°	.6009	.8572	.5150	76°	4.0108	.2419	.9703
32°	.6249	.8480	.5299	77°	4.3315	.2250	.9744
33°	.6494	.8387	.5446	78°	4.7046	.2079	.9781
34°	.6745	.8290	.5592	79°	5.1446	.1908	.9816
35°	.7002	.8192	.5736	80°	5.6713	.1736	.9848
36°	.7265	.8090	.5878	81°	6.3138	.1564	.9877
37°	.7536	.7986	.6018	82°	7.1154	.1392	.9903
38°	.7813	.7880	.6157	83°	8.1443	.1219	.9925
39°	.8098	.7771	.6293	84°	9.5144	.1045	.9945
40°	.8391	.7660	.6428	85°	11.4301	.0872	.9962
41°	.8693	.7547	.6561	86°	14.3007	.0698	.9976
42°	.9004	.7431	.6691	87°	19.0811	.0523	.9986
43°	.9325	.7314	.6820	88°	28.6363	.0349	.9994
44°	.9657	.7193	.6947	89°	57.2900	.0175	.9998
45°	1.0000	.7071	.7071	90°		.0000	1.0000

and larger. Finally, when the angle equals 90°, there is again no triangle. But in this case there isn't even a ratio such as

$$\frac{\text{opposite side}}{0},$$

since division by zero is not possible. Hence we say that tan 90° does
not exist; that is, the function tan x is not defined when $x = 90°$.

interpolation

Suppose we wish to find the value of a function of an angle between
two successive integral angles, as, for example, the value of tan 26° 40'.
We then make use of linear interpolation, similar to that used when
interpolating values of logarithms.

Example 1. Find the value of tan 26°40'. From the table:

$$\begin{aligned}
\tan 26° &= 0.4877 \\
\tan 27° &= \underline{0.5095} \\
\text{difference} &= 0.0218
\end{aligned}$$

The difference of 0.0218 corresponds to an interval of 1 degree, or 60 minutes;
we wish to find the difference in tangents corresponding to 40' (between
26° and 27°); so, by "proportional parts," we simply take $^{40}\!/_{60}$ or $\frac{2}{3}$ of
0.0218 and add it to 0.4877; hence tan 26°40' = 0.4877 + $\frac{2}{3}$ (0.0218) =
0.4877 + 0.0145 = 0.5022.

Example 2. Find the value of tan 58°24'.

$$\begin{aligned}
\tan 58° &= 1.6003 \\
\tan 59° &= \underline{1.6643} \\
\text{difference} &= 0.0640
\end{aligned}$$

$$\begin{aligned}
^{24}\!/_{60}\ (0.0640) &= 0.0256 \\
\tan 58° 24' &= 1.6003 + 0.0256 = 1.6259.
\end{aligned}$$

Example 3. Find angle x, if tan $x = 0.8205$. From the table

$$\begin{aligned}
0.8098 &= \tan 39° \\
\underline{0.8391} &= \tan 40° \\
0.0293 &= \text{difference}
\end{aligned}$$

$$\begin{aligned}
0.8098 &= \tan 39° \\
\underline{0.8205} &= \tan x \\
0.0107 &= \text{difference}
\end{aligned}$$

$$\left(\frac{0.0107}{0.0293}\right) (60) = 21.9 \text{ minutes; hence } x = 39° 22'.$$

Example 4. Find angle ϕ if $\tan \phi = 4.9822$.

$$4.7046 = \tan 78°$$
$$\underline{5.1446 = \tan 79°}$$
$$0.4400 = \text{difference}$$

$$4.7046 = \tan 78°$$
$$\underline{4.9822 = \tan \phi}$$
$$0.2776 = \text{difference}$$

$$\left(\frac{0.2776}{0.4400}\right)(60) = 37.9'; \text{ hence } \phi = 78° \, 38'.$$

using tangent ratios

With a table of tangent ratios at hand, many simple practical problems in indirect measurement can readily be solved.

Example 1. An observer at P, whose eyes are 5 feet above the ground, notes that the "angle of elevation" of the top of a tower is 32°. From where he is standing to the base of the tower is 342 feet. How high is the tower?

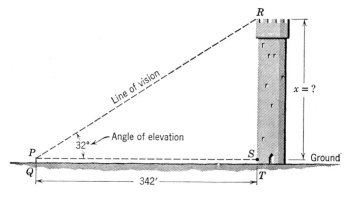

Fig. 8-55

Let the distance RS be represented by x feet. Then

$$\tan 32° = \frac{x}{342}.$$

From the table, we find $\tan 32° = 0.6249$;

$$\text{so, } \frac{x}{342} = 0.6249, \text{ or } x = (342)(0.6249).$$

Rounding to 3 significant figures,

$$x = (342)(0.625) = 213.75, \text{ or } 214 \text{ feet.}$$

Hence the tower is $5 + 214 = 219$ feet high.

Example 2. From the top of a cliff 195 feet high, an observer finds that the "angle of depression" ($\measuredangle PQR$) of a steamship at sea is $12°$ $30'$. How far out from the base of the cliff is the steamship?

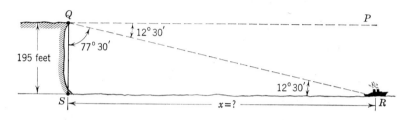

Fig. 8-56

$$\measuredangle PQR = \measuredangle QRS \text{ (Why?)}$$

$$\tan 12° = 0.2126$$
$$\tan 13° = \underline{0.2309}$$
$$\text{difference} = 0.0183$$

$${}^{30}\!/_{60}(0.0183) = 0.0092$$
$$\tan 12° 30' = 0.2126 + 0.0092 = 0.2218.$$

$$\frac{195}{x} = \tan 12° 30' = 0.2218,$$

$$\text{or} \quad x = \frac{195}{0.2218}.$$

Rounding to 3 significant figures and dividing:

$$x = \frac{195}{0.222} = 878 \text{ feet, to 3-figure accuracy.}$$

Note: The necessity for an awkward division can be avoided by using the following procedure.

$$\measuredangle RQS = 77° 30' \text{ (Why?)}$$
$$\tan 77° 30' = 4.5181.$$

$$\frac{x}{195} = \tan 77° 30', \text{ or } x = (195)(4.5181).$$

Rounding to 3 significant figures:

$$x = (195)(4.52) = 881 \text{ feet, to 3-figure accuracy.}$$

Why is this answer slightly different from the first answer, 878 feet?

Example 3. Find $\angle A$ and $\angle B$ in the right triangle ABC if $AC = 9$ feet and $BC = 42$ feet.

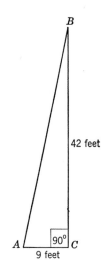

$$\tan A = \frac{42}{9} = 4.6667$$

$$
\begin{aligned}
\tan 77° &= 4.3315 \\
\tan 78° &= \underline{4.7046} \\
\text{difference} &= 0.3731
\end{aligned}
$$

$$
\begin{aligned}
\tan 77° &= 4.3315 \\
\tan A &= \underline{4.6667} \\
\text{difference} &= 0.3352
\end{aligned}
$$

$$\left(\frac{0.3352}{0.3731}\right)(60) = 53.9; \ \angle A = 77° \, 54'.$$

$$\angle B = 90° - 77° \, 54' = 12° \, 6'.$$

Fig. 8-57

EXERCISE 8–7

1. Find the tangent of:

(a) 17° 30'   (b) 43° 10'   (c) 66° 20'
(d) 50° 40'   (e) 38° 45'   (f) 12° 12'

2. Find the angle whose tangent is:

(a) 1.0724   (b) 0.2493   (c) 6.25
(d) 0.2000   (e) 0.0600   (f) 3.5000

3. When the angle of elevation of the sun is 48°, a tower 85 feet high will cast a shadow how long? (Fig. 8–58)

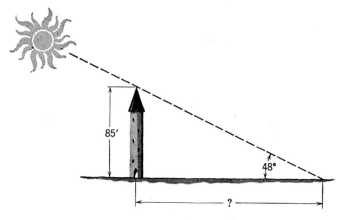

Fig. 8-58

4. A man standing at A, one mile from C, sights an airplane at B. If the angle of elevation is 4°, how far above the ground is the plane?

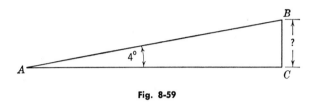

Fig. 8-59

5. The gable roof of a shed is 44 feet wide. The rafters make an angle of 22° with the horizontal. How high above the crossbeams is the ridgepole? Find AB in Fig. 8–60.

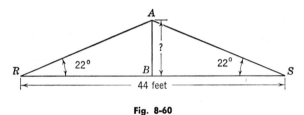

Fig. 8-60

6. When a helicopter is directly over a certain groundmarker at M, an observer at S, 500 yards from M, finds that the angle of elevation is 68°. How high is the helicopter?

7. Given right triangle ABC, with $AC = 4.2$ and $BC = 9.5$; find $\angle A$, $\angle B$ and AB in Fig. 8–61.

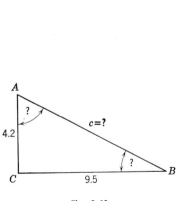

Fig. 8-61

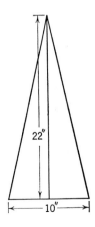

Fig. 8-62

8. Given the base of an isosceles triangle equal to 10 inches and the altitude, 22 inches; find the base angles and the vertex angle (Fig. 8-62).

9. The Empire State Building in New York is about 1250 feet high. If from the top of the building, the angle of depression to Washington Square Arch is 9°, about how far from the base of the Empire State building is the Arch?

10. In this railroad trestle, $AB = 40$ feet, and AC makes an angle of 56° with AB. Find the length of BC; also, the length of AC.

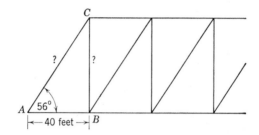

Fig. 8-63

the sine and cosine ratios

Any pair of sides of a right triangle may be used to form a ratio which then becomes a measure of either acute angle. For example, just as the ratio

$$\tan A = \frac{a}{b} = \frac{\text{opposite side}}{\text{adjacent side}}$$

is a measure of angle A, so two other ratios can be used as measures of angle A:

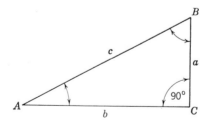

Fig. 8-64

1. Sine of angle A: $\sin A = \dfrac{a}{c} = \dfrac{\text{opposite side}}{\text{hypotenuse}}$;

2. Cosine of angle A: $\cos A = \dfrac{b}{c} = \dfrac{\text{adjacent side}}{\text{hypotenuse}}$.

The numerical values of these functions are given to four decimal places in the table on page **270**.

Study the diagram and the definitions once more, and you will see that these three statements are also true:

1. $\tan B = \dfrac{b}{a}$;   2. $\sin B = \dfrac{b}{c}$;   3. $\cos B = \dfrac{a}{c}$.

Remember, the side that is opposite $\angle A$ is adjacent to $\angle B$, and the side that is adjacent to $\angle A$ is opposite $\angle B$.

Note also that in a right triangle ABC whose acute angles are A and B that

$$\begin{cases} \sin A = \cos B, \\ \cos A = \sin B. \end{cases} \qquad \begin{cases} \tan A = \dfrac{1}{\tan B}, \\[2mm] \tan B = \dfrac{1}{\tan A}. \end{cases}$$

using sines and cosines

Example 1. Find the base (BC) and altitude (h) of an isosceles triangle whose vertex angle at A is $38°$ and whose equal sides are each 20 inches long.

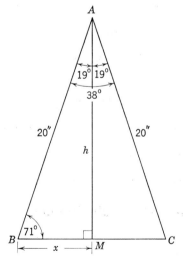

Fig. 8-65

Angle $BAM = \frac{1}{2}$ of $\angle BAC$, or 19° (Why?)

BM, or x, equals half the base BC.

$\dfrac{h}{20} = \sin 71°; \sin 71° = 0.9455;$

so, $h = (20)(0.9455) = 18.9$ inches, or 19 inches.

$\dfrac{x}{20} = \cos 71°; \cos 71° = 0.3256;$

so, $x = (20)(0.3256) = 6.51$ inches, or 6.5 inches, and $BC = 2x = 13$ inches.

Example 2. The radius of a circle is 3.28 inches. The chord PR subtends an angle of 108° at the center ($\angle POR = 108°$). Find (a) the length of chord PR, and (b) the distance from M to O.

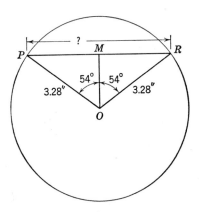

Fig. 8-66

(a) $\dfrac{PM}{3.28} = \sin 54° = 0.8090$, or $0.809;$

$PM = (3.28)(0.809) = 2.65$ inches, and $PR = 5.30$ inches.

(b) $\dfrac{OM}{3.28} = \cos 54° = 0.5878$, or $0.588;$

$OM = (3.28)(0.588) = 1.93$ inches.

finding the angles of a right triangle

It is easy to see how these functions can also be used to find the acute angles of a right triangle.

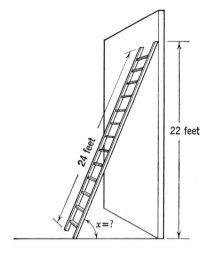

Fig. 8-67

Example 1. A 24-foot ladder leaning against a wall reaches a point 22 feet above the ground. What angle does the base of the ladder make with the ground?

$$\sin x = \frac{22}{24} = \frac{11}{12} = 0.9167.$$

From the table:

$$\sin 66° = 0.9135$$
$$\sin 67° = 0.9205$$

Interpolating, $x = 66°\ 27'$.

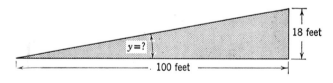

Fig. 8-68

Example 2. A ramp rises 18 feet vertically in a horizontal distance of 100 feet. Find the angle of inclination (Fig. 8–68).

$$\tan y = \frac{18}{100} = 0.1800.$$

$$\tan 10° = 0.1763$$
$$\tan 11° = 0.1944$$

Interpolating, $y = 10°\ 12'$.

EXERCISE 8–8

1. The base of an isosceles triangle is 18 inches, and its vertex angle is 100°. Find (a) the length of each of the equal sides, and (b) the altitude of the triangle.

2. Find the side of an equilateral triangle whose altitude is 20 inches.

3. A rectangle is 24 inches × 18 inches. Find the angle between the diagonal and the long side.

4. The altitude of an isosceles triangle is 24 inches and the base (AB) is 8 inches. Find the length of AC and BC, and the angles at A, B, and C.

5. The slope of a roof is 5 inches in each horizontal foot. What angle does it make with the horizontal?

6. A chord AB of a circle is 20 inches, and its central angle AOB is 140°. Find (a) the radius AO, and (b) the distance of the chord from the center of the circle.

7. A road rises 23 feet in a horizontal distance of 100 feet. How much will the road rise in a distance of 2000 feet measured along the roadway?

8. Find the area of a parallelogram whose sides are 6 inches and 8 inches and include an angle of 40°.

9. The bases of an isosceles trapezoid are 10 inches and 18 inches. If the base angles are each 66°, find the equal sides and the altitude (Fig. 8–69).

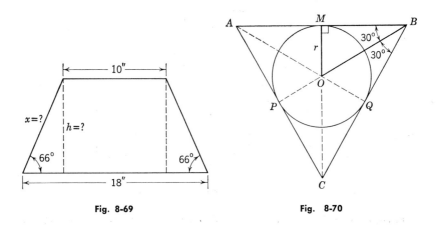

Fig. 8-69   Fig. 8-70

10. Find the radius of a circle inscribed in an equilateral triangle whose perimeter is 60 inches. (How long are AB, MB in Fig. 8–70?)

11. Find the area of a regular polygon of 12 sides inscribed in a circle whose radius is 100 feet.

12. Two adjacent sides of a parallelogram are 6 in. and 8 in., and the included angle is 112°. Find the area.

PRACTICAL APPLICATIONS

projections and vectors

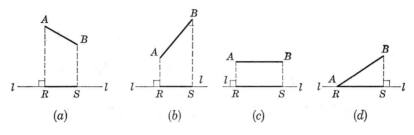

Fig. 8-71

In science and mechanics we frequently use the idea of horizontal and vertical projections. The projection of a line segment upon a line is the segment on the second line included between the feet of the perpendiculars drawn to the second line from the ends of the first segment. For example: in each of the parts of Fig. 8-71, RS is the projection of segment AB upon line ll. Since ll is a horizontal line in these instances, RS is called the horizontal projection of AB. Similarly, the segments PQ are the vertical projections of AB upon line ll.

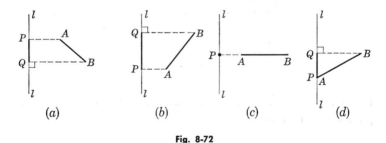

Fig. 8-72

Notice that as the slope of a given segment changes, the length of its projection changes. The maximum length of the projection occurs when the original segment is parallel to the line upon which it is projected. The length of the projection then equals the length of the segment.

The more oblique the segment is to the original line, the shorter its
projection. When the segment is at its maximum steepness, that is,
perpendicular to the line, the projection is at its minimum and then
becomes a point, or a segment of zero length (Fig. 8-73).

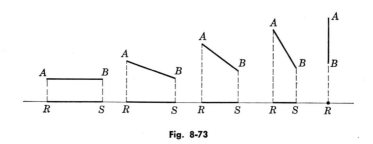

Fig. 8-73

Problems in mechanics and physics often require the use of projections of vectors upon horizontal and vertical axes.

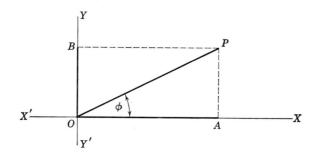

Fig. 8-74

In Fig. 8-74, the projection of OP upon the XX' axis equals OA; the
projection of OP upon the YY' axis is OB.

But $$\frac{OA}{OP} = \cos \phi, \text{ or } OA = (OP)(\cos \phi),$$

and $$\frac{OB}{OP} = \sin \phi, \text{ or } OB = (OP)(\sin \phi).$$

So we see that

horizontal projection of $OP = (OP)(\cos \phi)$,
vertical projection of $OP = (OP)(\sin \phi)$.

This leads to two simple but important rules about projections:

1. The horizontal projection of any line segment equals the length of the segment multiplied by the cosine of the angle of inclination, or the angle with the horizontal.

2. The vertical projection of any line segment equals the length of the segment multiplied by the sine of the angle of inclination.

component forces and velocities

These principles can be applied to the component parts of forces or velocities acting obliquely to the horizontal and vertical directions. If PR represents a force F acting at an angle of inclination ϕ, the two perpendicular component forces F_x and F_y are equivalent, when taken together, to the single original force F. Saying that they are "equivalent" means that F_x and F_y acting at the same time, would produce the same effect as F acting alone. The force F is called the *resultant* of F_x and F_y. The forces F_x and F_y are called the horizontal

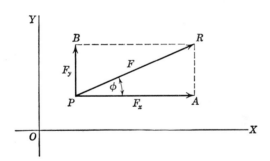

Fig. 8-75

and vertical components, respectively, of the force F. From what we have already learned, it is easy to see that

$$F_x = F \cos \phi,$$
$$\text{and} \quad F_y = F \sin \phi.$$

We can also see that, since

$$F_y = PB = RA,$$
$$\text{and since } (PA)^2 + (AR)^2 = (PR)^2,$$
$$\text{then, } F_x^2 + F_y^2 = F^2.$$

These simple relations are helpful in solving problems about forces and velocities. We have already solved similar problems by using scale drawings.

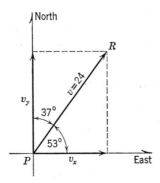

Fig. 8-76

Example 1. A ship is steering a course N. 37° E. at 24 miles per hour. Where will it be one hour after leaving point P? (See Fig. 8–76.)

Here $\qquad v = 24$, and $\phi = 90° - 37° = 53°$.

So, $\qquad v_x = v \cos \phi = (24)(\cos 53°)$
$\qquad\qquad\qquad = (24)(0.6018) = 14.4$ miles

and $v_y = v \sin \phi = (24)(\sin 53°)$
$\qquad\qquad\qquad = (24)(0.7986) = 19.2$ miles.

At the end of one hour, the ship will be 14.4 miles east of point P and 19.2 miles north of point P.

Check: $(14.4)^2 + (19.2)^2 = (24)^2$,
or $207.36 + 368.64 = 576$.

Example 2. A trailer is fastened to a car, as shown at an angle of 16°. If the car exerts a pull of 1000 pounds in the direction of PR, with how much force is the trailer actually pulled forward horizontally? What is the force tending to lift the trailer vertically upwards?

Fig. 8-77

$F_x = F \cos 16°$
$\quad = (1000)(0.9613)$
$\quad = 961$ pounds, forward pull.
$F_y = F \sin 16°$
$\quad = (1000)(0.2756) = 276$ pounds, upward pull.

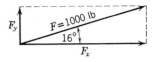

Fig. 8-78

Example 3. A block of metal weighing 500 grams is resting on an inclined plane which makes an angle of 22° with the horizontal. Find (a) the force F tending to pull the block down along the incline, and (b) the force N with which the block presses perpendicularly against the incline. If the angle at $A = 22°$, then the angle ROQ also equals 22° (Triangle ABC is similar to $\triangle ROQ$).

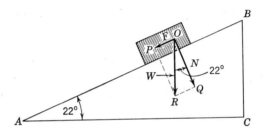

Fig. 8-79

So,
$$\frac{RQ}{OR} = \sin 22°, \text{ or } RQ = (OR)(\sin 22°).$$

But
$RQ = OP =$ force F; and $OR =$ force W;
so, $F = W \sin 22°$
$\quad = (500)(0.4040) = 202$ grams

Also,
$$\frac{OQ}{OR} = \cos 22°, \text{ or } OQ = (OR)(\cos 22°).$$

But
$OQ =$ force N;
so, $N = W \cos 22°$
$\quad = (500)(0.9272) = 464$ grams

EXERCISE 8–9

1. A plane is headed north at the rate of 220 miles per hour; at the same time, a 40-mile-per-hour wind is blowing from the west. What is the speed of the plane relative to the ground? In what direction is the plane actually moving? (Fig. 8–80, following page.)

2. A man rows a boat directly across a river, but the current carries him downstream at the rate of 240 feet per minute. At the end of one minute he has covered a distance of 480 feet. What was his rate of rowing (feet per minute)? Hint: First find angle ϕ (Fig. 8–81, following page).

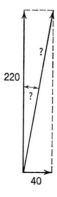

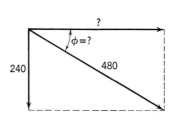

Fig. 8-80   Fig. 8-81

3. A plane is flying northwest (N 45° W) at the rate of 250 miles per hour. At what rate is it moving northward? at what rate, westward?

4. The horizontal and vertical components of a force acting on an object are 30 pounds and 40 pounds, respectively. Find the original force, and its direction of action.

5. What is the side of the largest square that can be cut from a circular disc 6.8 inches in diameter?

6. A chord of a circle is 28 inches long. The perpendicular distance from the center of the chord to the center of the circle is 8.4 inches. Find (a) the radius of the circle, and (b) the central angle subtended by the chord.

7. Five holes are equally spaced on a circle whose radius is 20 inches. Find the center-to-center distance AB between any two adjacent holes.

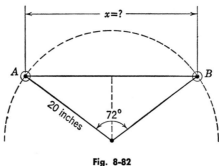

Fig. 8-82

8. Describe the principle and use of the hypsometer-clinometer.

9. Find out and report to the class on the method used by Eratosthenes (*circa* 200 B.C.) to measure the circumference of the earth. (See Hogben, page 233 ff.)

10. Discuss the nature and use of each of the following: (*a*) astrolabe; (*b*) transit; (*c*) sextant; (*d*) angle mirror; (*e*) theodolite; (*f*) alidade.

FOR FURTHER READING AND STUDY

1. Axelrod, Aaron. *Machine Shop Mathematics*. New York: McGraw-Hill, 1951. Chapter 6: "Shop Trigonometry."
2. Boyer, L. E. *An Introduction to Mathematics: A Historical Development*. New York: H. Holt, 1956. Chapters 24 and 25: "Trigonometry."
3. Gardner, Randolph. *Instruments for the Enrichment of Secondary School Mathematics*. Ann Arbor, Mich.: Edwards Bros., 1951.
4. Hogben, Lancelot. *Mathematics for the Million*. New York: W. W. Norton, 1937. Chapter 6: "The Size of the World, or What We Can Do with Trigonometry."
5. Hooper, A. *The River Mathematics*. New York: H. Holt, 1945. Chapters 9, 10, 12: "Earth Measurement; Trigonometry."
6. James, E. J. *The Teaching of Modern School Mathematics*. Oxford University Press, 1958. Chapter 12: "Surveying; Mapwork; Navigation." Chapter 13: "Sun and Shadows: Astronomy."
7. Kline, Morris. *Mathematics in Western Culture*. New York: Oxford University Press, 1953. Chapter 5: "Placing a Yardstick to the Stars."
8. McSwain, E. T. and Cooke, Ralph J. *Understanding and Teaching Arithmetic in the Elementary School*. New York: H. Holt, 1958. Chapter 10: "Meaning and Use of Measures and Measurement."
9. Shuster, C. N. and Bedford, F. L. *Field Work in Mathematics*. New York: American Book Company, 1935. Chapters 8 and 9.

CHAPTER 9

Functions and Graphs

Everyone knows what a curve is, until
he has studied enough mathematics to
become confused through the countless
number of possible exceptions.

> —Felix Klein: *Elementary*
> *Mathematics from an*
> *Advanced Standpoint*

VARIABLES, RELATIONS, AND FUNCTIONS

relations once more

We have already learned something about the nature of mathematical relations. As used in the everyday vernacular, the meaning
of the word relation is rather broad and somewhat loose. In mathematics, the word relation concerns a scheme (whether explicit or
implied) whereby it becomes possible to answer a specific question
with regard to specific items, as, for example: (*a*) Is $3 < 8$? (*b*)
Is A an ancestor of B? (*c*) Is 7 the square root of 49? You will
perhaps recall that, in rigorous terms, a mathematical relation is a
set of ordered pairs. This simply means that if a given relation is
represented by R, and if (x, y) is an ordered pair of elements, the

order pair (x, y) may or may not belong to the set R. For example, if the relation R is "greater than," and we consider the ordered pair $(6, 2)$, then $(6, 2)$ is an element of R, or $(6, 2)$ ϵ $>$. We may also say that xRy, or $6 > 2$. Clearly the order of the objects in the pair is crucial; thus $(2, 6)$ is not an element of the relation "greater than," since $2 < 6$. In other words, we must give our attention to which is the "first" of an ordered pair and which is the "second." One can think of a relation between x's and y's such that a given x may have several different y's; for example, if R should mean "is an ancestor of," then in xRy, xRy', xRy'', y might represent the son of x, y' the grandson of x, and y'' the great-grandson. Thus in some relations, two or more ordered pairs may have the same first element, but different second elements. In other relations, the same second element of several ordered pairs may have different first elements. For example, in aRb, where R means "is a descendant of," we may have aRb, $a'Rb$, and $a''Rb$.

It is also true that there are relations in which no two ordered pairs have the same first element and different second elements. Consider these examples.

1. The ages of the pupils in a given class:

Alice	15
Billy	16
Charles	14
Diana	15
etc.	

2. The cost of screw-drivers:

4-inch screw driver	25¢
5-inch screw driver	35¢
6-inch screw driver	49¢
8-inch screw driver	69¢
etc.	

3. The squares of the natural numbers:

1	1
2	4
3	9
4	16
etc.	

In each of these relations, when the first element of a pair is known, there is no doubt as to what the second element is, since only one pair in the relation in question has the specified first element. (The fact that different first elements may have the same second element is immaterial.) Any relation in which the first element of every ordered pair has a unique second element is called a *function*. In other words, a function is a special kind of a relation—one in which with a given first element, there are never two different second elements.[1]

variable and domain

The statement that "Jefferson was a signer of the Declaration of Independence" is a true statement. If we replace "Jefferson" by a blank, we obtain what is called an open sentence:

"—————— was a signer of the Declaration of Independence."

This open sentence is neither true nor false; it becomes true or false depending upon what is substituted for the blank. If we replace the blank with "Hancock" or "Franklin," it is true; if we substitute "Lincoln" or "Roosevelt" for the blank, it is false. In mathematics we usually use letters or other symbols instead of blanks in such open sentences; for example,

$$x \text{ is a man}$$
$$y - 5 = 8$$
$$z < 3$$
$$\square + 6 = 10$$
$$y^2 - 8y + 15 = 0$$

A letter or symbol used in this way is called a *variable*. A variable should be thought of as a *placeholder* for any one of a given set of elements.[2] The set of elements is very often some set of numbers. For example, the set of all odd numbers,

$$S = \{1, 3, 5, 7, \ldots\},$$

may be represented by the sentence "$2x + 1$ is an odd number." Here x is a variable; it is a symbol which can be replaced by any element

---

[1] Some authorities use the term function in the broader sense to include all relations. What has been here defined as a function is then called a "single-valued function."

[2] Such traditional characterizations of a variable as a "general number," a "literal number," an "unknown quantity," or a "number which may take on any value" are to be avoided, since they lack logical rigor and are ambiguous or confusing, if not meaningless.

of the set of natural numbers $N = \{1, 2, 3, 4, \ldots\}$. Substituting any element of set N for the variable x will identify an element in set S.

In order to understand the full significance of the concept of a variable, we must also give attention to the set of elements which may be substituted for the variable. This set of possible replacements for the variable is called the *domain* of the variable. When dealing with a variable, it is important that the domain of the variable be clearly stated. Thus: $2x + 1$ is an algebraic expression; x is a variable; the domain of the variable x might be the set of natural numbers. Or again: in the expression $y + 3\frac{1}{2}$, the variable is y, and its domain might be the set of positive integers and fractions. In short, a symbol in a mathematical expression is a variable if and only if it can be replaced by an element of a specified set of elements called the domain of the variable. More specifically, a variable is a symbol which is replaceable by a number. The set of numbers that can be dubbed in for the variable constitutes the domain of the variable. When a particular number has been substituted for the variable in a given expression, the number so obtained is called the *value* of the expression for that particular replacement of the variable.

The importance of the domain of a variable cannot be over-emphasized. The question as to what are the possible replacements of a variable is crucial. Consider the statement $x + 3 = 8$. If the universal set S—the totality of numbers to be considered—consists of the set of natural numbers, then the sentence $x + 3 = 8$ divides S into two subsets, one of which contains all the substitutions for x that make $x + 3 = 8$ a true statement, and the other containing all the substitutions that make $x + 3 = 8$ false. Here the first subset contains only one element, 5. This element is the only natural number which makes the sentence true. Thus the sentence $x + 3 = 8$ may be thought of as a *set-selector;* it selects, from the set of numbers under consideration, only those numbers which make the sentence true when they are substituted for the variable. The set so selected is called the *solution set* of the sentence. For example, in the sentence $x + 8 = 3$, if S is the set of integers, then the solution set is the integer -5; if S is taken as the set of natural numbers, then the sentence $x + 8 = 3$ has no solution set; it is neither true nor false.

more about ordered pairs

You will recall from an earlier chapter (page 90) that the points in a plane may be identified by ordered pairs of numbers, such as

(5, 3) or (6, −2). Such numbers are called the Cartesian coordinates of the ordered pairs, or simply the *coordinates*. Thus, in the ordered pair (5, 3), we consider 5 the "first," and 3 the "second"; in the pair (x, y), x is the first and y is the second. Sets of ordered pairs can be derived from any set of numbers, say $S = \{1, 2, 3, 4\}$; for example,

(1, 1)	(2, 1)	(3, 1)	(4, 1)
(1, 2)	(2, 2)	(3, 2)	(4, 2)
(1, 3)	(2, 3)	(3, 3)	(4, 3)
(1, 4)	(2, 4)	(3, 4)	(4, 4)

This new set of 16 ordered pairs is the Cartesian set of S and is expressed as $S \times S$. It can be represented graphically, using the idea of coordinates, in the familiar manner shown below, where the set of ordered pairs $S \times S$ is pictured by a network or lattice of 16 points.

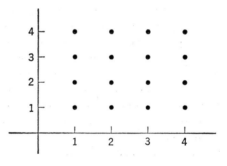

Fig. 9-1

If $S' = \{1, 2, 3, 4, 5, \ldots\}$, then the set of ordered pairs $S' \times S'$ is represented by all points with positive integral coordinates. If S'' is the set of all real numbers, the graphic representation of $S'' \times S''$ is the entire plane. There is exactly one point of the plane corresponding to each element of the set $S'' \times S''$ and there is exactly one element of $S'' \times S''$ corresponding to each point of the plane.

Ordered pairs are useful when dealing with sentences involving two variables, such as

(1) $x - 3 = y$; (2) $y = x^2 + 4$; (3) $x + 1 < y$.

As they stand, such sentences are neither true nor false; but with appropriate substitutions they may be true. Thus (1) becomes a true sentence when $x = 7$ and $y = 4$; similarly, (2) is true when $x = 3$ and $y = 13$. In other words, to make such sentences true, an ordered pair of numbers is required. Any ordered pair that makes the sentence true is called a *solution* of the sentence, and the set of all such ordered pairs is called the *solution set* of the sentence. The ordered pairs (3, 13), (−3, 13) are but two elements of the solution set of equation 2. Thus sentences in two variables may be regarded as set-selectors. Sentences in two variables may also be regarded as expressing a relation that may or may not hold for the coordinates of an ordered pair (x, y) belonging to a given set $S \times S$.

Example 1. Consider the relation $x < y$. If $S = \{1, 2, 3\}$, and $S \times S$ consists of a lattice of 9 points, the relation $x < y$ singles out a subset of just 3 points, or ordered pairs, namely (1, 2), (1, 3), (2, 3). We can think of the relation R, that is, $x < y$, as that subset consisting of exactly those ordered pairs (x, y) of $S \times S$ in which x is less than y. (See Fig. 9–2.)

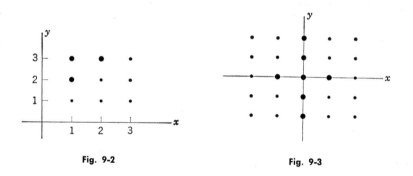

Fig. 9-2   Fig. 9-3

Example 2. Consider the relation $x^2 + y < 3$. If $S = \{-2, -1, 0, 1, 2\}$, and $S \times S$ consists of 25 points, then the relation $x^2 + y < 3$ singles out the subset of those seven points or ordered pairs (x, y) in which it is true that $x^2 + y < 3$; namely (0, 0), (0, 1), (0, 2), (0, −1), (0, −2), (1, 0) and (−1, 0). (See Fig. 9–3.)

Example 3. The relation $x = 4$, where S is the set of all real numbers, selects the subset of all ordered pairs (x, y) in which the first coordinate is 4, namely, the set

$$\{ \ldots (4, -3), (4, -2), (4, -1), (4, 0), (4, 1), (4, 2), (4, 3) \ldots \}.$$

This subset of the set of ordered pairs of all real numbers $S \times S$ is represented by the continuous line AB, parallel to the axis of the y's, and extending indefinitely both ways (Fig. 9–4).

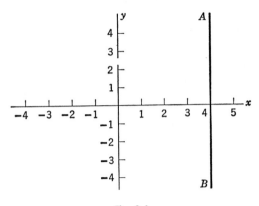

Fig. 9-4

Example 4. Again considering S as the set of all real numbers, the relation $x = -y$ selects the subset of all ordered pairs (x, y) in which x and y are inverse numbers (that is, "numerically equal but opposite in sign"). The graph of the relation $x = -y$ is thus the continuous line AB, extending indefinitely both ways (Fig. 9–5).

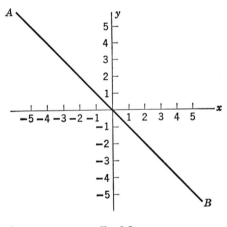

Fig. 9-5

Example 5. Taking S as the set of all real numbers, the relation $y = x^2$ yields the subset of ordered pairs represented by the totality of points on the continuous curve shown, which extends "upwards both ways" indefinitely (Fig. 9–6).

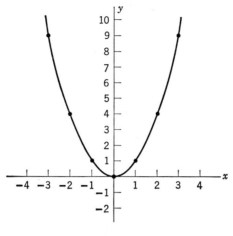

Fig. 9-6

domain and range

We speak of a subset of $S \times S$ as *a relation in S*. A relation may be designated by the letter R, as we have already seen. If we have a relation R in S, then R is a set of ordered pairs (x, y). The subset of S for which x is a placeholder, that is, the numbers that may be substituted for x, is called the *domain* of the relation. The subset of S for which y is a placeholder—the numbers that may be substituted for y—is called the *range* of the relation. Thus we have, in the foregoing examples:

Example	Domain	Range
1.	$\{1, 2\}$	$\{2, 3\}$
2.	$\{-1, 0, 1\}$	$\{-2, -1, 0, 1, 2\}$
3.	$\{4\}$	set of real numbers
4.	set of real numbers	set of real numbers
5.	set of real numbers	set of positive real numbers and 0.

The domain and range of a relation may consist of a number of isolated points, either finite or infinite, in which both the domain and range, as well as the graph, are characterized as *discrete,* as in examples 1 and 2. If, on the other hand, there are no points "missing" in the domain and range, the domain and range as well as the graph are said to be *continuous.* We thus think of a continuous curve as a smooth curve with no "gaps"; admittedly this language describes the ideas from an intuitive standpoint rather than the standpoint of logical rigor, but it will suffice for our purpose here.

functions

As already intimated, a *function* is a special kind of relation, to wit, one in which for each x in the domain of the relation, there is *one and only one* y in the range such that (x, y) belongs to the relation. This is suggested by the following graphs (Figs. 9-7, 9-8), in which we are concerned only with functions of x.

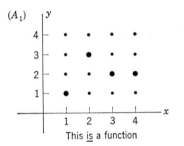

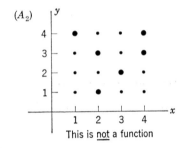

Fig. 9-7

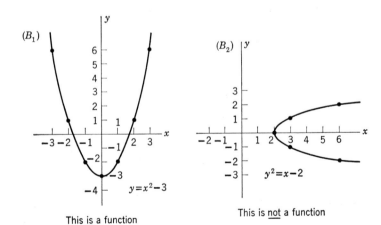

Fig. 9-8

Stated more formally: *A function in S is a relation in S such that for every x in the domain of the relation, there is exactly one corre-*

sponding y in the range of the relation. Or, to put it another way, a function in S is a set of ordered pairs (x, y) which belongs to $S \times S$, such that for each pair (x, y) there is one and only one y associated with the x. Thus in the relation $y = x^2 - 3$, we say that "y is a function of x," since to every x selected there corresponds one and only one y (the fact that two different x's may yield the same y is immaterial). But in the relation $y^2 = x - 2$ we cannot say that y is a function of x, since to any x there correspond *two* possible y's. However, if the relation in question is restated as $x = y^2 + 2$, then we can say that x is a function of y, since to every y there corresponds a unique x.[3]

A function, that is, a relation between variables, may be designated or specified in several different ways. The most commonly used methods, at least in elementary mathematics, are by means of (1) a *table*, (2) a *graph*, and (3) a *formula*. A table is simply a schematic arrangement for exhibiting ordered pairs of numbers. The numbers may represent empirical data, such as the population of a given community by years, or the sales volume by months. Or, the numbers may originate in some other way, as suggested in *b* and *c* below.

TABLE 6. Examples of Functions Expressed by Means of Tables

Year	(a) Number of TV sets (in millions)	(b) x	x^3	(c) x	$\sin x$
1948	0.9	0	0	0	0.000
1950	8.0	1	1	$\pi/6$	0.500
1952	22.0	2	8	$\pi/4$	0.707
1954	33.0	3	27	$\pi/3$	0.866
1956	42.2			$\pi/2$	1.000
		.	.	.	.
		.	.	.	.
		.	.	.	.

The graph is another common device for indicating a functional relation. It may be a curve drawn automatically by a recording instrument such as a barograph or a thermograph, which represent,

---

[3] When we consider y as a function of x in the relation $y = x^2 - 3$, we think of y as an *explicit* function. By writing $x = +\sqrt{y+3}$ and $x = -\sqrt{y+3}$, we could properly speak of x as an *implicit* function of y. Our definition of a function, as given above, clearly refers to explicit functions only.

respectively, the atmospheric pressure and temperature at a fixed place as a function of the time. Or the graph may be a curve drawn to fit a given table of paired values, where each ordered pair in the table is represented by a point in the lattice or in the plane, and the points are then "connected" by a broken line, a smooth curve, or a series of disconnected line segments.

EXAMPLES OF FUNCTIONS EXPRESSED BY MEANS OF GRAPHS

A third common way of expressing a functional relation is by means of a mathematical formula.

$$1.\ y = kx + b \qquad 2.\ y = ae^x \qquad 3.\ u = \frac{\log v}{v^2}$$

$$4.\ y = 2 \cos 2x \qquad 5.\ t = 2\pi \sqrt{\frac{l}{g}}$$

Such explicit symbolic statements of functional relations are called *analytic* expressions. The reader is cautioned, however, not to think of the formula as being the function—formulas merely help us to find the pairs of numbers which constitute the function.

functional notation

Since a functional relation is a collection of pairs of numbers, we may express a functional relation as

$$\{(x, y) \mid y = 3x + 5\},$$

which is read:

"the set of ordered pairs (x, y) such that $y = 3x + 5$."

Inasmuch as a function is a special relation which associates with each element x of its domain exactly one element y of its range, we often use the symbols $F(x)$ or $f(x)$ to denote the second element of the ordered pair whose first element is x. (The symbol $f(x)$ is read "f at x.") Thus the "f" represents the function, and we may write

$$f = \{(x, y) \mid 3x + 5\},$$
$$\text{or} \quad f(x) = 3x + 5$$
$$y = 3x + 5$$
$$y = f(x)$$

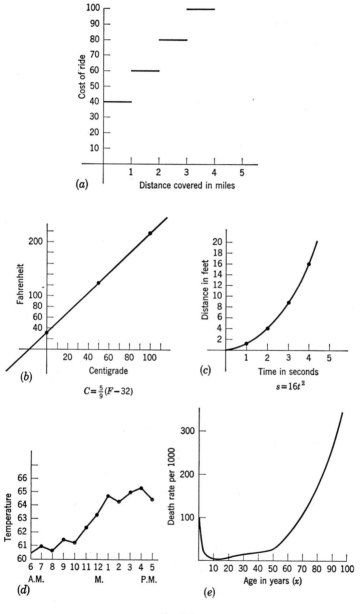

(a)

(b)

$C = \frac{5}{9}(F-32)$

(c)

$s = 16t^2$

(d)

(e)

Fig. 9-9

The variables x and y are said to be in functional relation, or "y is a function of x." Since the numbers representing the first element (x) of the ordered pairs are selected arbitrarily or at will, x is called the *independent* variable. The number which replaces the corresponding second element (y) is determined only after the x-number has been selected, and so y is called the *dependent* variable. The meaning of the conventional function notation will be clearer from the following examples.

$$\text{If} \quad f(x) = 3x + 5,$$
$$\text{then} \quad f(1) = 3(1) + 5 = 8$$
$$f(-4) = 3(-4) + 5 = {}^-7$$
$$f(\tfrac{1}{2}) = 3(\tfrac{1}{2}) + 5 = 6\tfrac{1}{2}$$
$$f(0) = 3(0) + 5 = 5$$

$$\text{Or again, if} \quad F(x) = x^2 - 2x + 1,$$
$$\text{then} \quad F(3) = (3)^2 - (2)(3) + 1 = 4$$
$$F(^-1) = (^-1)^2 - (2)(^-1) + 1 = 4$$
$$F(\tfrac{1}{10}) = (\tfrac{1}{10})^2 - 2(\tfrac{1}{10}) + 1 = 0.81$$

To summarize, we note the following points:

1. A function may be thought of as a set of ordered pairs of elements such that all the first elements are from one set and all the second elements are from another set, and no two pairs have equal first elements and unequal second elements.

2. A function may also be thought of as a rule which characterizes the relation explicitly so that the ordered pairs which constitute the function may readily be found.

3. The concept of function involves the idea of a domain, a range, and a rule.

4. The domain is the set of all first coordinates of the ordered pairs that comprise the function; these first coordinates are the numbers which may be used in the rule, or, they are the set of possible values of the independent variable.

5. The range is the set of all second coordinates of the ordered pairs that comprise the function. These second coordinates are the numbers obtained by following the rule, or, they are the set of possible values of the dependent variable.

6. The rule *is* the function, or set-selector. It assigns a unique second coordinate in the range to a given first coordinate in the domain.

7. A function (i.e., the rule) may be indicated by a table, a graph, or a formula.

8. A function may be denoted by the symbolism

$$y = F(x) = ax^2 + bx + c,$$
$$\text{or} \quad F = \{(x, y) \mid ax^2 + bx + c\}.$$

EXERCISE 9–1

1. If the set of all positive odd integers is represented by the expression $2n + 1$, what is the domain of the variable n?

2. Any two-digit numbers may be expressed as $10t + u$; what is the domain of the variable t? Of the variable u?

3. What is the set of integers which leave a remainder of 2 when divided by 5? If $n = 5k + 2$, and n is any one of these integers, what is the domain of the variable k? What are the corresponding values of n (that is, the corresponding values of the expression $5k + 2$)?

4. What is the difference in meaning (a) between (5, 7) and (7, 5)? (b) between (5, 7) and {5, 7}?

5. If $s = 16t^2$, and the domain of t is the set of natural numbers, write the first three corresponding values of s.

6. Find two or three values of the expression $x^2 - 2x$ when the domain is: (1) the set of positive integers; (2) the set of positive rationals; (3) the set of all positive real numbers.

7. What is the domain of r in the expression for simple interest, Prt, if the interest rate r may vary by steps of $\frac{1}{4}$ per cent and if r may not exceed 0.06?

8. Considering the universal set U as the set of all real numbers, as on the number line below, indicate verbally or geometrically

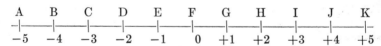

the domain of the variable in each of the following instances:

(a) $x - 1 < 4$ (b) $x^2 > 9$
(c) $x + 2 > 6$ (d) $3x$ is an odd integer
(e) $3x$ is an even integer   (f) $4 > x < 5$
(g) $4 < x < 5$ (h) $x < 4, x > 5$
(i) $4 < x > 5$ (j) $x < x + 1$

9. Explain the meaning of each of the following:

(a) $\{(x, y) \mid y = x^2 - 4\}$
(b) $\{(x, y) \mid y^2 = 4x\}$
(c) $\{(x, y) \mid x^2 + y^2 < 9\}$

10. (a) If $F(x) = x^2 + 2x - 4$, find $F(0); F(3); F(-5)$.
(b) If $f(u) = u^3 + 3u$, find $f(1); f(-3); f(\frac{1}{2}); f(0)$.
(c) If $y = f(x) = 10^x$, find $f(1); f(2); f(0); f(-2); f(\frac{1}{2})$.

11. (*a*) Which of the relations in Fig. 9–10 are functions either of x or y?
(*b*) State the domain and range of each relation.

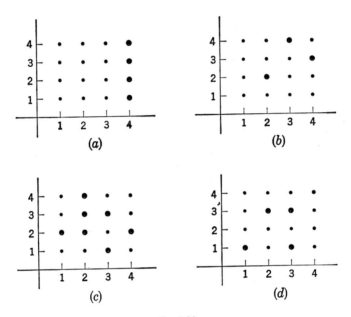

Fig. 9-10

12. The graphs below represent relations in which the universal set is the set of all real numbers. Which of these relations are functions of x? (Fig. 9–11.)

13. Given the universal set {0, 1, 2, 3, 4, 5}, for each of the following functions determine the domain and the range, and draw the graph:

(*a*) $F(x) = 2x - 3$ (*b*) $f(x) = 2x$
(*c*) $y = 4x^2$ (*d*) $F = \{(x, y) \mid x^2 + y^2 = 25\}$

14. Given the function $F(x) = x^2 + 2x - 1$, where the universal set is the set of real numbers:

(*a*) Find $F(1)$; $F(0)$; $F(-1)$; $F(3)$; $F(k)$; $F(\frac{1}{2})$; $F\left(\dfrac{1}{x}\right)$; $\dfrac{1}{F(x)}$.

(*b*) Draw the graph of $F(x)$.
(*c*) Determine the domain and the range of $F(x)$.

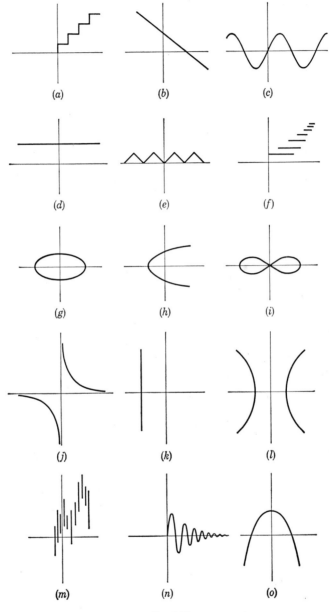

(a)

(b)

(c)

(d)

(e)

(f)

(g)

(h)

(i)

(j)

(k)

(l)

(m)

(n)

(o)

Fig. 9-11

ALGEBRAIC FUNCTIONS

linear functions; direct variation

As we have seen, the dependent variable of a function does not necessarily have to be an analytic expression in x. The function simply states that the relation is definite and that a method exists by which the uniquely associated y value can be determined for any given x. If, however, a function is defined by setting forth a finite number of indicated additions, subtractions, multiplications, divisions, powers, and root extractions upon a variable x, the resulting expression is an *algebraic function*. The following are algebraic functions:

(a) $px^2 + qx + r$

(b) $x^n + p_1x^{n-1} + p_2x^{n-2} + \ldots + p_{n-1}x + p_n$, where n is a positive integer

(c) $\dfrac{ax^2}{x+1}$

(d) $\sqrt{kx + 2}$

Here a and b are *integral*, *rational* functions of degree 2 and n,

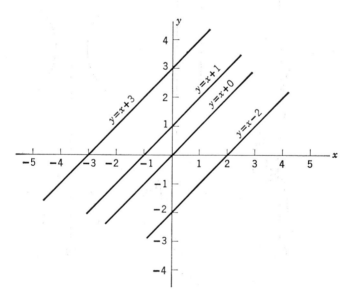

Fig. 9-12

respectively, and are also known as polynomial functions; c is a *rational* function of x, and d is an *irrational* function of x.

One of the simplest relations between two variables is that in which one of them is always more or less than the other, as in the relation $y = f(x) = x + b$, where b is a constant. Here the two variables differ by the constant amount b. That is, one variable is always b more than (or less than) the other. Figure 9-12 shows the function $f(x) = x + b$ for various values of b. The fact that these graphs are parallel (have the same slope) indicates that in each case the variables x and y are "changing" at the same rate; for each increase of one unit in the independent variable there is an increase of one unit in the dependent variable. Note also that by taking different values of the constant b we cause a corresponding horizontal shift in the position of the graph, but no change in its slope.

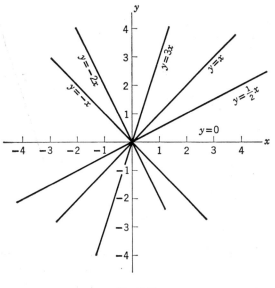

Fig. 9-13

Another simple relation between two variables is that in which one variable is always a given number of times as great as the other; or, $y = f(x) = kx$, where k is a constant. Figure 9-13 shows the function $f(x) = kx$ for various values of k. Note that by taking different values of the constant k we cause the slope to change, but that the graph always passes through the origin at $(0,0)$. Note also that there is no value of k for which the graph is the y axis, although when $k = 0$ the graph is the x axis. (Why?)

This type of relation is often called *direct variation*, and is illustrated by the relation between distance and time when the velocity is uniform $(s = vt)$, between the elongation of a spring and the force applied $(e = kF)$, between the electromotive force and the current when the resistance is constant $(E = RI)$, between volume and mass when the density is constant $(M = dV)$, between the volume and temperature of a gas when the pressure is constant $(V = kT)$, or between the simple interest on a fixed principal at a fixed rate $(I = Prt)$.

A more general form of relation is obtained by combining these two types, namely, functions of the form

$$y = f(x) = kx + b,$$

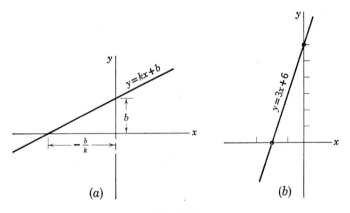

Fig. 9-14

graphs of which are shown below, Fig. 9-14, a and b. Such functions are called *linear functions*, since it can be proved (1) that the graph of every function of the type $y = kx + b$ is a straight line, and (2) that every straight line graph represents a function of the type $y = kx + b$. If $b = 0$, the relation is a simple direct variation. If $k = 0$, the graph is a straight line parallel to the x axis, showing that y is constant for all x's. In the function $y = kx + b$, the value of b is called the y-intercept; that is, the value of b indicates the value of y when $x = 0$, and therefore tells where the graph cuts across the y axis. The value of k indicates the slope of the graph. It tells the ratio of the vertical change to the horizontal change as we go from one point to another, as shown in the diagram (Fig. 9-15).

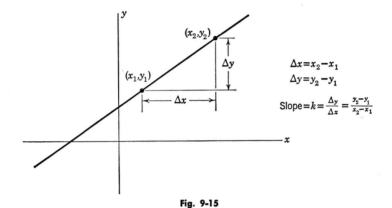

$$\Delta x = x_2 - x_1$$
$$\Delta y = y_2 - y_1$$
$$\text{Slope} = k = \frac{\Delta y}{\Delta x} = \frac{y_2 - y_1}{x_2 - x_1}$$

Fig. 9-15

It will be seen that the slope of any particular linear function is constant, since the right triangles so obtained for any pair of points are similar triangles.

Linear functions of the form $y = kx + b$ are exemplified by the following:

1. Final speed after constant acceleration has been acting for a time t, with initial velocity of v_o: thus $v = v_o + at$.

2. The relation between Fahrenheit and centigrate temperature readings: $F = \frac{9}{5}C + 32$.

3. The total amount due at simple interest when the principal and rate are fixed: $A = P + Prt$.

inverse variation

When one variable increases as the other decreases in such a way that their product is always constant, we have what is called *inverse variation*. Expressed algebraically, as an implicit function, we write $xy = k$; expressing y as an explicit function of x, we write $y = k/x$. In this form we see that the dependent variable varies directly as the reciprocal of the independent variable, or $y = k(1/x)$. The graph of this type of function is not a straight line; instead, it is one form of a curve known as an *hyperbola*. There are two parts or branches to the curve, neither of which ever touches either axis, although they keep

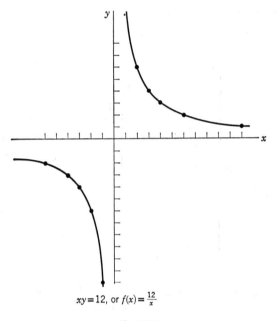

$xy = 12$, or $f(x) = \frac{12}{x}$

Fig. 9-16

getting closer and closer to the respective axes. The inverse relation is illustrated by the relation between the pressure and volume of a gas at constant temperature $(PV = k)$, by the relation between electric current and resistance when the voltage is constant $(IR = E)$, by the concentration of ions in chemical solution, as given by $[H^+] \cdot [OH^-]$

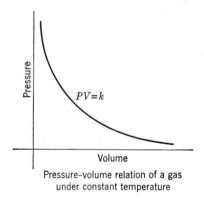

Pressure–volume relation of a gas
under constant temperature

Fig. 9-17

$= k$. Again, consider the familiar "time-rate-distance" relation, where, for a given fixed distance, the faster the rate, the less the time taken, or, the more time taken, the slower the rate:

$$r = \frac{D}{t}, \text{ where } r \text{ is a function of } t,$$

or $\quad t = \frac{D}{r}, \text{ where } t \text{ is a function of } r.$

the quadratic function

When two variables are related so that one varies directly as the square of the other, the relation is simply stated as $y = kx^2$. For example: the distance traversed by a freely falling body varies with the square of the time elapsed, and is given by (1) $s = \frac{1}{2}gt^2$; (2) the kinetic energy of a body in motion as given by $E = \frac{1}{2}Mv^2$; (3) the heat generated by an electric current flowing through a constant resistance, $H = I^2R$; (4) or the quantity of coal consumed by a steam locomotive, which depends upon the square of the speed, $c = kv^2$.

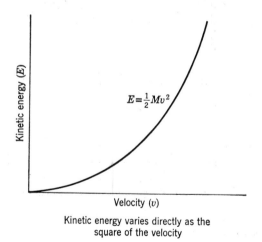

Kinetic energy varies directly as the square of the velocity

Fig. 9-18

The general form of the quadratic function is given by

$$y = f(x) = ax^2 + bx + c,$$

in which a, b, and c are constants, and $a \neq 0$. In this form, the graph is a parabola, an "open" curve which always has an axis of symmetry, although this need not be the x axis or the y axis. The parabola is illustrated by the path of a body thrown into space, neglecting air resistance: for example, a canon fired at an angle of elevation, a baseball pitch, or the particles of water from a hose nozzle or a fountain.

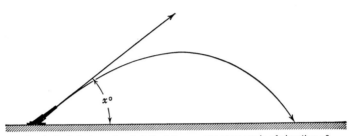

Parabolic-trajectory of a shell fired from a gun at an angle of elevation $x°$

Fig. 9-19

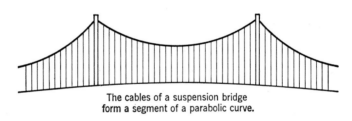

The cables of a suspension bridge
form a segment of a parabolic curve.

Fig. 9-20

Comets hurtling through space sometimes travel in a parabolic orbit. The cables of a suspension bridge, when carrying a uniformly loaded horizontal floor, assume the shape of a parabolic segment. Typical parabolas, together with their equations, are shown in Fig. 9-21.

power functions

Functions of the type $y = kx^n$, in which k is a constant and n is a real number, are known as *power functions*. Many physical quantities vary in accordance with a power law. When n is positive, we obtain parabolic type functions. If n is a positive integer greater than 1, the function becomes simply

$$y = kx^2, \quad \text{or} \quad y = kx^3, \quad \text{or} \quad y = kx^4, \quad \text{etc.}$$

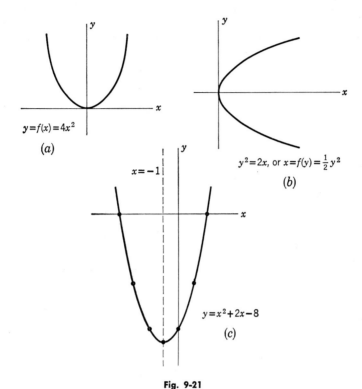

$y=f(x)=4x^2$

(a)

$x=-1$

$y^2=2x$, or $x=f(y)=\frac{1}{2}y^2$

(b)

$y=x^2+2x-8$

(c)

Fig. 9-21

If n is a positive fraction, we have

$$y = kx^{1/2}, \quad \text{or} \quad y = kx^{1/3}, \quad \text{or} \quad y = kx^{1/4}, \quad \text{etc.,}$$

which may also be expressed as

$$y = k\sqrt{x}, \quad \text{or} \quad y = k\sqrt[3]{x}, \quad \text{or} \quad y = k\sqrt[4]{x}, \quad \text{etc.}$$

When rewritten as a function of y, the relation becomes

$$x = Ky^2, \quad \text{where} \quad K = \frac{1}{k^2}, \quad \text{etc.}$$

If n is a negative integer or a negative fraction, we obtain hyperbolic type functions. Thus,

$$y = kx^{-1}, \quad \text{or} \quad y = \frac{k}{x}, \quad \text{or} \quad xy = k;$$

$$y = kx^{-2}, \quad \text{or} \quad y = \frac{k}{x^2}, \quad \text{or} \quad x^2y = k; \quad \text{etc.}$$

EXERCISE 9–2

1. Write the function whose graph is (a) a line parallel to the x axis and 3 units above it; (b) a line parallel to the y axis and 2 units to the left of it.

2. Write the function whose graph is the x axis; the y axis.

3. Draw the graph of the function $y = 4x - 6$; show that the slope of this function is constant by finding the ratio of the vertical to the horizontal change in going from $(2, 2)$ to $(4, 10)$, and from $(4, 10)$ to $(7, 22)$.

4. Explain why the slope of a linear function such as $y = kx + b$ is numerically equal to the tangent of the angle that the graph makes with the x axis.

5. (a) Plot the graph of the function $xy = 24$ for values of x: ± 2, ± 3, ± 4, ± 6, ± 8, ± 12. (b) Tell why the curve might appropriately be called a *rectangular* hyperbola. (c) What can you say of y when $x = 0$? of x, when $y = 0$?

6. Plot and discuss the graph of $F(x) = -12/x$, that is, $xy = -12$.

7. Plot and discuss the graphs of each of the following:

(a) $y = 2x^2$	(b) $y = x^2 - 4$
(c) $x = 4y^2$	(d) $y = x^2 - x - 6$
(e) $y = x^2 + x + 1$	(f) $y = x^2 - 6x + 9$

8. Draw the graphs of: (a) $y = x^3$; (b) $y = x^4$; (c) $y = x^{1/2}$; (d) $y = x^{3/2}$.

9. Draw the graphs of: $x = y^3$; $x = y^4$; $x = y^{1/2}$; $x = y^{3/2}$. Compare these curves with the curves for number 8.

10. Draw the graphs of: $y = 1/x$; $y = 1/x^2$; $y = 1/x^3$.

11. Prove that in any power function of x, if x changes by a fixed multiple, y must also change by a fixed multiple.

EXPONENTIAL FUNCTIONS

the exponential function

Consider exponential functions of the type $y = k^x$, in which k is a positive constant > 1, and the independent variable is an exponent. Take the simple case of $y = 2^x$; there is a vast difference between the functions $y = x^2$ and $y = 2^x$. They "grow" in different ways. The value of x^2 is quadrupled whenever x is multiplied by 2; but the value of 2^x is quadrupled whenever x is *merely increased* by 2. In the first instance, a larger and larger number is raised to a constant power. In the second instance, a constant is raised to a higher and higher power. These functions are not only different in form, they are different kinds of functions. A variable raised to a constant power is called a *power function.* It is an algebraic function. A constant raised to a variable power is called an *exponential function.*

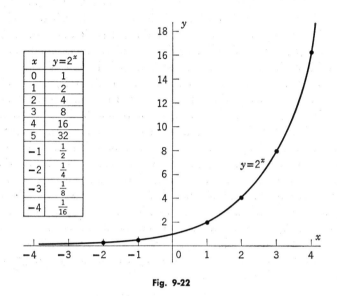

x	$y=2^x$
0	1
1	2
2	4
3	8
4	16
5	32
−1	$\frac{1}{2}$
−2	$\frac{1}{4}$
−3	$\frac{1}{8}$
−4	$\frac{1}{16}$

Fig. 9-22

Let us examine the graph in Fig. 9-22. At first the curve rises rather slowly; then, "gathering momentum," the rate of increase gradually becomes greater and greater. Indeed, the greater the value of x, the more rapidly y increases. In this respect, the growth of an exponential function resembles approximately the growth of money at compound interest (see Chapter 10). Hence variables that are related as in an exponential function are said to follow the *Compound Interest Law* (C.I.L.).

Any quantity which is doubled, or which increases by a fixed per cent of itself at regular intervals, increases exponentially, or according to the C.I.L. In any function of the type $y = ak^{bx}$, where a, b, and k are constants (k positive), the distinctive characteristic is that *adding a fixed amount* to x will *multiply y by a fixed amount.* Otherwise expressed, in an exponential function, the rate of increase of the dependent variable at any instant is proportional to the magnitude of the independent variable at that particular instant. That is why we sometimes refer to the C.I.L. as the "snowball law," since it resembles the growth of a snowball rolling down a hill; the ball gathers more and more snow the farther it rolls, and at any instant it might be said of it that "the bigger it is, the more rapidly it is growing bigger."

Exponential functions are extremely significant in higher mathematics. They are also of considerable importance in science and technology, since many phenomena follow the C.I.L. Thus if the net rate of increase (excess of births over deaths) of a given population, say of bacteria, or insects, or flowers or human beings, is fixed, the rate of increase is small when the population is small, and proportionately larger for a large population. Hence the C.I.L. is also called the *law of organic growth*. This type of growth is not limited to groups of living organisms. It is also manifested by other physical phenomena. For example, an electric current does not flow instantly to its full capacity, but "builds up" gradually in the conductor in accordance with the exponential function. Chemical reactions often increase accordingly, tension in a pulley belt involves an exponential function, atmospheric pressure varies with elevation above sea level in accordance with an exponential function. Even social and economic changes sometimes vary in accordance with the law of organic growth.

Furthermore, there is a corresponding law of decay—or growth in reverse—expressed in the forms

$$y = ak^{-bx} \quad \text{or} \quad Q_t = Q_o k^{-bt}.$$

This describes the fact that a quantity is *decreasing* at a rate which is constantly proportional to its magnitude at any given instant. In short, "the smaller it is, the more slowly it is getting smaller." Examples are: (1) Newton's law of cooling, as the temperature of a

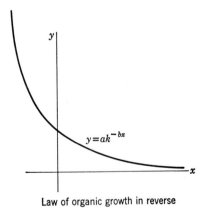

Law of organic growth in reverse

Fig. 9-23

body gradually approaches the temperature of its surroundings; (2) the gradual slowing up of a rotating wheel coming to rest of its own accord; (3) the hydrolysis of sugar solutions; (4) the action of disinfectants; (5) the dissipation of radio-active substances; (6) the amount of light which penetrates a series of glass plates; etc. In all these instances, the rate of diminution is constantly proportional to the amount remaining or surviving.

the logarithmic function

You will recall that if

$$y = k^x, \tag{1}$$
$$\text{then} \quad x = \log_k y. \tag{2}$$

It is clear that 1 is an exponential function, and 2 is a logarithmic function. If we interchange the variables in 2, we get

$$y = \log_k x, \tag{3}$$

which is the inverse of 1.

The graph of $y = \log_2 x$ is shown below in the same set of axes with the graph of $y = 2^x$. The line $y = x$, as can be seen, is an axis of symmetry for the two inverse functions in question.

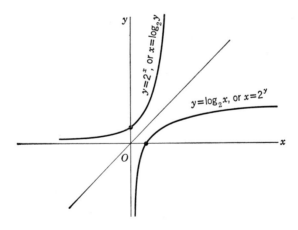

Fig. 9-24

exponential equations

The solution of equations involving exponents, either as constants or as variables, is easily effected by using common logarithms (Table 4, pages 192–193).

Example 1. Solve for x: $3.5^x = 12$. Taking logarithms of both sides of the equation,

$$\log (3.5)^x = \log 12$$
$$x \log 3.5 = \log 12$$

$$x = \frac{\log 12}{\log 3.5} = \frac{1.0792}{0.5441} = 1.98 \text{ (approximately)}.$$

Example 2. Solve for n: $(1.05)^{n+1} = 1.8$.

$$\log (1.05)^{n+1} = \log 1.8$$
$$(n + 1) \log 1.05 = \log 1.8$$

$$n + 1 = \frac{\log 1.8}{\log 1.05} = \frac{0.2553}{0.0212} = 12.04 \text{ (approximately)}.$$

$$n = 12.04 - 1 = 11.04 \text{ (approximately)}.$$

Example 3. Solve for y: $\sqrt[5]{60} = y$.

$$\log y = \tfrac{1}{5} \log 60$$
$$\log y = \tfrac{1}{5} (1.7782) = 0.3556$$
$$y = 0.2268 \text{ (approximately)}.$$

Example 4. Solve for t: $t^{\frac{2}{3}} = 14$.

$$\tfrac{2}{3} \log t = \log 14$$
$$\log t = \tfrac{3}{2} \log 14$$
$$= \tfrac{3}{2} (1.1461) = 1.7192$$
$$t = 52.39 \text{ (approximately)}.$$

EXERCISE 9–3

1. Solve the following exponential equations, using the table on page 192:

(a) $3^x = 10$

(b) $5^x = 16$

(c) $(1.03)^x = 1.5$

(d) $4^{x-1} = 5$

(e) $8.5 = (55)^{2x}$

(f) $(3.6)^x = 15.2$

(g) $2^x \cdot 10^x = 40$

(h) $(1.04)^{n+1} = 2.8$

(i) $\sqrt[x]{10} = 6$

(j) $\log_x 150 = 2.4$

2. Plot $y = 2^x$ and $y = x^2$ on the same set of axes for positive values of x from $x = 0$ to $x = 6$.

3. Plot the functions $y = 2^x$, $y = 3^x$, and $y = 4^x$ on the same axes for the values of $x = 0, 1, 2, 3, 4$.

4. Plot the graph of $y = (\tfrac{1}{2})^x$ for values of x from $x = -4$ to $x = +2$.

5. Plot the graph of $y = \log_{10} x$, using arbitrary units on the x-axis and y-axis to make convenient scales; use values of $x = 0.5, 1, 10, 20, 30, 50, 100$.

FOR FURTHER READING AND STUDY

1. Banks, J. Houston. *Elements of Mathematics*. Boston: Allyn and Bacon, 1956. Chapter 11: "Mathematical Functions."
2. Boyer, L. E. *An Introduction to Mathematics for Teachers*. New York: H. Holt, 1945. Chapters 17 and 18.
3. Hooper, Alfred. *The River Mathematics*. New York: H. Holt, 1945. Chapter 14: "Graphs of Functions."
4. Logsdon, Mayme I. *Elementary Mathematical Analysis*. Vol. I. New York: McGraw-Hill, 1932. Chapters I, V, IX, XII.
5. Richardson, M. *Fundamentals of Mathematics*. New York: Macmillan, 1958. Chapter X.

CHAPTER 10

Interest and Present Value

Despite the persistence of the idea that
interest is something unnatural and in-
defensible, . . . despite all attempts to
prohibit interest taking, there is not and
never has been in all recorded history
any time or place without the existence
of interest.

—Irving Fisher:
The Theory of Interest

SIMPLE INTEREST

money and interest

Interest is the cost of borrowing someone's money, or the premium
you receive for lending someone your money. The amount of the interest charge on a particular loan depends upon three factors:

1. *How much you borrow.* This amount is the face of the loan, or
the *principal.* If you have to pay $5 for the use of $100 for 1 year,
you naturally expect to pay twice as much for a loan of $200, or 10
times as much for a loan of $1000, etc., for the same period of time.

2. *The duration of the loan.* This is the time period of the loan, or the time, stated in years or fractions of a year. If you have to pay $5 for the use of $100 for 1 year, you naturally expect to pay twice as much for using the same amount for 2 years, three times as much if you borrow it for 3 years, etc.

3. *The prevailing "worth of money."* This is the interest rate. Usually expressed as a per cent, it varies roughly from 1 or 2 per cent to as much as 6 per cent or slightly more. In any particular instance the rate in a given transaction is determined by current business conditions, who the lender is, who the borrower is, the purpose of the loan, the security offered, and other economic factors.

The rate of interest may be defined as the per cent of premium paid on money at one date in terms of money to be in hand one year later. Although the interest rate is generally stated as a per cent, it need not be so expressed. Actually, it is more convenient mathematically, and more meaningful to the learner, to regard an interest rate as a common fraction or as a decimal fraction. Thus the rate of interest is that fractional part of the principal which must be paid for the use of that principal for a given unit of time. Unless otherwise specified, the unit of time is one year, which is the standard unit of time in the theory of finance. Thus an interest rate of "5 per cent," or, more completely, "5 per cent a year," means that $\frac{1}{20}$ of the principal is due at the end of one year. The borrower's obligation is $2\frac{1}{20}$ of the amount borrowed, whether that amount is $1, $100, or $1000.

It is clear from the foregoing statement that the amount of interest to be paid when a loan falls due is found by multiplying the principal by the annual rate, and then multiplying the product by the number of years for which the loan was made. In symbols:

$$I = Pni \tag{1}$$

where I = the total interest due
P = the principal
n = the time in years
i = the annual interest rate

Hence the total amount due when the loan matures is given by

$$A = P + I \tag{2}$$
Since $$A = P + Pni, \tag{3}$$
We have $$A = P(1 + ni) \tag{4}$$

Formula 4 can also be derived by reasoning as follows. Consider a loan of $1, or a unit principal of 1; at the end of one year, the interest due is i dollars, and the total amount at the end of the first year (A_1) is $(1 + i)$ dollars. At the end of 2 years, the amount due is $(1 + 2i) = A_2$; after 3 years, $A_3 = (1 + 3i)$; and so on, for n years, $A_n = (1 + ni)$. Therefore, on a principal of P dollars, the total amount due after n years is P times as great; or

$$A_n = P(1 + ni).$$

The basic formula 1 for simple interest can of course be used to find the rate, or the principal, or the time, since

$$i = \frac{I}{Pn}; \quad P = \frac{I}{ni}; \quad n = \frac{I}{Pi}.$$

Example 1. The interest on $900 for 2 years is $90. Find the rate.

Solving for i: $i = \dfrac{I}{Pn} = \dfrac{90}{(900)(2)} = \dfrac{1}{20} = 5$ per cent

Example 2. The interest on a certain principal for 6 months ($\frac{1}{2}$ year) at 4 per cent is $16. Find the principal.

Solving for P: $P = \dfrac{I}{ni} = \dfrac{16}{(\frac{1}{2})(0.04)} = \dfrac{16}{0.02} = \$800$

Example 3. In how many years will $500 yield $105 interest at 6 per cent?

Solving for n: $n = \dfrac{I}{Pi} = \dfrac{105}{(500)(0.06)} = \dfrac{105}{30} = 3\frac{1}{2}$ years

ordinary and exact time

For short term loans, that is, for periods of one year or less, the time between two dates can be determined either (1) in terms of calendar months, or (2) in terms of the exact number of days elapsed. In the first instance, we find the approximate number of days on the assumption that every month has 30 days. This is known as *ordinary time*.

Example 1. Find the ordinary time from May 3 to September 12. May 3 to September 3 = 4 months.

$$
\begin{aligned}
4 \times 30 &= 120 \text{ days} \\
12 - 3 &= \underline{9 \text{ days}} \\
& 129 \text{ days}
\end{aligned}
$$

Example 2. Find the ordinary time from March 16 to June 5. March 16 to June 16 = 3 months.

$$3 \times 30 = 90 \text{ days}$$
$$16 - 5 = \underline{11 \text{ days}}$$
$$79 \text{ days}$$

When we count the exact number of days elapsed, we are using *exact time*. When figuring exact time, the first day is not counted, but the last day is included in the total (just as in figuring ordinary time).

Example 3. Find the exact time from May 3 to September 12.

May,	28 days remaining
June,	30 days
July,	31 days
August,	31 days
September,	12 days
	132 days

Example 4. Find the exact time from March 16 to June 5.

March,	15 days remaining
April,	30 days
May,	31 days
June,	5 days
	81 days

Exact time is the time basis used for most interest calculations. When banks make loans, they usually compute the interest for the exact number of days, although they consider 360 days to the year. Ordinary time (30-day month) is generally used for long term loans; exact time is generally used for commercial, industrial and personal loans (except real estate loans and installment loans).

ordinary and exact interest

When interest is computed on a 360-day year, it is called *ordinary interest*. This is true whether the time used is "ordinary time" (30 days = 1 month) or "exact time" (actual number of days). However, interest is sometimes computed on a calendar year of 365 days (or 366 days for leap years), in which case it is called *exact interest*. When exact interest is computed, the time used is always exact time.

Example. Find (*a*) the ordinary interest, and (*b*) the exact interest on $1000 for 65 days at 4 per cent.

(*a*) Ordinary interest $= 1000 \times \dfrac{65}{300} \times \dfrac{4}{100} = \$7.22$

(*b*) Exact interest $= \$1000 \times \dfrac{65}{365} \times \dfrac{4}{100} = \$7.12$

Exact interest is not generally used in business transactions, but interest payments on government bonds and other federal transactions are based on exact interest, that is, calculated on a 365-day year.

As you can see from the foregoing examples, ordinary interest is always greater than exact interest for the same period of time. The reason for this is easily seen. Consider a given principal at a given rate and a given number of days, say N days:

$$O.I. = \frac{PNi}{360},$$

$$E.I. = \frac{PNi}{365};$$

$$\text{then} \quad \frac{O.I.}{E.I.} = \frac{365}{360} = \frac{73}{72},$$

$$\text{or} \quad O.I. = \frac{73}{72} E.I.,$$

$$\text{and} \quad E.I. = \frac{72}{73} O.I.$$

To summarize: interest between two dates is commonly computed in one of three ways:

1. *Ordinary interest* (base: 360-day year), with *ordinary time* (30-day-month time).

2. *Ordinary interest* (base: 360-day year), with *exact time* (actual days).

3. *Exact interest* (base: 365-day year), with *exact time* (actual days).

Example. Find the interest on $900 from July 2 to September 2 at 5 per cent by each of the three methods above.

1. $\$900 \times \dfrac{60}{360} \times \dfrac{5}{100} = \$7.50$

2. $\$900 \times \dfrac{62}{360} \times \dfrac{5}{100} = \$7.75$

3. $\$900 \times \dfrac{62}{365} \times \dfrac{5}{100} = \$7.64$

present value

You know that a given principal of P dollars today, at simple interest, will, in n years, amount to A_n dollars, where

$$A_n = P(1 + ni) \qquad (4)$$

Clearly then we can regard A_n as the *future value* of a sum of money whose *present value* is P dollars. Using formula 4 answers the question: What will so-and-so many dollars in cash today amount to, at simple interest, n years from now? Or, given a present value, find its future value.

Now let us reverse the question and ask: What sum of money (P) must be placed at interest today to obtain a specified amount (A_n) at some future time, say n years from now? Or, what is the present value of A_n dollars payable n years from today? To answer this, we need only solve equation 4 for P:

$$P = \frac{A_n}{1 + ni} \qquad (5)$$

where P = present value
A_n = future value
n = time in years
i = rate of interest

Equations 4 and 5 may be stated verbally as follows:

To find the *future* value of a sum whose present value is known, *multiply* the present value by $(1 + ni)$.

To find the *present* value of a sum whose future value is known, *divide* the future value by $(1 + ni)$.

The present value of a future sum is often called its *cash value*. The difference between the amount due on a sum placed at simple interest and the principal itself is called *true discount*. In other words, the true discount on an amount A_n is the same as the interest on a principal P; or, finding the true discount on the future value means finding the interest on the present value. We say that we have *discounted* the future value to its present or cash value.

EXERCISE 10–1

1. Quarterly interest is paid every 3 months, or every quarter-year. Find the quarterly interest on $2400 at $3\frac{1}{2}$ per cent a year.

2. Which is greater: the interest on $4000 for 3 months at 4 per cent a year, or for 1 year at $1\frac{1}{2}$ per cent a year?

3. A tax bill for $124 was paid 18 days after it was due. The penalty for delinquent tax payments is an interest charge of 7 per cent per year for the late period. What was the amount of the penalty?

4. If the interest on $1200 for 3 months amounts to $9, find the annual rate of interest.

5. A $1000 bond earns $21.25 interest semiannually. What is the annual rate of interest?

6. A principal of $1600 earns interest at 3 per cent. How long will it take to earn $24 interest?

7. What sum of money will earn $144 in 1½ year at 4 per cent?

8. Find the ordinary time and the exact time: (*a*) from March 3 to June 3, (*b*) from May 5 to August 8, (*c*) from July 10 to September 24, (*d*) from January 10, 1959 to March 4, 1959.

9. What is the ordinary interest on $600 at 4 per cent for 72 days?

10. A loan of $1200 at 4 per cent ran from May 10 to August 10:

(*a*) Find the ordinary interest, using ordinary time.
(*b*) Find the ordinary interest, using exact time.
(*c*) Find the exact interest, using exact time.

11. How much must a man invest at simple interest at 4 per cent to have $480 five years from now?

12. Find the present value of $300 due in 10 years at 5 per cent simple interest.

13. A man needs to have $1300 one year from now. If he can realize 5 per cent simple interest on his money, what amount should he invest now to obtain the desired amount at that time?

14. Mrs. Halsey bought a deep freeze unit, on a 3-month term basis, for $360. The cash price was $345. What rate of interest did she pay?

15. If a person borrows $500 at 4 per cent, how long may he use it and pay it back with $515?

16. Mr. Stewart bought a laundry machine for which he agreed to pay $303 two months later. If money is worth 6 per cent, what should the cash price be?

17. Mr. Jones can sell his house today for $15,000; two years from now he thinks he might get $16,000 for it. If money is worth 4 per cent, which is the better proposition?

18. Prove that (*a*) $O = E + E/72$ and (*b*) $E = O - O/73$, where $O =$ ordinary interest and $E =$ exact interest.

19. The current yield on a bond means that approximate rate of return on the investment, and may be defined as the annual income from the bond divided by the total cost of the bond. Find the current yield on a $1000 bond purchased at 94½, paying 4 per cent, with a brokerage cost of $5. (Nearest tenth of 1 per cent.)

20. What is the rate of return on a block of stock costing $1240, including brokerage and taxes, if the total dividends for one year amounted to $84?

21. Prove that to find the interest on any principal for 60 days at 6 per cent, we need only move the decimal point in the principal two places to the left.

22. How long will it take a sum of money to double itself at simple interest at 6 per cent?

COMPOUND INTEREST

converting interest into principal

Whenever interest, as it falls due, is added to the principal, the total interest so earned is called *compound interest*. During each succeeding period, the principal is greater than during the previous period, and so the interest earned during each succeeding period is greater than that earned during the previous period. The act of converting "interest" money to "principal" money is called compounding the interest, or, more accurately, converting interest into principal. The regular periods are called the *conversion intervals*. In financial theory, we assume that interest received is immediately invested as principal, and not spent or allowed to remain "idle."

Example 1. Find the compound interest on $500 for 4 years at 5 per cent a year, compounded annually. Here the conversion interval is one year; interest is converted 4 times.

Original principal	= $500.00
Interest on $500 for 1 year	= 25.00
Principal during second year	= $525.00
Interest on $525 for 1 year	= 26.25
Principal during third year	= $551.25
Interest on $551.25 for 1 year	= 27.56
Principal during fourth year	= $578.81
Interest on $578.81 for 1 year	= 28.94
Total amount due	= $607.75
Less original principal	= 500.00
Compound Interest	= $107.75

This compound interest compares with $100 simple interest at the same rate for the same period.

Example 2. Find the compound interest on $200 for 3 years at 4 per cent a year, compounded semiannually. Here the conversion interval is ½ year; there are 6 conversion intervals.

Original principal	= $200.00
Interest on $200 for 6 months	= 4.00
Principal during 2nd interval	= $204.00
Interest on $204 for 6 months	= 4.08
Principal during 3rd interval	= $208.08
Interest on $208.08 for 6 months =	4.16
Principal during 4th interval	= $212.24
Interest on $212.24 for 6 months =	4.24
Principal during 5th interval	= $216.48
Interest on $216.48 for 6 months =	4.33
Principal during 6th interval	= $220.81
Interest on $220.81 for 6 months =	4.42
Total amount due	= $225.23
Less original principal	= 200.00
Compound Interest	= $ 25.23

Simple interest for the same period at the same rate is only $24.00.

compound interest tables

To find the compound interest for longer periods by the above method would obviously be very tedious. In practice, we make use of special tables, such as Table 7, page 327. The table gives the total amount due on 1 dollar at compound interest at various rates and for various intervals. We find the total amount of a given principal by multiplying the amount of $1 by the given principal. Subtracting the original principal from the amount then gives us the compound interest earned.

Example 1. Find the compound interest on $500 for 4 years at 5 per cent a year, compounded annually. We find in the table, in the column headed "5 per cent," opposite "$n = 4$," the figure 1.21551, which is the amount of $1 for 4 years at 5 per cent. Multiplying:

$$A = (1.21551)(\$500) = \$607.76.$$

Subtracting the original principal:

$$\$607.76 - \$500 = \$107.76, \text{ interest.}$$

This is the same result as in example 1 (page 325), but for a difference of 1 cent. The discrepancy is due to the fact that the 5-place decimals in the table have been rounded; using a table with 6 or more decimal places would give the same result as by the long-hand method.

Example 2. Find the compound interest on $200 for 3 years at 4 per cent, compounded semiannually.

A rate of 4 per cent annually is equivalent to 2 per cent per half-year interval. In 3 years, there are 6 semiannual conversion intervals. So, in the table, we look for the value under "2 per cent," opposite "$n = 6$"; we find 1.12616, the amount of $1. Multiplying:

$$A = (1.12616)(\$200) = \$225.23$$
$$\$225.23 - \$200 = \$25.23, \text{ interest.}$$

This time the result agrees exactly with the result found by the long method in example 2 on page 326.

Example 3. Find the compound interest on $750 for 8 years at 6 per cent, compounded quarterly. Here the rate is $1\frac{1}{2}$ per cent per quarterly conversion

TABLE 7.   Compound Amount of One Dollar
$$A_n = (1 + i)^n$$

Periods	1 Per Cent	1¼ Per Cent	1½ Per Cent	2 Per Cent	Periods
1	1.01000	1.01250	1.01500	1.02000	1
2	1.02010	1.02516	1.03023	1.04040	2
3	1.03030	1.03797	1.04568	1.06121	3
4	1.04060	1.05095	1.06136	1.08243	4
5	1.05101	1.06408	1.07728	1.10408	5
6	1.06152	1.07738	1.09344	1.12616	6
7	1.07214	1.09085	1.10984	1.14869	7
8	1.08286	1.10449	1.12649	1.17166	8
9	1.09369	1.11829	1.14339	1.19509	9
10	1.10462	1.13227	1.16054	1.21899	10
12	1.12683	1.16075	1.19562	1.26824	12
14	1.14947	1.18995	1.23176	1.31948	14
16	1.17258	1.21989	1.26899	1.37279	16
18	1.19615	1.25058	1.30734	1.42825	18
20	1.22019	1.28204	1.34686	1.48595	20
22	1.24472	1.31429	1 38756	1 54598	22
24	1.26974	1.34735	1.42950	1.60844	24
26	1.29526	1.38125	1.47271	1.67342	26
28	1.32129	1.41599	1.51722	1.74102	28
30	1.34785	1.45161	1.56308	1.81136	30
32	1.37494	1.48813	1.61032	1.88454	32
34	1.40258	1.52557	1.65900	1.96068	34
36	1.43077	1.56394	1.70914	2.03989	36
38	1.45953	1.60329	1.76080	2.12230	38
40	1.48886	1.64362	1.81402	2.20804	40

TABLE 7.   Compound Amount of One Dollar (*Continued*)

$$A_n = (1 + i)^n$$

Periods	2½ Per Cent	3 Per Cent	4 Per Cent	5 Per Cent	Periods
1	1.02500	1.03000	1.04000	1.05000	1
2	1.05063	1.06090	1.08160	1.10250	2
3	1.07689	1.09273	1.12486	1.15763	3
4	1.10381	1.12551	1.16986	1.21551	4
5	1.13141	1.15927	1.21665	1.27628	5
6	1.15969	1.19405	1.26532	1.34010	6
7	1.18869	1.22987	1.31693	1.40710	7
8	1.21840	1.26677	1.36857	1.47746	8
9	1.24886	1.30477	1.42331	1.55133	9
10	1.28008	1.34392	1.48024	1.62890	10
12	1.34489	1.42576	1.60103	1.79586	12
14	1.41297	1.51259	1.73168	1.97993	14
16	1.48451	1.60471	1.87298	2.18287	16
18	1.55966	1.70243	2.02582	2.40662	18
20	1.63862	1.80611	2.19112	2.65330	20
22	1.72157	1.91610	2.36992	2.92526	22
24	1.80873	2.03279	2.56330	3.22510	24
26	1.90029	2.15659	2.77247	3.55567	26
28	1.99650	2.28793	2.99870	3.92013	28
30	2.09757	2.42726	3.24340	4.32194	30
32	2.20376	2.57508	3.50806	4.76494	32
34	2.31532	2.73191	3.79432	5.25335	34
36	2.43254	2.89828	4.10393	5.79182	36
38	2.55568	3.07478	4.43881	6.38548	38
40	2.68506	3.16703	4.80102	7.03999	40

interval, and there are 4×8, or 32 intervals. So, in the table, under "1½ per cent," opposite "$n = 32$," we find the amount of $1, or 1.61032.

$$A = (1.61032)(\$750) = \$1,207.74.$$
$$\$1207.74 - \$750.00 = \$457.74, \text{ interest.}$$

compound interest formulas

We have seen that the interest rate means that fractional part of the principal which must be paid at the end of a given period for the privilege of using the money during that period. As in the case of simple interest, the rate is always understood to be an annual rate unless otherwise indicated. Also, as with simple interest, it is con-

venient but not necessary to express the rate as a per cent. Sometimes it is actually more helpful to express the rate as a decimal part
of a monetary unit. For example: $100 at 5 per cent for 1 year
amounts to $100 + (0.05) ($100), or $105. Again, $1, at a rate of 0.05,
in one year amounts to $1 + $0.05, or $1.05. In other words, when
the interest rate i is in decimal form, it can be added to the principal
directly, since both are expressed in the same monetary units (dollars,
or francs, or pounds sterling, etc.).

Let us see what happens when interest is converted into principal
at regular intervals. We start with a principal of $1, at an annual
rate i. At the end of the first year the dollar has earned i dollars
(remember that i is a decimal fraction less than 1). Having earned
i dollars interest, the amount at the end of the first year (A_1) is given
by $A_1 = 1 + i$. This amount, A_1, becomes the principal for the second
year. So, interest for the second year equals $i(1 + i)$, and the amount
due at the end of the second year (A_2) becomes

$$A_2 = \underbrace{(1 + i)}_{\text{principal}} + \underbrace{i(1 + i)}_{\text{interest}}.$$

Factoring, $A_2 = (1 + i)(1 + i)$,   or $A_2 = (1 + i)^2$.

By similar reasoning, A_2, the amount due at the end of the second
year, automatically becomes the principal for the third year. So, interest for the third year equals $i(1 + i)^2$, and the amount due at the
end of the third year (A_3) becomes

$$A_3 = \underbrace{(1 + i)^2}_{\text{principal}} + \underbrace{i(1 + i)^2}_{\text{interest}}$$

Factoring, $A_3 = (1 + i)^2(1 + i)$,   or $A_3 = (1 + i)^3$.

Continuing in the same manner, we have:

$$A_4 = (1 + i)^3 + i(1 + i)^3$$
$$= (1 + i)^4$$
$$A_5 = (1 + i)^4 + i(1 + i)^4$$
$$= (1 + i)^5$$
$$A_6 = (1 + i)^6$$
$$A_{10} = (1 + i)^{10}$$
$$A_n = (1 + i)^n$$

Now, if in n years 1 dollar amounts to $(1 + i)^n$ dollars, then in the
same time and at the same rate, a principal of P dollars will amount
to P times as much, or

$$A_n = P(1 + i)^n \qquad (1)$$

The multiplier of P, namely $(1 + i)^n$, is called the *accumulation factor*. The values of $(1 + i)^n$ for various values of n and i are given in Table 7. Note that by multiplying a given principal by the appropriate accumulation factor gives the compound amount. To find the compound interest, we must subtract the principal from the compound amount.

nominal and effective rates

Whenever the conversion interval is less than one year, an interesting situation arises: the rate of interest actually received is larger than the annual rate named. For example, if $100 is invested at 6 per cent, payable semiannually, the interest for the first half of the year is $3, and the amount available at the beginning of the second half is $103. The interest on $103 for the second half-year is $3.09 and the total amount at the end of the year is $106.09. So, the total yearly interest actually received is $6.09; the rate of interest received on $1 is therefore 0.0609, or 6.09 per cent. This is called the *effective rate*. If the first $3 had not been added to the principal until the end of the year, the rate would actually have been 6 per cent.

When interest is compounded oftener than once a year, say m times a year, formula 1 becomes

$$A_n = P\left(1 + \frac{j}{m}\right)^{mn}, \tag{2}$$

where $j =$ the nominal annual rate
$m =$ the number of conversions per year
$n =$ the number of years of the loan
$mn =$ the number of conversion intervals

The rate of interest *actually* earned, or the *effective rate*, is designated by i; the *nominal* rate is designated by j. Thus, by definition, we have the following identity:

$$(1 + i)^n = \left(1 + \frac{j}{m}\right)^{mn}, \tag{3}$$

$$\text{or } 1 + i = \left(1 + \frac{j}{m}\right)^{m}. \tag{4}$$

It is easily seen that to every j there corresponds a unique value of i; and, conversely, to every i there corresponds a unique value of j. Solving equation 4 first for i and then for j, we have:

$$i = \left(1 + \frac{j}{m}\right)^m - 1 \qquad (5)$$

$$\text{and} \quad j = m[(1 + i)^{1/m} - 1]. \qquad (6)$$

It can be shown that the effective rate i is always greater than the nominal rate j except when $m = 1$, that is, when compounded annually, in which case $i = j$. Furthermore, for any given j, the effective rate i increases as m increases; and for any given i, the nominal rate j decreases as m increases.

Example 1. Find i when $j = 0.06$ and $m = 4$. From equation 5,

$$\log (1 + i) = m \log \left(1 + \frac{j}{m}\right)$$

Hence

$$\log (1 + i) = 4 \log (1.015)$$
$$\log (1 + i) = (4)(0.0065) = 0.0260$$
$$(1 + i) = 1.062$$
$$i = 0.062, \text{ approximately.}[1]$$

Example 2. Find j when $i = 0.06$ and $m = 4$.

$$m \log \left(1 + \frac{j}{m}\right) = \log (1 + i)$$

$$4 \log \left(1 + \frac{j}{4}\right) = \log (1.06)$$

$$\log \left(1 + \frac{j}{4}\right) = \frac{1}{4} \log (1.06) = 0.0063$$

$$\left(1 + \frac{j}{4}\right) = 1.0147$$

$$\frac{j}{4} = 0.0147$$

$$j = (4)(0.0147) = 0.0588 \text{ (approximately).}$$

EXERCISE 10–2

1. Find, without using tables, the compound interest on:

(a) $500 at 6 per cent for 2 years compounded annually.
(b) $1000 at 5 per cent for 1½ years compounded semiannually.
(c) $200 at 3 per cent for 3 years compounded annually.
(d) $100 at 4 per cent for 1 year compounded quarterly.

[1] For more precise results, logarithmic tables of at least 6-place mantissas are required.

2. Using Table 7, page 327, find the compound interest on:

(*a*) $300 for 20 years at 3 per cent annually.
(*b*) $1000 for 5 years at 4 per cent annually.
(*c*) $500 for 12 years at 2½ per cent semiannually.
(*d*) $450 for 6 years at 5 per cent quarterly.
(*e*) $2000 for 15 years at 3 per cent semiannually.
(*f*) $750 for 10 years at 6 per cent quarterly.
(*g*) $1500 for 5 years at 4 per cent semiannually.
(*h*) $2400 for 5 years at 4 per cent quarterly.

3. Find i when $j = 0.04$ and $m = 4$.

4. Find j when $i = 0.05$ and $m = 2$.

5. Approximately how long will it take for a given principal to double itself (*a*) at 5 per cent compounded annually? (*b*) at 4 per cent compounded semiannually? (Use Table 7 and linear interpolation.)

6. How long will it take $1000 to amount to $1500 at 3¼ per cent compounded annually? (Use basic formula and logarithms.)

7. How long will it take $500 to amount to $1200 at 5 per cent compounded quarterly?

8. At what annual rate (effective) will $600 amount to $1000 in 15 years?

9. Is the compound interest on a given sum for 3 years at 4 per cent, compounded quarterly, the same as the interest on the same sum for 6 years at 2 per cent, compounded semiannually?

10. When interest is compounded semiannually for half a year, that is, when $m = 2$ and $n = \frac{1}{2}$, prove that $i = j + \frac{1}{4}j^2$.

PRESENT VALUE AND DISCOUNT

present value

A debt which is due at some future time is sometimes paid before it is due. For example, someone owes you $100 which isn't due until 5 years from now, but he wants to pay you now. Are you entitled, mathematically, to receive $100 today in payment of a $100 debt due in 5 years? The answer is "no"; you should be willing to accept, today, $78.35, which if invested at once for 5 years at 5 per cent will amount to ($78.35)(1.27628) = $99.9965, or $100. In other words, whether you wait 5 years and then accept $100; or whether you accept $78.35 now, invest it at 5 per cent and wait 5 years—either way you will have exactly $100 five years from now. This is just what the debt amounted to: $100 due 5 years from today. The $78.35 is called the present worth, or the *present value* of $100 due in 5 years (at 5 per cent). Of course, if money is "worth" only 3 per cent, if that's all you can "get for it" at interest, then the present value is more—exactly \$86.26—because more dollars are required to accumulate to \$100 in 5 years at a lower rate.

The present value of a sum due at some future date is that sum which, put at compound interest now, will amount to the sum in question on the given future date. If v_n represents the present value of \$1 due in n years (without interest), and if i represents the effective rate of interest that could be obtained if that cash or present value were in hand to put out at interest; then

$$v_n(1 + i)^n = 1, \tag{7}$$

$$\text{or} \quad v_n = \frac{1}{(1 + i)^n}. \tag{8}$$

If instead of a unit principal we have a general principal P, formula 8 becomes

$$V_n = \frac{P}{(1 + i)^n}. \tag{9}$$

where V_n represents the present value of P dollars payable n years hence at a rate i.

the discount factor

We say that a sum of money is accumulated to a certain date, meaning that it is put at compound interest until that date; its future value is found by multiplying its present value by the accumulation factor, $(1 + i)^n$. We also say that a sum of money is discounted to a certain date, meaning the value of the sum at the date in question as compared with its value at some later date. The present value of a sum due at some future date is found by dividing its value at that future date by $(1 + i)^n$.

The processes of accumulation and discounting are thus exactly the reverse of one another. Since it is more convenient to multiply by a 5-place decimal than it is to divide, we generally write formulas 8 and 9 as follows:

$$v_n = (1 + i)^{-n}, \tag{10}$$
$$V_n = P(1 + i)^{-n}, \tag{11}$$

where $(1 + i)^{-n} = \frac{1}{(1 + i)^n}$ and is called the *discount factor*. When $n = 1$, we have

$$v = \frac{1}{1 + i}, \qquad (12)$$

an expression which occurs throughout the theory of interest. The values of the discount factor v^n, for various values of n and i, are given in Table 8. Any given sum is discounted simply by multiplying it by v^n. Note carefully that v and all powers of v are less than 1.

Example 1. What is the present value of $500 due in 6 years if money is worth 4 per cent? From Table 8, for $n = 6$, under 4 per cent, we find

$v^6 = 0.79031.$
$V_6 = (0.79031)(\$500) = \$395.16$, present value.
Check: From Table 7, for $n = 6$, under 4 per cent, we find
$\qquad (1 + i)^6 = 1.26532;$
$\qquad (1.26532)(\$395.16) = \$500.00$, future value.

TABLE 8.   Present Value of One Dollar
$$v^n = (1 + i)^{-n}$$

Periods	1 Per Cent	1¼ Per Cent	1½ Per Cent	2 Per Cent	Periods
1	0.9901	0.98765	0.98522	0.98039	1
2	0.98030	0.97546	0.97066	0.96117	2
3	0.97059	0.96342	0.95632	0.94232	3
4	0.96098	0.95152	0.94218	0.92385	4
5	0.95147	0.93978	0.92826	0.90573	5
6	0.94205	0.92817	0.91454	0.88797	6
7	0.93272	0.91672	0.90103	0.87056	7
8	0.92348	0.90540	0.88771	0.85349	8
9	0.91434	0.89422	0.87459	0.83676	9
10	0.90529	0.88318	0.86167	0.82035	10
12	0.88745	0.86151	0.83639	0.78849	12
14	0.86996	0.84037	0.81185	0.75788	14
16	0.85282	0.81975	0.78803	0.72845	16
18	0.83602	0.79963	0.76491	0.70016	18
20	0.81954	0.78001	0.74247	0.67297	20
22	0.80340	0.76087	0.72069	0.64684	22
24	0.78757	0.74220	0.69954	0.62172	24
26	0.77205	0.72398	0.67902	0.59758	26
28	0.75684	0.70622	0.65910	0.57437	28
30	0.74192	0.68889	0.63976	0.55207	30
32	0.72730	0.67198	0.62099	0.53063	32
34	0.71297	0.65549	0.60277	0.51003	34
36	0.69892	0.63941	0.58509	0.49022	36
38	0.68515	0.62372	0.56792	0.47119	38
40	0.67165	0.60841	0.55126	0.45289	40

TABLE 8.   Present Value of One Dollar *(Continued)*
$$v^n = (1 + i)^{-n}$$

Periods	2½ Per Cent	3 Per Cent	4 Per Cent	5 Per Cent	Periods
1	0.97561	0.97087	0.96154	0.95238	1
2	0.95181	0.94260	0.92456	0.90703	2
3	0.92860	0.91514	0.88900	0.86384	3
4	0.90595	0.88849	0.85480	0.82270	4
5	0.88385	0.86261	0.82193	0.78353	5
6	0.86230	0.83748	0.79031	0.74622	6
7	0.84127	0.81309	0.75992	0.71068	7
8	0.82075	0.78941	0.73069	0.67684	8
9	0.80073	0.76642	0.70259	0.64461	9
10	0.78120	0.74409	0.67556	0.61391	10
12	0.74356	0.70138	0.62460	0.55684	12
14	0.70773	0.66112	0.57748	0.50507	14
16	0.67362	0.62317	0.53391	0.45811	16
18	0.64117	0.58739	0.49363	0.41552	18
20	0.61027	0.55368	0.45639	0.37689	20
22	0.58086	0.52189	0.42196	0.34185	22
24	0.55288	0.49193	0.39012	0.31007	24
26	0.52623	0.46369	0.36069	0.28124	26
28	0.50088	0.43708	0.33348	0.25509	28
30	0.47674	0.41199	0.30832	0.23138	30
32	0.45377	0.38834	0.28506	0.20987	32
34	0.43191	0.36604	0.26355	0.19035	34
36	0.41109	0.34503	0.24367	0.17266	36
38	0.39128	0.32523	0.22529	0.15661	38
40	0.37243	0.30656	0.20829	0.14205	40

Example 2. Find the present value of \$1000 due in 3 years if money is worth 5 per cent, compounded quarterly. From Table 8, for $n = 12$ at $1\frac{1}{4}$ per cent, we find $v^{12} = 0.86151$.

Therefore $V_n = (0.86151)(\$1000) = \$861.51.$
Check: From Table 7, for $n = 12$ at $1\frac{1}{4}$ per cent,
we find $(1 + i)^{12} = 1.16075$;
$(1.16075)(\$861.51) = \$1000.00.$

Sometimes we need to find the present value of a sum due n years hence with interest, where k is the effective rate of interest carried by the unit principal, i the current effective rate, and v_n' the present value. In this case the sum due in n years is not 1, but rather the amount of 1 for n years at rate k, that is, $(1 + k)^n$.

Hence
$$v_n' = (1 + k)^n \cdot (1 + i)^{-n};$$
and, for a principal of P dollars,
$$V_n' = P(1 + k)^n \cdot (1 + i)^{-n}.$$

Example 3. Find the present value of $200 with interest payable at 5 per cent and due in 4 years, when money is worth 4 per cent nominal, payable semiannually.

$$V_n' = (\$200)(1.05)^4 (1.02)^{-8}$$
$$= (\$200)(1.21551)(0.85349) = \$207.49.$$

equation of value

We often wish to compare one or more sets of sums due at various times with other sets due at other times. In order to compare several sums due at various times, all the sums must be accumulated or discounted to the same date.

Example 1. A debtor owes $500 due in 3 years, and $1000 due in 4 years. He wishes to pay off both debts 2 years from now. How much should he pay then, if money is worth 4 per cent?

Let S equal the sum which he must pay 2 years hence; it is to be mathematically equivalent to the combined outstanding debts. Hence, discounting all sums to the present time, we have

$$Sv^2 = 500v^3 + 1000v^4$$
$$S(0.92456) = (500)(0.88900) + (1000)(0.85480)$$
$$(0.92456)S = 444.50 + 854.80 = 1299.30,$$
$$S = \$1405.32.$$

Example 2. A owes B $800, due in 5 years; B owes A $1200 due in 4 years. Money being worth 5 per cent, how much should change hands if they discharged their debts today? As of today:

A owes B 800v^5$ = (800)(0.78353) = \$626.82$
B owes A 1200v^4$ = (1200)(0.82270) = \$987.24$
So, $987.24 − 626.82 = \$360.42$, the amount B must pay A today.

EXERCISE 10–3

1. Using Table 8, page 334, find the present value of:

(a) $300 due in 3 years with interest at 4 per cent annually.
(b) $1000 due in 5 years with interest at 5 per cent quarterly.
(c) $500 due in 2 years with interest at 6 per cent semiannually.
(d) $100 due in 10 years with interest at 4 per cent quarterly.
(e) $200 due in 4 years with interest at $2\frac{1}{2}$ per cent annually.
(f) $1500 due in 6 years with interest at 3 per cent, semiannually.

2. Miss Jordan plans to make an investment so that she will have $6000 five years from now. How much should she invest now at 4 per cent compounded quarterly to have the amount she wants?

3. When his son was 8 years old, Mr. Halsey planned to invest a sum which would yield $8000 for his college expenses beginning 10 years later. How much should he invest at 5 per cent compounded semiannually to yield $8000 in 10 years?

4. A college class at graduation plans to raise a fund which will yield $25,000 on its twenty-fifth anniversary. If there are 200 members in the class and they invest the money at 4 per cent compounded semiannually, what amount must each member contribute at graduation?

5. What single cash payment is required to pay off two debts, one of $500 due in 3 years, the other of $600 due in 5 years, if money is worth 4 per cent?

6. If Jones owes Anderson $500 due in 4 years, and Anderson owes Jones $600 due in 6 years, how much should change hands if they settled their debts today? (Assume money is worth 5 per cent.)

7. What amount due 2 years from today is equivalent to two debts of $500 each due in 3 years and 5 years, respectively? (Assume money is worth 5 per cent.)

8. Given: debts of $750 and $400 due in 4 years and 6 years, respectively. If money is worth 4 per cent, what single debt will settle the payments equitably at the end of 3 years?

9. A loan of $200 bearing interest at 3 per cent compounded semiannually is due at the end of 2 years and 6 months. If money is worth 4 per cent semiannually, what is the present value of the loan?

10. Mr. Crosby owes Mr. Ford $3000 which is due in three annual instalments beginning one year from now. He offers to settle by paying Mr. Ford $3000 in a single lump-sum payment 2 years from now. Would this be an equitable arrangement? (Assume money to be worth 5 per cent.)

FOR FURTHER READING AND STUDY

1. Hilborn, C. E. *Mathematics for Use in Business.* Boston: Houghton Mifflin, 1948. Chapters 12–15.
2. Lowenstein, L. L. *Mathematics in Business.* New York: John Wiley, 1958. Chapters 5, 6 and 7.
3. Snyder, Llewellyn R. *Essential Business Mathematics.* New York: McGraw-Hill, 1958. Chapter 3.
4. Stelson, H. E. "A Comparison of Simple and Compound Interest," *National Mathematics Magazine* 19:336–342; 1945.
5. Trimble, H. C. "The Arithmetic of Growth," *The Mathematics Teacher* 47: 180–183; February 1954.
6. Van Voorhis, W. R. and Topp, C. W. *Fundamentals of Business Mathematics.* New York: Prentice-Hall, 1948. Chapter 10.

CHAPTER 11

Probability and Insurance

It is remarkable that a science [prob-
abilities] which began with the consideration of games of chance, should
have become the most important object
of human knowledge.

—Laplace

SELECTIONS AND ARRANGEMENTS

the idea of choices

Let us suppose that a tourist has a choice of three steamships, A, B, C, to take him to Europe. Having arrived, he is again confronted with the same three choices on the return trip. Let us further suppose that he wishes to return by a different steamship from the one he chooses in going abroad. Then, regardless of which one he uses to go abroad, he has only two choices for returning. Now let us answer this question: in how many different ways can he go on one steamship and return by a different one? The total number of ways in which he can perform both acts (as specified by the question) is six:

Going—Returning

1. $A—B$
2. $A—C$
3. $B—A$
4. $B—C$
5. $C—A$
6. $C—B$

In other words, the first choice (going abroad) may be exercised in three ways, and, that having been done, the second choice may be exercised in two ways. The total number of ways of exercising both choices is $3 \times 2 = 6$ different ways. If the restriction about returning on a different steamship were removed, each act could be performed, respectively, in 3 different ways, so that both acts can be performed in a total of $3 \times 3 = 9$ different ways:

AA	BA	CA
AB	BB	CB
AC	BC	CC

a fundamental principle

The above illustration suggests the following generalization:

If an act can be performed in any one of a different ways, and when it has been done in any one of those ways, a second act can be performed independently in any one of b different ways, the two acts can be successively performed in a total of $a \times b$, or ab different ways.

Example 1. A traveling salesman has a choice of four different airlines to reach his destination; he can return by any one of three different railroads. In how many different ways can he fly out and return by rail? Clearly, both acts can be performed in $4 \times 3 = 12$ ways. Actually, this principle can be extended to any number of successive, independent acts to be performed.

Example 2. A boy has 3 pairs of slacks, 4 shirts, and 2 jackets. In how many different ways can he "get dressed"? He can get dressed in $3 \times 4 \times 2 = 24$ different ways. The assumption is, of course, that he dons 1 pair of slacks, 1 shirt and 1 jacket at a time. This can be visualized by means of a tree diagram, Fig. 11–1.

Such tree diagrams are particularly useful when the number of branches is not the same at each stage.

Example 3. How many different quartets can be chosen from 6 sopranos, 3 contraltos, 5 tenors, and 2 basses?

$$6 \times 3 \times 5 \times 2 = 180$$

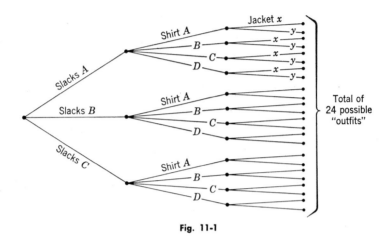

Fig. 11-1

Note that no two of these 180 sets are identical in all respects. Each one of them differs from all the other 179 sets in at least one respect. Note also that tabulating or using a tree diagram is quite impracticable.

Example 4. In how many different ways can 4 letters be posted in 5 different letter boxes? The first letter may be dropped in any one of 5 boxes, or in 5 ways; the second letter can also be disposed of in any one of 5 different ways. The same is true for each of the two remaining letters. Hence,

$$5 \times 5 \times 5 \times 5 = 5^4 = 625.$$

Note that we put the letters into the boxes, not the boxes into the letters; the answer is not 4^5, but 5^4.

Example 5. Four people enter a room in which there are 7 vacant chairs. In how many different ways may they choose their seats? The first person may choose his chair in 7 different ways; the second person may choose his chair in only 6 different ways, since one of the 7 originally vacant chairs is now occupied; etc. Hence,

$$7 \times 6 \times 5 \times 4 = 840.$$

Note that we are putting the people into the chairs, not the chairs into the people.

EXERCISE 11–1

1. From 8 women and 6 men, how many different couples can be formed for dancing?

2. In how many different ways can we put 4 pencils in 3 pockets, assuming that each pocket can hold all the pencils?

3. If 2 dice are thrown, in how many different ways can they fall?

4. Three coins are pitched; in how many different ways can they come up?

5. An ace and a jack are to be selected from an ordinary deck of 52 cards. In how many different ways can the selection be made?

6. Six people enter a bus in which there are 10 vacant seats. In how many ways may they be seated?

7. Three rival salesmen stop in a city in which there are 6 hotels. In how many ways may they stop over so that each one stays at a different hotel?

8. How many different kinds of passenger tickets will a railroad company need to print for use on a line on which there are 18 stations, if only one-way tickets are sold between all stations?

9. A woman has 3 pairs of differently colored gloves. In how many ways may she select a right glove and a left glove? How many of these selections will not be mates?

10. At a banquet there are 8 men and their wives. How many different couples can be formed for dinner, if no man escorts his wife?

permutations

When a set of objects is placed in some definite order or sequence, the particular arrangement is called a *permutation*. For example, the 3 letters A, B, and C can be arranged in 6 possible ways, reading from left to right understood:

$$ABC \qquad BAC \qquad CAB$$
$$ACB \qquad BCA \qquad CBA$$

No two of these permutations are alike, if we agree always to read from left to right.

Similarly, 4 bottles may be arranged on a shelf (from left to right) in exactly 24 different ways:

1234	2134	3124	4123
1243	2143	3142	4132
1324	2314	3214	4213
1342	2341	3241	4231
1423	2413	3412	4312
1432	2431	3421	4321

Such a tabulation is for illustrative purposes only. More generalized reasoning would run as follows: consider 4 *empty spaces*, in sequence, to be "filled" by the 4 bottles:

The first space can be "filled" in four different ways (that is, by any one of the 4 bottles). Then the second space can be filled in three different ways (that is, by any one of the 3 remaining bottles; the third space, in two different ways; the last space can be filled in only one way (since there is only 1 book left). Hence the total number of possible permutations is

$$4 \times 3 \times 2 \times 1 = 24.$$

Note that this is simply an application of the fundamental principle mentioned earlier.

permutations of *n* things, all at a time

The reasoning of the previous paragraph can be generalized to apply to the total number of permutations of n different things, taken all at a time. Thus if there are n objects in a set, the number of possible permutations (in a row, from left to right) is given by

$$_nP_n = n(n-1)(n-2)(n-3)\ldots 3 \times 2 \times 1, \quad \text{or} \quad _nP_n = n!$$

where $_nP_n$ means the total number of possible different arrangements of a set of n different things taken n at a time, and where the continued product $n(n-1)(n-2)\ldots 3 \times 2 \times 1$ is abbreviated $n!$ (read "factorial n"). Thus

$$4! = 4 \cdot 3 \cdot 2 \cdot 1 = 24$$
$$5! = 5 \cdot 4 \cdot 3 \cdot 2 \cdot 1 = 120$$
$$6! = 6 \cdot 5 \cdot 4 \cdot 3 \cdot 2 \cdot 1 = 720$$
$$k! = k(k-1)(k-2)\ldots 4 \cdot 3 \cdot 2 \cdot 1$$

Note that in a factorial product, the last factor is 1, and the number of factors is equal to the highest factor. The factors are consecutive integers in descending order.

Example 1. Find the total number of different possible arrangements of the letters of the word *rhombus*, taking them all at a time.

$$_7P_7 = 7 \cdot 6 \cdot 5 \cdot 4 \cdot 3 \cdot 2 \cdot 1 = 5040.$$

Example 2. How many 4-place numbers may be formed from the digits 2, 4, 6, 8, allowing no repetitions of digits? How many, if a digit may be repeated one or more times?

With no repetitions: $\quad _4P_4 = 4! = 4 \cdot 3 \cdot 2 \cdot 1 = 24.$
With repetitions: $\quad \quad 4^4 = 256.$

permutations of *n* things, some at a time

Here we want to know the number of possible arrangements of n things taken r at a time. For example, how many arrangements of 4 letters each can be made from the letters of the word *harvest?*

$$_7P_4 = 7 \cdot 6 \cdot 5 \cdot 4 = 840.$$

In general,

$$_nP_r = n(n-1)(n-2)\ldots(n-r+1),$$

where n things are arranged by taking r at a time.

Example 1. How many 4-place numbers can be formed from the digits 1, 2, 3, 4, 5, 6, 7, 8, 9, no digit being repeated?

Here $n = 9$ and $r = 4$; so, $_9P_4 = 9 \cdot 8 \cdot 7 \cdot 6 = 3024.$

Example 2. How many telephone dial call-names of 2 letters each can be made from the 26 letters of the alphabet, allowing no repetitions, and disregarding the fact that some of them cannot be "pronounced"?

Here $n = 26$, $r = 2$; so, $_{26}P_2 = 26 \cdot 25 = 650.$

Note that in using this formula, the number of factors is r; the highest factor is n; and the last factor is always one more than the difference between n and r, that is, $(n - r + 1)$. Note also that $r \leq n$; if $r = n$, then the last factor $(n - r + 1)$ reduces to 1.

If some of the objects of a set are alike, that is, indistinguishable from one another, we use a slightly modified formula. Thus if, of n things, p are alike of one kind, q are alike of another kind, etc., the rest being all different, then the number of possible different permutations is given by

$$\frac{n!}{p!\,q!\cdots}.$$

Example 1. In how many distinct ways can 4 identical pennies and 6 identical nickels be arranged in a row? Here $n = 10$, $p = 4$, $q = 6$; so

$$\frac{10!}{4!\,6!} = \frac{10 \cdot 9 \cdot 8 \cdot 7 \cdot 6 \cdot 5 \cdot 4 \cdot 3 \cdot 2 \cdot 1}{(4 \cdot 3 \cdot 2 \cdot 1)(6 \cdot 5 \cdot 4 \cdot 3 \cdot 2 \cdot 1)} = 210.$$

Example 2. How many distinct arrangements can be made by using all the letters of the word *parallel?* Here $n = 8$, $p = 3$, $q = 2$ (3 l's, 2 a's); so

$$\frac{8!}{3!\,2!} = \frac{8 \cdot 7 \cdot 6 \cdot 5 \cdot 4 \cdot 3 \cdot 2 \cdot 1}{(3 \cdot 2 \cdot 1)(2 \cdot 1)} = 3360.$$

EXERCISE 11–2

1. The Greek alphabet has 24 letters. How many names of Greek letter fraternities can be formed having three letters each, (*a*) if no repetitions are allowed? (*b*) if repetitions are allowed?

2. In how many ways can 6 pupils be seated in 6 seats? in 8 seats?

3. A railway signal tower has 3 arms, each of which may be set in 4 different positions (including the position of rest). How many different signals can be made using all three arms?

4. In how many ways may a child insert 8 different coins in 2 piggy banks?

5. In how many ways may a coach assign his players on a basketball team if he has a squad of 9 men, each of whom can play in any one of the 5 positions?

6. In how many different ways may a baseball team be formed from a squad of 9 men, if one of them is always the catcher, but the other 8 can play in all positions?

7. In how many ways can a number of 4 figures be formed from the digits 0 to 6 inclusive without repeating any digit?

8. If $_nP_4$ equals 8 times $_nP_3$, find the value of n.

9. In how many different ways can the letters of the word *isosceles* be arranged?

10. In how many ways can 2 pennies, 3 nickels, and 5 dimes be distributed among 10 children so that each child receives one coin?

combinations

A particular set of things without any regard to how they are arranged among themselves is called a combination of things, or simply a *combination*. The symbol for the number of possible combinations or sets of n things taken r at a time is $_nC_r$. For example, with the 5 letters u, v, x, y, z, taking 3 letters at a time, it is possible to form 10 different combinations:

uvx	*uvz*	*vxz*	*xyu*	*vyz*
uvy	*vxy*	*xyz*	*uyz*	*uxz*

To derive a formula determining the number of combinations of n things taken r at a time, we suppose there are x such combinations, that is, $_nC_r = x$. Remember that each of these x sets differs in composition from each of the others. Now imagine that the r objects in any one of these x sets are rearranged in all possible ways among themselves, and further, that this is done with all x sets. This would yield $(x) \cdot (r!)$ arrangements in all. But this is precisely the total number of possible arrangements of n things taken r at a time, or $_nP_r$.

Hence, $$x \cdot r! = {}_nP_r,$$

or $$x = \frac{_nP_r}{r!}.$$

In other words:

$$_nC_r = \frac{_nP_r}{r!} = \frac{n(n-1)(n-2)\ldots(n-r+1)}{r!}.$$

Note that there are the same number of factors in the numerator as in the denominator, namely, r factors.

Example 1. In how many ways can a group of three cheerleaders be selected from a group of 8 candidates?

$$_8C_3 = \frac{8 \cdot 7 \cdot 6}{3 \cdot 2 \cdot 1} = 56.$$

Example 2. How many straight lines are determined by 10 points, no 3 of which lie in the same straight line? To determine a line we must select 2 points; selecting pairs of points from among 10 points gives

$$_{10}C_2 = \frac{10 \cdot 9}{2 \cdot 1} = 45.$$

Example 3. In how many ways may a committee of 4 seniors and 2 juniors be selected from 9 seniors and 6 juniors?

$$_9C_4 \cdot _6C_2 = \frac{9 \cdot 8 \cdot 7 \cdot 6}{4 \cdot 3 \cdot 2 \cdot 1} \cdot \frac{6 \cdot 5}{2 \cdot 1} = 1890.$$

If we set $r = n$ in the formula $_nC_r$ we obtain

$$_nC_n = \frac{_nP_n}{n!} = \frac{n!}{n!} = 1,$$

a result which is consistent with "common sense," since the only way to select a set of n things from a set of n things, is to take them all, which can be done in only one way.

Furthermore, every time we select a set of r things from a set of n things $(r < n)$, there is obviously a set of $(n - r)$ things which remains. Hence the number of sets of n things taken r at a time is the same as the number of sets taken $(n - r)$ at a time, or

$$_nC_r = _nC_{n-r}.$$

Finally, in the relation $_nC_r = _nC_{n-r}$, if we set $r = n$, we have

$$_nC_n = _nC_{n-n},$$
$$\text{or} \quad _nC_n = _nC_0.$$

But we saw above that

$$_nC_n = 1; \quad \text{so} \quad _nC_0 = 1,$$

which is again consistent with common sense. There is only one way to select a set of zero things from a set of n things: leave them alone.

total combinations of *n* things

If a mechanic has 5 different tools in his kit, how many different selections of tools can he make by using some or all of them?

$$\begin{aligned}
\text{Using 1 at a time: } {}_5C_1 &= 5 \\
\text{Using 2 at a time: } {}_5C_2 &= 10 \\
\text{Using 3 at a time: } {}_5C_3 &= 10 \\
\text{Using 4 at a time: } {}_5C_4 &= 5 \\
\text{Using 5 at a time: } {}_5C_5 &= \underline{1} \\
\text{Total number of combinations} &= 31
\end{aligned}$$

In general, the total number of combinations (T) of n things taken in sets of one, two, three, . . . up to all n at a time is given by the expression

$$T = {}_nC_1 + {}_nC_2 + {}_nC_3 + \ldots + {}_nC_n.$$

Example 1. A group of 8 children attends a birthday party. Each child is introduced to every other child once. How many introductions are there? It takes 2 individuals to constitute an "introduction," regardless of the order in which they are presented to each other. Hence

$$_8C_2 = \frac{8 \cdot 7}{2 \cdot 1} = 28.$$

Example 2. How many squads of 4 can be chosen from 7 soldiers (a) so as to include one particular soldier? (b) so as to exclude a particular soldier?

$$(a) \; {}_6C_3 = \frac{6 \cdot 5 \cdot 4}{3 \cdot 2 \cdot 1} = 20;$$

$$(b) \; {}_6C_4 = \frac{6 \cdot 5 \cdot 4 \cdot 3}{4 \cdot 3 \cdot 2 \cdot 1} = 15.$$

Example 3. In how many ways can 7 presents be given to 2 children so that one child receives 3 and the other receives 4?

$$_7C_4 = {}_7C_3 = \frac{7 \cdot 6 \cdot 5}{3 \cdot 2 \cdot 1} = 35.$$

Note that every time we select a set of 3 prizes for one child, the 4 remaining prizes form a set for the other child.

EXERCISE 11–3

1. In how many ways may a set of 12 objects be divided into 2 equal sets?

2. What is the maximum number of points in which 6 straight lines can intersect each other?

3. Given a set of 8 points, no three of which lie in the same straight line; what is the maximum number of triangles that can be formed by joining these points?

4. A club consists of 15 members; they elect a president, a secretary and a treasurer. In how many ways can this be done?

5. In how many ways can 4 prizes be awarded to 6 people, if each person may receive any number of prizes?

6. On a test there are 10 questions. Pupils are required to answer the first question and any 7 others. In how many ways can they do this?

7. At a certain trial, 7 jurors voted for acquittal and 5 voted for conviction. In how many ways might this have occurred?

8. How many different "hands" of 4 cards can be dealt from a deck of 52 cards?

9. From among 5 professors and 8 students, how many publications committees of 6 members can be appointed containing (*a*) at least 2 professors; (*b*) exactly 2 professors; (*c*) not more than 2 professors?

10. Eight basketball teams wish to arrange a schedule of games such that each team shall play every other team twice. How many games must they schedule?

11. Four men and 3 women decide to play a game of doubles at tennis. If each side is to consist of one man and one woman, in how many ways can they choose sides?

12. Explain why $_nC_n = 1$; why $_nC_0 = 1$.

13. Prove, by using formulas, that $_nC_r = {_nC_{n-r}}$.

14. The total number of combinations of n things taken some or all at a time can be shown to be equal to $2^n - 1$, as follows. There are two ways of dealing with each of the n things—either choosing it, or rejecting it. So the total number of ways of dealing with the n things is 2^n. But 2^n includes the case in which *each* of the n things was rejected. Hence the total number of combinations of n things taken some or all at a time is $2^n - 1$. Now prove that

$$_nC_0 + {_nC_1} + {_nC_2} + {_nC_3} + \ldots + {_nC_n} = 2^n.$$

PROBABILITY

the concept of probability

We are constantly alluding to the "chances" that a certain event will or will not take place: "it won't rain tomorrow"; "the train is very likely to be late"; "it is extremely unlikely that the bank made a mistake"; and so on. The concept of mathematical probability dates back to about 300 years ago, when Pascal, Fermat, Gauss, Bernoulli, De Moivre and Laplace contributed to the theory of games of chance. The idea of probability may be interpreted in four or five ways, or, from another point of view, it may be argued that there is only one kind of probability. Nevertheless, it suits our purpose to regard probability from two rather different approaches: (1) the so-called classical, or *a priori* probability, and (2) the statistical or *empirical* probability.

Consider a coin tossed at random, where by the phrase "random toss" we imply that the coin is allowed to fall freely, without any bias or interference, or "left completely to chance." We intuitively feel that it can land in one and only one of two possible ways—either heads or tails. (We dismiss the possibility of its "landing" on its edge—in the sand, for example.) We know, *a priori*, that there are only two possibilities (H or T); we know that it must land, one way or the other (that much is certain); and we tacitly assume that there is no reason to expect one eventuality rather than the other. We express these intuitive ideas mathematically by saying that the chance of obtaining a "head" is one out of two, or $\frac{1}{2}$; the chance of obtaining a tail is equally likely, also one out of two, or $\frac{1}{2}$. Or again, suppose that a bag contains 3 apples and 2 oranges. If we draw one of these 5 objects from the bag at random (blindfolded, etc.), we may say that the probability of drawing an apple, in one trial, is $\frac{3}{5}$; the probability of drawing an orange, in one trial, is $\frac{2}{5}$.

These two examples illustrate a simple but fundamental principle of *a priori* probability, namely, that of several equally likely events, the probability that a given event will happen is the ratio of the number of favorable possibilities to the total number of possibilities. Expressed symbolically, we say that of n possible ways, if an event can happen in x ways and fail to happen in y ways, where $x + y = n$, and each of these ways is equally liable to occur, then the probability that the event will happen (p) is $\dfrac{x}{x + y}$, and the probability that it will fail (q) is $\dfrac{y}{x + y}$.

Obviously, $p + q = \dfrac{x}{x + y} + \dfrac{y}{x + y} = 1$, which may be interpreted to mean that it is certain that an event will happen or fail; that is, $p + q = 1$, where certainty is represented by unity. Note that if an event is certain to happen, $y = 0$, and $p = \dfrac{x}{x + 0} = \dfrac{x}{x} = 1$. Also, if the probability that an event will happen is p, then the event that it will not happen (that is, it will fail) is $q = 1 - p$.

Example 1. What are the chances of a deuce showing on one toss of a die? Since a die has 6 faces, each numbered differently, it can "land" in any one of 6 different ways. If the toss or roll has been a random act (die not "loaded," no "faked roll," etc., etc.), only one of these six ways is "favorable," that is, a two-spot. Hence (1) chance of a deuce (happening) $= \frac{1}{6}$; (2) chance of no deuce (failing) $= \frac{5}{6}.$

Example 2. If 1 letter of the name "Carol" be selected at random, what are the chances that it will be a vowel? Here five choices are possible. Only two of them are vowels, and therefore "favorable." So, the chances of a vowel on one selection are 2 out of 5, or $\frac{2}{5}.$

Example 3. If 3 coins are tossed at random, what is the chance that there will be 2 heads and 1 tail? The total possible number of ways in which 3 tossed coins can land is $2^3 = 8$ ways, tabulated below for convenience:

1. *HTT*	2. *HHT*
3. *HTH*	4. *HHH*
5. *THT*	6. *THH*
7. *TTH*	8. *TTT*

Only 2, 3, and 6 will show 2 heads and 1 tail; hence, the chance is $\frac{3}{8}.$

Example 4. Two cards are drawn from a suit of 13 cards. What is the probability of drawing an ace and a king? The total possible number of ways of selecting 2 cards from 13 cards equals $_{13}C_2 = \frac{13 \cdot 12}{1 \cdot 2} = 78$ ways. Only one of these 78 possibilities is an ace-king. Hence, $p = \frac{1}{78}.$

Example 5. If 2 dice are tossed, what is the probability that a total of 7 will turn up? The total number of ways in which 2 dice can fall equals 6×6, or 36 ways. Of these 36 possibilities, only 6 will yield a total of 7, namely 1 and 6, 6 and 1, 2 and 5, 5 and 2, 3 and 4, 4 and 3. Hence the probability of a total of 7 equals $\frac{6}{36}$, or $\frac{1}{6}.$

The reader should be aware of two pertinent considerations with regard to *a priori* probability. To begin with, the notion of genuine "randomness" is clearly an ideal which can only be approximated when dealing with physical objects. Secondly, the probability ratios expressing favorable to total possibilities, etc., are to be interpreted as meaningful only when a very large number of trials is involved; these ratios cannot be applied to a single event. For example, if a coin is tossed 10 times, it might very well come up heads 7 times and tails 3 times; upon 100 tosses, one might obtain 56 heads and 44 tails; with 1000 trials, one might obtain 503 heads and 497 tails. In short, the larger the number of trials, the more closely the ratio will approach ½.

EXERCISE 11–4

1. What is the chance of an ace showing on one toss of a 6-sided die? The chance of an ace or a deuce on one throw?

2. What is the chance of an even number appearing on one throw of a 6-sided die?

3. What is the chance of selecting (*a*) a vowel on the first trial from "Arnold"; (*b*) a consonant on the first trial from "Marie"?

4. From a deck of 52 cards, what are the chances of drawing, in one trial: (*a*) an ace; (*b*) the king of spades; (*c*) an honor card (A, K, Q, J, or 10).

5. A bag contains 5 white balls and 3 black balls. What is the chance of drawing a black ball? A white ball?

6. The chance of a certain event happening is $\frac{2}{9}$. We say that "the odds in favor" of it happening are "2 to 7." What are the odds that it won't happen?

7. If the odds are 5 to 1 against an event, what is the chance that it won't happen? That it will happen?

8. If the odds are 1 to 3 that an event will take place, what is the chance that it will happen? How many more times is it likely to fail than to take place?

9. At a card party there were 5 door prizes and 95 blanks. What is the chance of a person holding one ticket receiving a door prize?

10. A man buys a book of 10 chances on a television set to be raffled. If the total number of chances sold is 2000, what is the probability that he will win the set?

11. Two coins are tossed. What is the probability that *at least* one tail will turn up? (*Hint:* 2 coins can come up in 4 possible ways, *HH; HT; TH, TT*).

12. Two coins are tossed. (*a*) What is the probability that just one tail will turn up? (*b*) What is the probability that exactly two heads will turn up?

13. In a class of 18 girls and 12 boys, 1 pupil is chosen at random. What is the chance that the pupil chosen will be a girl?

14. In a single toss of 2 dice, what is the probability of obtaining a total of 4?

15. If 4 cards are selected from a deck of 52 cards containing 13 spades, what is the probability that they will all be spades?

16. A hostess has 7 guests; she invites 3 of them to play bridge. What are the chances that 2 particular ones will be among those invited?

17. If 5 coins are tossed at one time, what is the probability that all 5 will fall heads?

18. Five coins are tossed at random. What is the chance that exactly two of them will turn up heads?

19. If 3 cards are drawn from a deck of 52 cards, what is the chance that they will be ace, king and queen of the same suit?

20. Of a group of 10 children, 4 have red hair. If 2 children are selected from the group at random, what is the probability that both will have red hair?

21. If there are 8 instructors in a given department and they are assigned to classes at random, what is the chance that you will have a particular instructor in a given semester? What is the probability that you will have this same instructor for two successive semesters?

22. What is the probability that a year, not a leap year, will have 53 Sundays?

probability of several events

If two events are of such a nature that the happening or failing of one of them has no influence upon the happening or failing of the other, they are called *independent* events. The probability that two independent events will occur simultaneously or in succession is called a *compound probability*. The compound probability of two independent events equals the product of the two events taken singly. This principle is easily proved. It can be extended to more than two independent events. Thus for n independent events whose respective probabilities are $p_1, p_2, p_3, \ldots, p_n$, the compound probability (p) that all n events will occur simultaneously (or successively) is given

$$p = p_1 \cdot p_2 \cdot p_3 \cdot \ldots p_n.$$

Example. What is the probability of obtaining a deuce on the first throw of a die, followed by a 6 on the second throw? The probability of the first event is $\frac{1}{6}$; that of the second event is also $\frac{1}{6}$. Hence the probability of both happening is $\frac{1}{6} \times \frac{1}{6} = \frac{1}{36}$. (An alternative method of reasoning would be to say that in 2 throws, 2 dice may fall in 36 ways, only one of which is favorable; hence $p = \frac{1}{36}$, as before.)

If the occurrence of one event affects the occurrence of another, the two events are said to be *dependent* events. For example, given 4 coins (a penny, a nickel, a dime and a quarter), if any coin is selected and not replaced, the probability of drawing the nickel on the second draw is affected. It can be proved that if p_1 is the probability of one event, and p_2 the probability of a second event after the first has occurred, then the probability that the two events will occur in the specified order is $p_1 \cdot p_2$. This principle can also be extended to three or more dependent events.

Example. What is the probability of drawing a king and then a queen from a deck of 52 cards containing 4 kings and 4 queens?

$$p_1 = \frac{4}{52}, \text{ and } p_2 = \frac{4}{51};$$

Hence, probability of both events

$$= \frac{4}{52} \times \frac{4}{51} = \frac{16}{2652}.$$

mutually exclusive events

It sometimes happens that when one event has occurred, the possibility of another event is excluded, it being understood that we are referring to the same given occasion or trial. Such events are known as *mutually exclusive* events. For example, throwing a coin once can yield a 5 or a 6, but not both, in the same toss. It can be proved that if the separate probabilities of two mutually exclusive events are p_1 and p_2, respectively, then the probability that *one* of these events will happen on any particular occasion when either could happen is $p_1 + p_2$.

Example 1. What is the chance of throwing either a 1 or a 6 in a single throw of a die?

$$p = \frac{1}{6} + \frac{1}{6} = \frac{1}{3}.$$

Example 2. What is the probability of drawing either an ace, or a king or a queen from a suit of 13 cards?

$$\frac{1}{13} + \frac{1}{13} + \frac{1}{13} = \frac{3}{13}.$$

Example 3. What is the chance of throwing either a head or a tail in one toss of a coin?

$$\tfrac{1}{2} + \tfrac{1}{2} = 1$$

EXERCISE 11–5

1. What are the chances of throwing 2 threes in two successive throws of a single die?

2. What is the chance of throwing 2 tails in a single throw of 2 coins? In two successive throws of 1 coin?

3. Is the probability of throwing 3 fours in three throws of a single die the same as the probability of throwing 3 fours in one throw of 3 dice? What is the probability?

4. In drawing 3 balls from a bag containing 4 red balls, 5 white balls, and 2 blue balls, what is the chance of drawing 1 red, 1 white and 1 blue ball, in that order?

5. From a group of 5 men and 4 women, 2 persons are selected at random. (*a*) What is the probability that the first will be a man and the second a woman? (*b*) What is the chance that they are both women?

6. What is the probability of either a 1, a 2, or a 6 in a single throw of a die?

7. (*a*) What is the chance of throwing either a total of 3 or a total of 12 in a single throw of two dice? (*b*) What is the probability of throwing a total of 7 in one throw of 2 dice? (*c*) What are the odds in favor of the second of these eventualities?

8. Prove that the compound probability of two independent events equals the product of their respective probabilities taken singly. (*Hint:* Let $p_1 = a_1/n_1$, and $p_2 = a_2/n_2$.)

9. If a die is thrown four times in succession, what is the chance that a one-spot is not thrown?

10. If two dice are thrown, what is the chance that both will turn up 6?

empirical probability

There are many situations in which the number of favorable events and the total possible events cannot be counted, as in connection with *a priori* probability discussed thus far. For example, of 1000 automobiles on the highway, we cannot know beforehand how many will meet with an accident; out of 5000 men aged 40, we cannot determine from *a priori* considerations how many will survive one year. If, however, adequate statistical records are kept of such phenomena, the probability of occurrence or non-occurrence can be approximately determined. This is called *empirical probability.* For example, if it has been observed that an event happens h times out of n possible times, and if n is a comparatively large number, the probability that the event in question will happen in general may be taken as h/n. Please note that we have avoided saying just how large n must be, but clearly the greater the number of observed instances, the more "dependable" the probability ratio becomes. Thus if many thousands of recorded instances of the number of survivors from age 40 to age 41 yield a ratio of 0.99382, we are justified in saying that of a group of 100,000 persons aged 40, very nearly 99,382 will live to reach age 41. Experience has shown that empirical probabilities, if carefully determined on the basis of adequate samples, can be applied to large groups in the aggregate. In the long run, predicted results and actual results agree quite closely. On the other hand, applying such a probability ratio to a single individual is virtually meaningless, as ordinary experience and observation readily testify.

In all life insurance transactions, it is necessary to consider the probability of living or dying in any year and the present value of money at interest. The probability of living or dying is usually found by means of a mortality table.

MATHEMATICAL BASIS OF LIFE INSURANCE

death rates

The operations and calculations of a life insurance company are based upon the vital statistics collected on the lives of large numbers of policyholders. One of the most important tools in this connection is the determination of death rates at various ages. For example, the records of a life insurance company might show the following facts concerning some of their policyholders:

Age	Number of Policyholders at Beginning of the Year	Number Dying during the Year	Death Rate per 1000
18	11,340	26	2.30
19	8861	21	2.37
20	9876	24	2.43
21	8012	20	2.50
22	10,770	28	2.60

Again, a life insurance company may have had the following experience with its 21-year-old policyholders over a period of 6 years:

Year	Number of Policyholders Age 21 at Beginning of Year	Number Dying during Year	Death Rate per 1000
1954	9250	23	2.49
1955	8654	22	2.54
1956	9417	24	2.55
1957	9603	26	2.71
1958	10,275	25	2.43
1959	11,432	28	2.45
			6)15.17
			2.53

From these figures, the average death rate per 1000 at age 21 during this 6-year period was $15.17 \div 6 = 2.53$.

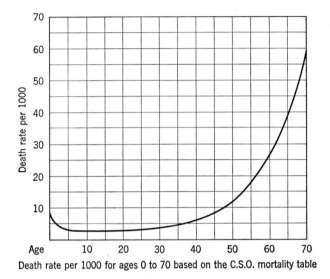

Death rate per 1000 for ages 0 to 70 based on the C.S.O. mortality table

Fig. 11-2

the mortality table

A mortality table may be described as a statistical device for exhibiting probabilities of life and of death at various ages. If it were possible to trace accurately say 100,000 individuals from the date of their birth until the date of death in each case, recording the number dying in each year of age and the number surviving each year, we would have the basis for a mortality table. Obviously it is impossible to trace a given group of individuals in exactly this way. Fortunately it is not necessary to proceed by this method. Since we are primarily concerned with the probability that a person of a given age will live or die within a year, these respective probabilities for two different ages may be determined independently of each other. Thus the number dying (or surviving) within a year out of a group aged 35 and the number dying (or surviving) out of a group aged 36 might be obtained from two different groups; moreover, these two groups need not even be equally numerous, provided that both groups are sufficiently large in number to yield statistically valid data. The important consideration is the relative number of individuals at each age as compared with the number alive at the preceding age. The actual numbers are of comparatively little importance; it is the ratios that count.

In short, a mortality table shows approximately how many people in a given age group will survive one year, or, how many will die within the year. With such tables as a basis, a life insurance company can determine rather closely how much each policyholder must contribute each year in the form of premiums, and about how much money it may expect to have to pay out in claims during the year. Mortality tables form the basis not only of the life insurance business, but they are also indispensable in connection with life annuities, inheritance taxes, retirement pensions, old-age insurance, social security, and similar problems. To be sure, there will be differences in these life and death probabilities for different nationalities, for different races, for different periods of time, for males and females, and for various occupational groups. But such differences need not concern us here.

the c.s.o. table

We reproduce here a part of the mortality table widely used by American life insurance companies today, the table which for many purposes superseded the famous "American Experience Table." It is called the "Commissioners 1941 Standard Ordinary Mortality Table," and is based on the lives and deaths of many thousands of policyholders of several leading life insurance companies for the period 1930–1940.

Let us see how such a table may be used. The symbol l_x represents the number of persons living at any age (x). For example, the number of persons living at age 20, from the table, is $l_{20} = 951,483$. The number of survivors from this group who attain age 21 is 949,171, since 2312 persons died between ages 20 and 21. The symbol d_x represents the number of persons dying in the year of age from (x) to $(x + 1)$; for example, $d_{20} = 2312$, the number of persons who died between ages 20 and 21 out of l_{20} persons who had attained the age of 20.

The probability p_{20} that a person 20 years of age will survive to age 21 is given by the ratio

$$\frac{l_{21}}{l_{20}} = \frac{949,171}{951,483} = 0.99757.$$

Hence the probability that a person age 20 will die within the year q_{20} is given by the relation

TABLE 9.   Commissioners 1941 Standard Ordinary Mortality Table

Age (x)	Number Living (l_x)	Deaths in Year (d_x)	Probability of Dying within a Year (q_x)	Age (x)	Number Living (l_x)	Deaths in Year (d_x)	Probability of Dying within a Year (q_x)
1	1,000,000	5770	0.00577	51	800,910	10,628	0.01327
2	994,230	4116	0.00414	52	790,282	11,301	0.01430
3	990,114	3347	0.00338	53	778,981	12,020	0.01543
4	986,767	2950	0.00299	54	766,961	12,770	0.01665
5	983,817	2715	0.00276	55	754,191	13,560	0.01798
6	981,102	2561	0.00261	56	740,631	14,390	0.01943
7	978,541	2417	0.00247	57	726,241	15,251	0.02100
8	976,124	2255	0.00231	58	710,990	16,147	0.02271
9	973,869	2065	0.00212	59	694,843	17,072	0.02457
10	971,804	1914	0.00197	60	677,771	18,022	0.02659
11	969,890	1852	0.00191	61	659,749	18,988	0.02878
12	968,038	1859	0.00192	62	640,761	19,979	0.03118
13	966,179	1913	0.00198	63	620,782	20,958	0.03376
14	964,266	1996	0.00207	64	599,824	21,942	0.03658
15	962,270	2069	0.00215	65	577,882	22,907	0.03964
16	960,201	2103	0.00219	66	554,975	23,842	0.04296
17	958,098	2156	0.00225	67	531,113	24,730	0.04656
18	955,942	2199	0.00230	68	506,403	25,553	0.05046
19	953,743	2260	0.00237	69	480,850	26,302	0.05470
20	951,483	2312	0.00243	70	454,548	26,955	0.05930
21	949,171	2382	0.00251	71	427,593	27,481	0.06427
22	946,789	2452	0.00259	72	400,112	27,872	0.06966
23	944,337	2531	0.00268	73	372,240	28,104	0.07550
24	941,806	2609	0.00277	74	344,136	28,154	0.08181
25	939,197	2705	0.00288	75	315,982	28,009	0.08864
26	936,492	2800	0.00299	76	287,973	27,651	0.09602
27	933,692	2904	0.00311	77	260,322	27,071	0.10399
28	930,788	3025	0.00325	78	233,251	26,262	0.11259
29	927,763	3154	0.00340	79	206,989	25,224	0.12186
30	924,609	3292	0.00356	80	181,765	23,966	0.13185
31	921,317	3437	0.00373	81	157,799	22,502	0.14260
32	917,880	3598	0.00392	82	135,297	20,857	0.15416
33	914,282	3767	0.00412	83	114,440	19,062	0.16657
34	910,515	3961	0.00435	84	95,378	17,157	0.17988
35	906,554	4161	0.00459	85	78,221	15,185	0.19413
36	902,393	4386	0.00486	86	63,036	13,198	0.20937
37	898,007	4625	0.00515	87	49,838	11,245	0.22563
38	893,382	4878	0.00546	88	38,593	9378	0.24300
39	888,504	5162	0.00581	89	29,215	7638	0.26144
40	883,342	5459	0.00618	90	21,577	6063	0.28099
41	877,883	5785	0.00659	91	15,514	4681	0.30173
42	872,098	6131	0.00703	92	10,833	3506	0.32364
43	865,967	6503	0.00751	93	7327	2540	0.34666
44	859,464	6910	0.00804	94	4787	1776	0.37100
45	852,554	7340	0.00861	95	3011	1193	0.39621
46	845,214	7801	0.00923	96	1818	813	0.44719
47	837,413	8299	0.00991	97	1005	551	0.54826
48	829,114	8822	0.01064	98	454	329	0.72467
49	820,292	9392	0.01145	99	125	125	1.00000
50	810,900	9990	0.01232				

$$q_{20} = 1 - p_{20},$$
$$\text{or} \quad q_{20} = 1 - 0.99757 = 0.00243,$$

which appears in the third column of the table.

We can generalize these relations as follows

$$l_{x+1} < l_x \tag{1}$$
$$d_x = l_x - l_{x+1} \tag{2}$$

The deaths over any number of years may be found by deducting the number of living at the end of a given period of years from the number living at the beginning of the period. For example, the deaths over a 3-year period from age (x) to age $(x + 2)$ would be $d_x + d_{x+1} + d_{x+2}$; or

$$l_x - l_{x+3} = d_x + d_{x+1} + d_{x+2}. \tag{3}$$

In general,

$$l_x - l_{x+n} = d_x + d_{x+1} + d_{x+2} + \ldots + d_{x+n-1}, \tag{4}$$
$$\text{and} \quad l_x = d_x + d_{x+1} + d_{x+2} + \ldots \text{ to the end of the table.} \tag{5}$$

For example, from the third column of the table we see that the probability of dying in the year of age 49 to age 50 is $q_{49} = 0.01145$. Hence the probability of living another year at age 49 is $p_{49} = 1 - q_{49} = 1 - 0.01145 = 0.98855$. In other words,

$$p_x = \frac{l_{x+1}}{l_x}, \tag{6}$$

which may also be written as

$$p_x \cdot l_x = l_{x+1} \tag{7}$$

Of course, as always,

$$\left. \begin{array}{l} p_x + q_x = 1, \\ \text{or} \quad p_x = 1 - q_x, \\ \text{and} \quad q_x = 1 - p_x. \end{array} \right\} \tag{8}$$

The probability of surviving 2 years at age (x) is expressed as $_2p_x$, and the probability of surviving n years is $_np_x$. Thus the probability of living 3 years may be regarded as the compound probability of three separate events happening, namely,

1. That a person age (x) will survive one year to age $(x + 1)$.
2. That he will then live a second year to age $(x + 2)$.
3. That he will survive another year to age $(x + 3)$.

Therefore

$$_3p_x = p_x \cdot p_{x+1} \cdot p_{x+2}. \tag{9}$$

This is easily seen to be equivalent to $\dfrac{l_{x+3}}{l_x}$, since

$$p_x \cdot p_{x+1} \cdot p_{x+2} = \frac{l_{x+1}}{l_x} \cdot \frac{l_{x+2}}{l_{x+1}} \cdot \frac{l_{x+3}}{l_{x+2}},$$

$$\text{or,} \quad {}_3p_x = \frac{l_{x+3}}{l_x}. \tag{10}$$

In general, then,

$$\,_np_x = \frac{l_{x+n}}{l_x}. \tag{11}$$

computing the premium

To determine the premium to be charged, the "mortality factor" is combined with the "compound interest factor" (that is, present value) as suggested in what follows. To begin with, the *net single premium* is the mathematical equivalent of the benefit according to the mortality table and the rate of interest employed in the calculation. This will be best understood by considering the benefit under a whole life policy. We shall assume that the premiums are paid at the beginning of each year, and that the claims are paid at the end of the year of death. Suppose that each one of the l_x persons in a group at age (x) has contracted a policy for $1 on his life. Since the number of deaths in the first year would be d_x, the value (at the beginning of the year) of the death claims due at the end of the year would be $v \cdot d_x$. The deaths in the second year being d_{x+1}, the value of these death claims at the beginning of the first year would be $v^2 \cdot d_{x+1}$, and so on for succeeding years. The total present value of all the death claims would therefore be given by

$$v d_x + v^2 d_{x+1} + v^3 d_{x+2} + \ldots.$$

If this present value is distributed among the l_x persons, then each one's share will be this total present value of the benefit divided by l_x. Thus the net single premium (A_x) to be borne by each one of l_x persons whose life is insured for a benefit of $1 is given by

$$A_x = \frac{v d_x + v^2 d_{x+1} + v^3 d_{x+2} + \ldots}{l_x}.$$

This amount represents the present value of each individual's benefit at his death, and hence represents the smallest single premium which could be accepted by a company as the consideration for undertaking such an obligation.

Life insurance contracts are, however, rarely purchased by the payment of a single premium. The usual procedure is to pay for it in annual instalments. Thus the *net single premium* determined as above is commonly transformed, by suitable mathematical processes, into an equivalent *net annual premium*.

EXERCISE 11–6

1. Of 1,000,000 children 1 year old, how many will live to be 21? (Refer to the table on page 357).

2. The table shows that of 1,000,000 babies one year of age, only 181,765 will live to be 80 years old. How many will die before reaching that age?

3. Of the 1,000,000 babies age 1 year, 960,201 live to be 16 years old. What fractional part of the group lives to that age? (Express as a decimal fraction to the nearest ten-thousandth.)

4. If 960,201 of the babies live to be 16 years old but 2103 die during that year, how many live to be 17 years old? What part of those 16 years old die? Express to the nearest $\frac{1}{10}$ of 1 per cent.

5. 0.99775 of those living at the beginning of age 17 survive to age 18. This is how many per 1000? This is what per cent to the nearest tenth?

6. If 837,413 live to be 47 years old but only 454,548 become 70 years old, how many die between these two ages?

7. If 0.01327 of those living to age 51 die during that year, what part lives to be 52 years old?

8. From the table, find the probability that a person 25 years of age will live to be 30; to be 60; to be 80.

9. What are the chances that a person of 60 will live two years? 5 years? 10 years?

10. What is the probability that a person of 40 will die within 2 years? Within 5 years? Within 10 years?

11. Why does $p_x + q_x = 1$?

12. Why does $l_x - d_x = l_{x+1}$?

13. Of 50,000 persons aged 35, how many may be expected to survive to age 36? (Multiply by p_{35}.)

14. Of 200,000 persons aged 28, how many will probably die during the year? (Multiply by q_{28}.)

15. Of 400,000 persons aged 18, how many will probably die during the next two years?

16. If each of 10,000 persons at age 30 was insured for $1000, what would be the amount of death claims the company would expect to pay during the following year, assuming that all persons carried the same type policy, and neglecting overhead expense?

17. If each of 200,000 individuals at the age of 18 has his life insured for $500, how much would the company expect to pay in death benefits for this group during the next 5 years?

18. What per cent of the individuals taking out a 20-year endowment policy at age 25 live long enough to collect the face value of the policy themselves?

19. Prove that $q_x = \dfrac{l_x - l_{x+1}}{l_x}$.

20. Explain why $p_{x+n} = \dfrac{l_{x+n+1}}{l_{x+n}}$; what do the symbols mean?

FOR FURTHER READING AND STUDY

Probability

1. Bakst, Aaron. *Mathematics: Its Magic and Mastery*. New York: Van Nostrand, 1941. Pp. 329–353: "How to Have Fun with Lady Luck."
2. Cohen, J. and Hansel, M. *Risk and Gambling*. New York: Philosophical Library, 1956.
3. Compton, A. H. "Do We Live in a World of Chance?" *Yale Review* 21:86–99; September 1931.
4. Good, I. J. "Kinds of Probability." *Science* 129:443–447; Feb. 20, 1959.
5. Kraitchik, Maurice. *Mathematical Recreations*. New York: W. W. Norton, 1942. Pp. 117–141: "Probabilities."
6. Levinson, Horace. *The Science of Chance: from Probability to Statistics*. New York: Rinehart, 1950.

Life Insurance

7. Clifford, Paul, Sobel, Max, and Keiffer, Mildred. *The Mathematics of Life Insurance*. New York: Institute of Life Insurance, Educational Division, 488 Madison Ave., New York 22, N. Y. (Pamphlet) 1958.
8. Dublin, Louis. *The Facts of Life from Birth to Death*. New York: Macmillan, 1951.
9. Dublin, Louis and Lotka, A. J. *Money Value of a Man*. New York: Ronald Press Co., 1946.
10. Larson, Robert and Gaumnitz, E. A. *Life Insurance Mathematics*. New York: John Wiley, 1951.

GENERAL READING LIST

I. The Nature of Mathematics

1. Adler, Irving. *The New Mathematics*. New York: John Day, 1958. 187 p.
2. Bell, E. T. *Mathematics, Queen and Servant of Science*. New York: McGraw-Hill, 1951. 437 p.
3. Court, Nathan A. *Mathematics in Fun and in Earnest*. New York: Dial Press, 1958. 250 p.
4. Hardy, G. *A Mathematician's Apology*. Cambridge University Press, 1940. 93 p.
5. Hogben, Lancelot. *Mathematics for the Million*. New York: W. W. Norton and Company, 1955. 647 p.
6. Hogben, Lancelot. *The Wonderful World of Mathematics*. New York: W. W. Norton and Company, 1955. 69 p.
7. Kasner, Edward and Newman, James. *Mathematics and the Imagination*. New York: Simon and Schuster, 1940. 380 p.
8. Kline, Morris. *Mathematics in Western Culture*. New York: Oxford University Press, 1953. 484 p.
9. Kramer, Edna E. *The Main Stream of Mathematics*. New York: Oxford University Press, 1951. 319 p.
10. National Council of Teachers of Mathematics. Twenty-third Yearbook. *Insights into Modern Mathematics*. Washington, D. C.: The Council, 1957. 440 p.
11. National Council of Teachers of Mathematics. Twenty-fourth Yearbook. *The Growth of Mathematical Ideas: Grades K-12*. Washington, D. C.: The Council, 1959. 507 p.
12. Ogilvy, C. Stanley. *Through the Mathescope*. New York: Oxford University Press, 1956. 162 p.
13. Pedoe, D. *The Gentle Art of Mathematics*. London: The English Universities Press, Ltd., 1958. 143 p.
14. Rademacher, H. and Toeplitz, O. *The Enjoyment of Mathematics*. Princeton, N. J.: Princeton University Press, 1957. 204 p.
15. Sawyer, W. W. *Mathematician's Delight*. New York: Penguin Books, Inc., 1946. 215 p.
16. Schaaf, Wm. L. (Editor). *Mathematics: Our Great Heritage*. New York: Harper and Bros., 1948. 291 p.
17. Shackle, G. L. S. *Mathematics at the Fireside*. Cambridge (England): Cambridge University Press, 1952. 156 p.
18. Whitehead, A. N. *An Introduction to Mathematics*. New York: Oxford University Press, 1948. 256 p.
19. Whitehead, A. N. *Science and the Modern World*. New York: Pelican Mentor, 1948. 212 p. Chapter 2: "Mathematics as an Element in the History of Thought."

II. History of Mathematics

20. Ball, W. W. R. *A Short Account of the History of Mathematics*. New York and London: Macmillan, 1927. 522 p.

21. Bell, E. T. *Men of Mathematics*. New York: Simon and Schuster, 1937. 592 p.
22. Cajori, F. *A History of Mathematics*. New York: Macmillan, 1929. 516 p.
23. Eves, Howard. *An Introduction to the History of Mathematics*. New York: Rinehart, 1953. 422 p.
24. Hofman, Joseph. *The History of Mathematics*. New York: Philosophical Library, 1957.
25. Hooper, Alfred. *Makers of Mathematics*. New York: Random House; London: Faber and Faber, Ltd., 1948. 402 p.
26. Karpinski, L. C. *The History of Arithmetic*. Chicago: Rand McNally, 1925. 200 p.
27. Sanford, Vera. *A Short History of Mathematics*. Boston: Houghton Mifflin, 1930. 402 p.
28. Smith, David Eugene. *History of Mathematics*. Vol. 2. Special Topics of Elementary Mathematics. Boston: Ginn and Company, 1925; Dover Publications.
29. Smith, David Eugene. *Number Stories of Long Ago*. Washington, D. C.: National Council of Teachers of Mathematics, 1955. 160 p.
30. Smith, D. E. and Karpinski, L. C. *The Hindu-Arabic Numerals*. Boston: Ginn and Company, 1911. 160 p.
31. Struik, D. J. *A Concise History of Mathematics*. New York: Dover Publications, 1948. 299 p.
32. Sullivan, J. W. N. *The History of Mathematics in Europe*. London: Oxford University Press, 1930. 109 p.
33. Turnbull, H. W. *The Great Mathematicians*. London: Methuen, 1929. 128 p.
34. Yeldham, Florence. *The Story of Reckoning in the Middle Ages*. London: Harrap, 1926. 95 p.

III. Mathematical Recreations

35. Adler, Irving. *Magic House of Numbers*. New York: The John Day Company, 1957; Signet Key Books, 1958; 128 p.
36. Bakst, Aaron. *Mathematical Puzzles and Pastimes*. New York: D. Van Nostrand Company, 1954. 206 p.
37. Degrazia, Joseph. *Math Is Fun*. New York: The Gresham Press, 1948. 159 p.
38. Friend, J. Newton. *Numbers: Fun and Facts*. New York: Charles Scribner's Sons, 1954. 208 p.
39. Gamow, George and Stern, Marvin. *Puzzle-Math*. New York: Viking, 1958. 119 p.
40. Gilles, William. *The Magic and Oddities of Numbers*. New York: Vantage Press, 1953. 65 p.
41. Heath, Royal V. *Mathemagic, Magic Puzzles and Games with Numbers*. Simon and Schuster, 1933; Dover Publications, 1953; 138 p.
42. Hunter, J. A. H. *Fun with Figures*. New York: Oxford University Press, 1956. 160 p.
43. Hunter, J. A. H. *Figurets: More Fun with Figures*. New York: Oxford University Press, 1958. 116 p.
44. Johnson, Donovan. *Paper Folding for the Mathematics Class*. Washington, D. C.: National Council of Teachers of Mathematics, 1957. 32 p.

45. Lee, Wallace, W. *Math Miracles*. Durham, N. C.: Privately printed, 1950. 83 p.
46. Meyer, Jerome S. *Fun with Mathematics*. Cleveland and New York: World Publishing Company, 1952. 176 p.
47. Mott-Smith, Geoffrey. *Mathematical Puzzles for Beginners and Enthusiasts*. Philadelphia: Blakiston Company, 1946; Dover Publications, 1955. 248 p.
48. Northrop, Eugene. *Riddles in Mathematics*. New York: Van Nostrand, 1944. 262 p.
49. Steinhaus, H. *Mathematical Snapshots*. New York: Oxford University Press, 1950. 135 p.
50. Storme, P. and Stryfe, P. *How to Torture Your Friends*. New York: Simon & Schuster, 1941. 170 p.

ANSWERS TO PROBLEMS

EXERCISE 1-3, page 20

3. Number of elements in $P \cup Q$ is 9 or more; the number of elements in $P \cap Q$ is 4 or less.
7. $P \cap Q = \{\text{Alice, Betty}\}$; $P \cup Q = \{\text{Alice, Betty, Cora, Dot, Fred, Bill}\}$
8. (b) $[1, 7]$; (c) $[2, 8]$
9. (a) $[4, 4]$; (b) $[3, 5]$; (c) $[3, 5]$
10. (a) $[2, 4]$ and $[12, 16]$; (b) the null set

EXERCISE 1-4, page 23

3. (a) Transitive (b) None (c) Transitive (d) Transitive (e) Symmetric (f) Reflexive, transitive (g) Symmetric, transitive
4. Yes; no

EXERCISE 2-2, page 39

1. John Harris is a Hoosier.
2. Troy is north of Albany.
3. Troy is south of Albany.
4. Their corresponding angles are equal.
5. If unemployment has increased, taxes will be reduced.
9. All triangles are plane figures.
10. All squares have equal angles.
11. All *umpi* are *soli*.
12. If $a < b$, then $r < s$.
13. If $ABCD$ is a rhombus, its diagonals bisect its angles.
15. (a) p, or not-p, or both p and not-p.
    (b) p and q, or p and r, or p and both q and r.
    (c) p and q, or r, or both p and q and r.
    (d) it is not true that p and not-p.
    (e) not-p, or q, or both not-p and q.
    (f) not-p implies not-q.
    (g) it is not true that p implies q and q implies p.
    (h) p implies q if and only if not-q implies not-p.

EXERCISE 2-3, page 45

8. (*a*) Valid   (*b*) Not valid   (*c*) Not valid   (*d*) Valid   (*e*) Not valid.

EXERCISE 2-4, page 54

1. (*a*) If the corresponding sides of two triangles are not proportional, the triangles are not similar.
 (*b*) If a vehicle does not have two wheels, it is not a bicycle.
 (*c*) If he is a cripple, he is not an athlete.
 (*d*) If angle *A* is an acute angle, it is not a right angle.
 (*e*) If Smith does not increase social security benefits, he has not been elected.
6. (*a*) If two sides of a triangle are equal, the opposite angles are equal.
 (*b*) If a point is not on the perpendicular bisector of a line, it is not equidistant from the ends of the line.
 (*c*) If a point is not on the bisector of an angle, it is not equidistant from the sides of the angle.
 (*d*) If alternate interior angles are equal, the lines are parallel.
 (*e*) If two chords of a circle are equal in length, they are equally distant from the center.
15. Valid   **16.** Not valid   **18.** (*c*) and (*e*)
19. (1), (2) and (3) are valid; (4) not valid.
20. (*a*) corresponds to #3; (*b*), #1; (*c*) #5

EXERCISE 3-1, page 62

1. (*a*) No   (*b*) No   (*c*) Not if freely suspended   (*d*) Yes   (*e*) Yes   (*f*) Yes, yes, no
2. (*a*) No   (*b*) Yes   (*c*) No
3. By (1) measuring the angles with a protractor, (2) "fitting" the angles into a straight angle, (3) "successively rotating" the three sides through a total of 180°.
4. *Point symmetry:* hub of a wheel; center of a sphere.
 Line symmetry: the diagonals of a square; the bisector of an angle.
 Plane symmetry: reflection in a plane mirror; the human body.
5. (*a*) Diagonal crosspiece in a gate or door; any truss, bracket, or support which forms a triangle.
 (*b*) Pantograph; parallel rule; collapsible egg carton; "folding" expansion gate; etc.
6. *Any* set of three non-collinear points must of necessity *all lie in the same plane;* this is not necessarily true of any four non-collinear points taken at random.
9. $RS = 10$ in.; did it take you very long to realize that $RS = OP =$ radius?

EXERCISE 3-2, page 71

1. $\angle BCR > \angle y$; $\angle y = \angle z$; $\angle z = \angle A$; $\therefore \angle y = \angle A$; $\therefore \angle BCR > \angle A$.
2. (*a*) $\angle x > \angle y$ by T_1.
 (*b*) $\angle x > \angle m$; $\angle m > \angle z$; $\therefore \angle x > \angle z$.

3. If l_1 and l_2 are each $\perp l_3$, the corresponding angles made by l_3 (transversal) are equal; $\therefore l_1 \parallel l_2$.

4. If $l_1 \perp l_2$, and $l_2 \parallel l_3$, then, since corresponding angles are equal, $l_1 \perp l_3$.

5. Corresponding angles of $\parallel$ lines are equal; $\therefore \angle a = \angle b$; and, since $\angle b + \angle c = 180°$, $\therefore \angle a + \angle c = 180°$.

6. Extend the vertical line and the oblique side of $\angle a$ until they meet to form a triangle; then $\angle a = \angle b$, since if two angles of one triangle equal two angles of another triangle, the third angles are equal; etc.

9. Their sides are respectively perpendicular.

10. $6\sqrt{3}$ inches

11. $h^2 + \left(\dfrac{s}{2}\right)^2 = s^2$; $h^2 = s^2 - \dfrac{s^2}{4} = \dfrac{3}{4}s^2$; $h = \sqrt{\dfrac{3s^2}{4}} = \sqrt{\dfrac{s^2}{4}} \cdot \sqrt{3} = \dfrac{s}{2}\sqrt{3}$.

12. Apply the Pythagorean theorem to each of the four right triangles formed by drawing the diagonals; then apply the axiom, "If equals are added to equals, etc."

EXERCISE 3-4, page 94

1. All these loci are straight lines; in (a), the line is parallel to the y axis; in (b), the line is parallel to the x axis; in (j), the line *is* the y axis.

2. All these loci are rectangular hyperbolas.

3. All these loci are parabolas.

4. (a) Circle   (b) Parabola   (c) Ellipse   (d) Hyperbola   (e) Two straight lines

5. (a) $y = 10$ (b) $x = -8$ (c) $y = 0$ (d) $x + y = 0$ (e) $x^2 + y^2 = 25$

6. (a) $x = 7\frac{1}{2}$ (b) $y = -1$

7. $y = 3x$ **8.** $x = 6$ **9.** $x = 2y + 6$

10. (a) $(3, 2)$; $(6, 4)$; $(6, 2)$ (b) 3; 2 (c) $2:3$ (d) $(9, 2)$; $RT = 4$; $PT = 6$; $4:6$, or $2:3$ (e) constant slope (i.e., uniform grade or slant)

EXERCISE 4-1, page 105

1. (c) "15," "10 + 5"   (e) "15"   (f) "6"   (g) "8," "2"   (h) "0"   (f) "88633"   (l) 4, 7; "4," "7"

5. (a) *Numbers* (except when proofreading, in which case they are *numerals;* (b) *Numeral;* (c) and (d), *Numbers;* (e) *Numerals;* (f), *Numbers;* (g) and (h), *Numerals*

10. (a) No   (b) No   (c) No

11. (a) There are just as many rifles as soldiers, and just as many soldiers as rifles; (b) because the two sets are in one-to-one correspondence

EXERCISE 4-2, page 118

1. No; no   **2.** No; no   **3.** (a), (c) and (e)

4. (a) A_1 (b) A_1 (c) C_1 (d) A_2 (e) A_2 (f) A_1 **5.** (c)

8. (a) M_2 (b) M_1 (c) M_3 (d) M_2

9. (a) 40   (b) 19   (c) 25   (d) 49

10. (a) M_1 (b) M_2 (c) M_3 (d) M_3 (e) M_1 (f) A_2

11. (a) $873 \times 10 = 8730$ (b) $129 \times 10 = 1290$
   (c) $700 + 456 = 1156$ (d) $37 \times 100 = 3700$

14. (a), (b)

15. $(m + n)$; mn; condition for $(m - n)$ is $m > n$; condition for $(m \div n)$ is $m = kn$, where k is any natural number.

16. No; no   **17.** No; no

18. $c + (ab) = (c + a)(c + b)$; no

19. $k(a + b + c + \cdots) = ka + kb + kc + \cdots$

20. (a) $72 \div (4)(2 + 1) = 6$ (b) $[72 \div (4 \cdot 2)] + 1 = 10$
   (c) $72 \div [(4)(2) + 1] = 8$ (d) $(72 \div 4)(2) + 1 = 37$

EXERCISE 5-2, page 147

4. (a) $0.777\ldots$ (b) $0.9090\ldots$ (c) $1.8333\ldots$
   (d) $6.374999\ldots$ (e) $0.142857142857\ldots$ (f) $0.384615384615\ldots$

5. (a) $\frac{9}{11}$ (b) $\frac{25}{111}$ (c) $\frac{8}{9}$ (d) $\frac{1}{2}$ (e) $\frac{89}{4950}$ (f) $\frac{69}{55}$

7. (a) Irrational   (b) rational   (c) irrational
   (d) rational   (e) rational   (f) rational

EXERCISE 5-4, page 162

1. (a) $8i$ (b) $24i$ (c) $-3\sqrt{2}i$ (d) $15\sqrt{2}i$ (e) $-40i$ (f) $-ai$ (g) 1   (h) 8
   (i) -5 (j) -1 (k) $-6i$ (l) $-2i$

2. (a) -12 (b) $-\sqrt{35}$ (c) 9   (d) $-8i$ (e) 30   (f) $-6i$

3. (a) $9 - 3i$ (b) $-8 + 9i$ (c) 0

4. (a) $-1 + 4i$ (b) $2 + 4i$ (c) 0

5. (a) $30 - 10i$ (b) 41   (c) $2i$
   (d) -4 (e) $2 + 2i$ (f) $m^2 + p$

10. $x = \pm 2\sqrt{5}i$

11. Causes 90° rotation, counterclockwise

14. (a) and (b) are incorrect; (c) is correct

15. All four are correct

16. (a), (c) and (e) are correct; (b) and (d) are incorrect

17. (a) A_2 (b) A_1 (c) M_1 and M_2 (d) M_3 (e) M_1 and M_2

18. (a) Imaginary   (b) Real, rational   (c) Real, irrational   (d) Real, rational
   (e) Real, irrational   (f) Complex

19. (d) and (f)

20. (a) 2 and 3;   (b) 1   (c) 1, 2 and 3   (d) 3

EXERCISE 6-1, page 172

4. (a) 29   (b) 192   (c) 613   (d) 107   (e) 44   (f) 66   (g) 369   (h) 1711   (i) 1944
(j) 1922   (k) 1922   (l) 1990

5. (a) CCCVIII   (b) XCVI   (c) XLIX   (d) DCCL   (e) MDCCCCVI, or MCMVI
(f) MDCCCCLX, or MCMLX   (g) MCCCCXCII, or MCDXCII
(h) MDCCCCXLII, or MCMXLII   (i) MDCCCCLVIII, or MCMLVIII
(j) MDCCCXCV   (k) MDCCCLXI   (l) MDCXIX

6. 1898; probably not; MDCCCXCVIII

7. (a) CCCCLXXII, or CDLXXII (472)
(b) MMMMMMXXXII (6032)
(c) MMMMMMMCCCCCCCCCLXXXXV (7995)

EXERCISE 6-2, page 182

1. (a) 0, 1, 2, 3, 4, 5, 6, 10, 11, 12, 13, 14, 15, 16, 20, 21, 22, 23, 24, 25, 26, 30, 31,
32, 33
(b) 0, 1, 2, 3, 4, 5, 6, 7, 8, 10, 11, 12, 13, 14, 15, 16, 17, 18, 20, 21, 22, 23, 24, 25, 26

2. 0, 1, 2, 3, 4, 5, 6, 7, 10, 11, 12, 13, 14, 15, 16, 17, 20, 21, 22, 23, 24, 25, 26, 27, 30,
31, 32, 33, 34, 35

3. (a) 110, 111, 112, 113, 120, 121, 122, 123, 130, 131, 132, 133, 200, 201, 202, 203,
210, 211, 212, 213, 220
(b) 32, 33, 34, 35, 40, 41, 42, 43, 44, 45, 50, 51, 52, 53, 54, 55, 100, 101, 102, 103,
104

4. 200, 201, 202, 203, 204, 210, 211, 212, 213, 214, 220, 221, 222, 223, 224, 230, 231,
232, 233, 234, 240, 241, 242, 243, 244, 300

5. 132, 133, 134, 135, 136, 137, 140, 141, 142, 143, 144

6. (a) 144_5 (b) 2012_4 (c) 1121_6 (d) 476_8 (e) 416_7 (f) 10102_3 (g) 561_9 (h) 415_{11}
(i) 161_{12} (j) $41E_{12}$

7. (a) 134   (b) 311   (c) 149   (d) 224   (e) 279   (f) 78   (g) 72   (h) 99   (i) 78
(j) 1752

8. (a) 11121_3 (b) 124_5 (c) 3211_4 (d) 33_8 (e) 132_9 (f) 2321_5

9. (a)

+	1	2	3	4
1	2	3	4	10
2	3	4	10	11
3	4	10	11	12
4	10	11	12	13

(b)

+	1	2	3	4	5	6
1	2	3	4	5	6	10
2	3	4	5	6	10	11
3	4	5	6	10	11	12
4	5	6	10	11	12	13
5	6	10	11	12	13	14
6	10	11	12	13	14	15

9. (*c*)

+	1	2	3	4	5	6	7	8	9	10	11
1	2	3	4	5	6	7	8	9	X	E	10
2	3	4	5	6	7	8	9	X	E	10	11
3	4	5	6	7	8	9	X	E	10	11	12
4	5	6	7	8	9	X	E	10	11	12	13
5	6	7	8	9	X	E	10	11	12	13	14
6	7	8	9	X	E	10	11	12	13	14	15
7	8	9	X	E	10	11	12	13	14	15	16
8	9	X	E	10	11	12	13	14	15	16	17
9	X	E	10	11	12	13	14	15	16	17	18
10	E	10	11	12	13	14	15	16	17	18	19
11	10	11	12	13	14	15	16	17	18	19	IX

10. (*a*)

×	1	2	3	4
1	1	2	3	4
2	2	4	11	13
3	3	11	14	22
4	4	13	22	31

(*b*)

×	1	2	3	4	5
1	1	2	3	4	5
2	2	4	10	12	14
3	3	10	13	20	23
4	4	12	20	24	32
5	5	14	23	32	41

(*c*)

×	1	2	3	4	5	6	7	8
1	1	2	3	4	5	6	7	8
2	2	4	6	8	11	13	15	17
3	3	6	10	13	16	20	23	26
4	4	8	13	17	22	26	31	35
5	5	11	16	22	27	33	38	44
6	6	13	20	26	33	40	46	53
7	7	15	23	31	38	46	54	62
8	8	17	26	35	44	53	62	71

11. $312_4 + 30_4 + 123_4 = 1131_4 = 93_{10}$

12. $433_7 + 45_7 + 15_7 = 526_7 = 265_{10}$

13. (*a*) 8   (*b*) 7   **14.** (*a*) No   (*b*) Yes

EXERCISE 6-3, page 187

1. (*a*) 2^9 (*b*) 3^{p+q} (*c*) a^{2k-1} (*d*) $\dfrac{r^3}{8}$ (*e*) $81y^8$ (*f*) b^{2x} (*g*) a^4 (*h*) ab^2 (*i*) y^{-4}
(*j*) p^{2n+1}

2. (*a*) 1,000,000   (*b*) a^{-3} (*c*) 0.01   (*d*) 72   (*e*) 7   (*f*) $\frac{1}{4}$ (*g*) 1   (*h*) $\frac{1}{2}$ (*i*) $4\frac{1}{9}$ (*j*) 9

3. (*a*) 2^6 (*b*) 2^{2n} (*c*) 2^{-1} (*d*) $5(2)^4$ (*e*) $3(2)^5$

4. (*a*) 3^8 (*b*) 3^{3n} (*c*) 3^{2x} (*d*) $2(3)^3$ (*e*) $4(3)^{-2}$

5. (*a*) 5^2 (*b*) 5^{6n} (*c*) 5^0 (*d*) $2(5)^3$ (*e*) 5^{-4}

6. (*a*) 10^7 (*b*) 10^{60} (*c*) 10^{-3} (*d*) 10^{-7}

7. Two taken 5 times as a factor; or, the product of five 2's.

8. (*d*), i.e., 2304.05

9. (*a*) 1   (*b*) 3   (*c*) 0   (*d*) −1   (*e*) −2

10. (*a*) 600,000,000   (*b*) 600,000,000   (*c*) 4750
(*d*) 0.000328   (*e*) 3,286,000   (*f*) 0.0000000021
(*g*) 26,900,000,000,000,000,000   (*h*) 0.0000000000016

11. (*a*) 2.941×10 (*b*) 2.08×10^{-3} (*c*) 2.08×10
(*d*) 2.08×10^{-1} (*e*) 1.728×10^3 (*f*) 6.03×10^6
(*g*) 3.284×10^{-3} (*h*) 8.16×10^{-8}

12. (*a*) 29,979,000,000   (*b*) $0.0_2 9106$
(*c*) $0.0_5 48024$ (*d*) 2,080,000,000

13. $\dfrac{1}{4.8024 \times 10^{-10}} = \dfrac{1}{4.8024} \times 10^{10} = 0.208 \times 10^{10} = 2.08 \times 10^9$

14. (1) $0.1\mu\mu = \frac{1}{10}(10^{-6})$ mm. $= 10^{-7}$ mm. $= 10^{-8}$ cm. $= 1$ A
(2) 0.001 A $= (10^{-3})(10^{-8})$ cm. $= 10^{-11}$ cm.

15. 1.0×10^{-23} **16.** (*b*)

EXERCISE 6-4, page 191

1. (*a*) 7   (*b*) 6   (*c*) 5   (*d*) 12   (*e*) 4   (*f*) 9   (*g*) 10   (*h*) 0

2. (*a*) $2^5 = 32$ (*b*) $5^2 = 25$ (*c*) $10^4 = 10,000$
(*d*) $10^1 = 10$ (*e*) $a^y = R$ (*f*) $n^x = M$
(*g*) $y^z = x$ (*h*) $17° = 1$

3. (*a*) 3   (*b*) 2   (*c*) 3   (*d*) 6
(*e*) -1 (*f*) 1   (*g*) $\frac{1}{2}$ (*h*) n

4. (*a*) $\log_3 243 = 5$ (*b*) $\log_{10} 100 = 2$ (*c*) $\log_A x = m$
(*d*) $\log_{10} 1 = 0$ (*e*) $\log_{10} 42.3 = 1.6263$ (*f*) $\log_{10} 8.67 = 0.9380$
(*g*) $\log_2 1 = 0$ (*h*) $\log_e x = k$

5. (*a*) 7   (*b*) 2   (*c*) 1   (*d*) 0   (*e*) 1   (*f*) 0
13. 2.485   **14.** (*d*)   **15.** 7
17. (*a*) False   (*b*) True   (*c*) False   (*d*) True   (*e*) False
18. $\frac{7}{8}$ **19.** (*c*)

EXERCISE 6-5, page 199

1. (*a*) $10^{1.4216} = 26.4$ (*b*) $10^{3.8751} = 7500$ (*c*) $10^5 = 100,000$
(*d*) $10^{-0.7447} = 0.18$ (*e*) $10^{0.7168} = 5.21$ (*f*) $10^{-5} = 0.00001$
(*g*) $10^{-2.4112} = 0.00388$ (*h*) $10^{6.9805} = 9,560,000$

2. (*a*) 2.4378   (*b*) 0.5966   (*c*) 1.7910
(*d*) $9.8451 - 10$ (*e*) 5.5145   (*f*) $9.6484 - 10$
(*g*) $8.7076 - 10$ (*h*) $7.8704 - 10$ (*i*) 3.9053
(*j*) $9.8129 - 10$

3. (*a*) 11.2   (*b*) 2980   (*c*) 8.73
(*d*) 0.373   (*e*) 470   (*f*) 0.0601
(*g*) 7.08   (*h*) 0.000211   (*i*) 636,000

4. (*a*) 2.0983   (*b*) 1.8298   (*c*) $8.9311 - 10$
(*d*) 0.4972   (*e*) $9.7256 - 10$ (*f*) $7.8803 - 10$
(*g*) 5.9328   (*h*) $6.3318 - 10$

5. (a) 483.3   (b) 9.045   (c) 0.03073
   (d) 75.55   (e) 0.6323   (f) 7.483
            (g) 3773   (h) 0.002173

EXERCISE 6-6, page 200

1. (a) 16.26   (b) 146.1   (c) 13.92   (d) 46.26   (e) 59.5
2. (a) 1.478   (b) 1.382   (c) 6.559
   (d) 3,282   (e) 0.6279   (f) 7.175
3. (a) 716.2   (b) 2,646,000,000,000   (c) 112.2   (d) 382.4
4. (a) 3   (b) 1   (c) 0
5. 23   6. $\frac{7}{3} = 10^{0.36798}$ 7. 0.15563
8. 4.444   9. (a) 4.3266   (b) 0.5829
10. 3,593   11. 2.378   12. (a) E (b) 8
13. -1.488 14. (a) $3 \log 5 = \log 125$ (b) 2
15. Let $\log_b a = N$, or $b^N = a$; taking logarithm of each side of the equation to base a, we get:
$$\log_a (b^N) = \log_a a, \text{ or } N \log_a b = 1.$$
Since $N = \log_b a$, we have: $\log_b a \cdot \log_a b = 1$.

EXERCISE 7-1, page 216

4. 1.158 to 1.162; 3.626 to 3.630; 2.498 to 2.502; 1.906 to 1.910; 0.073 to 0.077
5. (a) $2\frac{1}{32}$ in.   (d) $2\frac{1}{64}$ in.   (e) $1\frac{63}{64}$ in.   (f) $1\frac{31}{32}$ in.
6. (a) $3\frac{19}{32}$ (b) $3\frac{37}{64}$ (c) $3\frac{11}{16}$
7. $m = 12.35$ in.; a.d. $= 0.018$ in.; A.D. $= 0.009$ in.; best value $= 12.352 \pm 0.009$ in.
8. $m = 8.54$ cm.; a.d. $= 0.013$ cm.; A.D. $= 0.005$ cm.;
   best value $= 8.536 \pm 0.005$ cm.
9. $m = 5.43$ cm.; a.d. $= 0.014$ cm.; A.D. $= 0.005$ cm.;
   best value $= 5.431 \pm 0.005$ cm.
10. $m = 10.312$ g.; a.d. $= 0.0012$ g.; A.D. $= 0.0005$ g.;
    best value $= 10.3116 \pm 0.0005$ g.

EXERCISE 7-2, page 219

1. (a), (h) and (j) are exact numbers, because they can be counted or stated in discrete units; all other items are approximate numbers, since they are measurements, or estimates, or rounded numbers.
2. $\sqrt{16}$, $\sqrt{3}$, and 1.732 are exact; 1.732 ... is an approximate number.
3. π and $3\frac{1}{7}$ are exact numbers; 3.14159 ... is an approximate number.
4. $6\frac{1}{4}$ lies between $6\frac{1}{8}$ and $6\frac{3}{8}$; 6.25 lies between 6.245 and 6.255; 6.250 lies between 6.2495 and 6.2505.
5. For example: (a) "a price tag of \$3.75"; (b) "in about 15 minutes"; (c) "\$2.95 less $\frac{1}{3}$ off, or about \$.98."

6. (a) 0.05 ft.; 0.005 ft.; the more precise, 6.73 ft.
   (b) 0.5 in.; 0.05 in.; the more precise, 13.6 in.
   (c) 0.05 cm.; 0.005 cm.; the more precise, 28.84 cm.
   (d) 0.0005 in.; 0.005 in.; the more precise, 8.004 in.
   (e) 0.05 ft.; 0.5 ft.; the more precise, 135.8 ft.

EXERCISE 7-3, page 221

2. (a) 1.5 mi. and 2.5 mi. (b) 98.55°F and 98.65°F
   (c) $3\frac{1}{8}$ lb. and $3\frac{3}{8}$ lb. (d) 245.5 yd. and 246.5 yd.
   (e) 4.115 cm. and 4.125 cm. (f) $6\frac{9}{32}$ in. and $6\frac{11}{32}$ in.

3. (a) 0.1 (b) 0.02 (c) 0.013 (d) 0.001 (e) 0.002 (f) 0.001 (g) 0.042 (h) 0.25
   (i) 0.25 (j) 0.019

4. (a) 0.5 in.; 0.023; 2.3% (b) 0.5 ft.; 0.004; 0.4%
   (c) 0.05 yd.; 0.031; 3.1% (d) 0.05 cm.; 0.0007; 0.07%

5. (a) 2.8% (b) 0.3% (c) 2.2%
   (d) 0.17% (e) 0.04% (f) 0.3%

EXERCISE 7-4, page 227

1. (a) 0.002 in. (1) (b) 65 mi. (2)
      0.20 in. (2) 43.8 lb. (3)
      0.020 in. (2) 20.04 g. (4)
      0.012 in. (2) 9.006 cm. (4)
      0.21 in. (2) 27.3 mi. (3)
      0.201 in. (3) 10.24 cm. (4)
      0.210 in. (3) 20.0 mi. (3)
      0.0030 in. (2) 106.04 g. (5)
        3.060 in. (4)
        0.003025 (4)
   (c) 4520 (3); 1300 (2); 19,400 (3); 186,000 (3); 93,000,000 (2)

2. (a) 230, 32, 5.8, 0.04 (b) 852, 26.3, 125.36, 0.005
   (c) 0.1, 0.10, 0.001, 1.0001 (d) 123, 12.3, 1.23, 0.123, 0.0123

4. (a) More precise, 0.0080 mm.; equally accurate
   (b) More precise, 0.0080 mm.; equally accurate
   (c) More precise, 430 yd.; more accurate, 430 yd.
   (d) Precision cannot be compared; equally accurate
   (e) More precise, 12.90 lb.; more accurate, 12.90 lb.
   (f) More precise, 6 ft.; more accurate, 6 ft.
   (g) Equally precise; more accurate, 6 ft. 0 in.

5. (a) 2; 3; 3 (b) 1; 3; 1 (c) 2; 2; 2
   (d) 2; 1; 2 (e) 4; 1; 3 (f) 1; 2; 3

6. No   **7.** No

8. (a) 850 . . . (2) (b) 34oo . . . (2) (c) 6,290,000 . . . (3)
   (d) 93,000,000 . . . (2) (e) 63,000 . . . (3) (f) 280,000 . . . (3)
   (g) 237,000,000 . . . (3) (h) 186,000 . . . (3)

9. (a) 5.8×10^3 (b) 3.620×10^5 (c) 4.00×10^4
   (d) 2.00×10^5 (e) 7.50×10^4 (f) 3.690×10^6
10. (a) 375   (b) 8

EXERCISE 7-5, page 230

1. (a) 53.86   (b) 23.7   (c) 37.2
   (d) 60   (e) 31,000   (f) \$54
2. Greatest, 157.48; least, 157.30
3. Greatest, 43.408; least, 43.390
4. (a) 3.3   (b) 19.5   (c) 3.33
   (d) 5.4   (e) 7.53   (f) 51,000
5. 3.39; 19.514   **6.** 3.21; 19.406

EXERCISE 7-6, page 232

1. (a) 5680   (b) 60   (c) 13,000   (d) 95.2   (e) 52,800
2. 30   **3.** 1285.2825 sq. yd.
4. 6642.25 sq. ft.   **5.** Yes; to 3-figure accuracy   **6.** 47 ft.
7. (a) 20 ft.   (b) 76.4 in.   (c) 25.8 cm.   (d) 38.70 in.   (e) 20.4 in.
8. 55 sq. in.   **9.** 130 sq. in.   **10.** 80 sq. in.
11. (a) 1.2   (b) 12   (c) 22   (d) 81.2   (e) 3.15   (f) 15
12. 10.3 ft.   **13.** 120 sq. in.   **14.** 0.67 amperes   **15.** 4.8 seconds
16. (a) Correct   (b) Incorrect   (c) Correct   (d) Correct

EXERCISE 8-1, page 242

1. $216\sqrt{3}$ **2.** $64 - 16\pi$ **3.** $h = 6; P = 12\sqrt{3}$ **4.** $48\sqrt{5}$ **5.** 1:3
6. 2:3   **7.** $108\frac{1}{3}\pi$ **8.** $42\frac{1}{4}$ sq. in.   **9.** $12\frac{1}{4}\pi$, or $38\frac{1}{2}$ cu. in. (approx.)
10. $\frac{1}{3}\pi b^2 h$; $\frac{1}{3}\pi h^2 b$ **11.** 1:3
12. $A = 2\pi Rh$, where $h = 2R$; hence $A = (2\pi R)(2R) = 4\pi R^2$.
13. $r = n(1 + \sqrt{2}); n = r(\sqrt{2} - 1),$ or $n = -r(1 - \sqrt{2})$
14. (a) $\frac{4}{\pi}$, or about 1.27 in.

   (b) $C - c = 2\pi(r + \Delta r) - 2\pi r = 2\pi(r + \Delta r - r) = 2\pi \Delta r$; hence $\Delta r = \dfrac{C - c}{2\pi}$

   (c) Shrinking a metal rim onto a wagon wheel; changing the "size" of a finger ring; loosening a "frozen" glass stopper in a bottle by heating the neck of the bottle; etc.

EXERCISE 8-2, page 246

1. (a) 4:1   (b) 6:1   (c) 1:7   (d) 2:3
2. (a) 6:5   (b) 2:5   (c) 2:3   (d) 7:9

3. 3:5   **4.** 3:4; $\frac{4}{7}$; $\frac{3}{7}$
5. (a) 12   (b) 27½   (c) 105   (d) 28⅘
6. 5½   **7.** 504   **8.** 633⅓   **9.** About $88   **10.** $301

EXERCISE 8-3, page 250

1. 33 ft.; 2¼ in.   **2.** 6½ in.; 37½ ft.   **3.** 580 ft.; 3.2 in.
4. 1 in. = 2 ft., or ½ in. = 1 ft.; 4½ ft. by 9 ft.   **5.** 90 mi.; 3½ in.   **6.** ½ in.
7. ½ in.; ¾ in.; 3½ in.   **8.** 1:1,267,200   **9.** 1:253,440; 1:126,720; 1:63,360
10. (a) 2⅜ in.; (b) 1¾ in.   **11.** 1.4 mi.   **12.** 6.3 mi.

EXERCISE 8-4, page 255

(All answers are approximate)
1. MK = 2¼ in.; HK = 6⅛ in.; mast = 53 ft.
2. 44½ ft.   **3.** SL = 5400 yd.; TL = 3800 yd.
4. 20.4 mi. per hr.; N 11° E
5. OA = 23 lb.; OB = 33 lb.
6. 13.4 lb.; 27° from the horizontal
7. 21¼ lb.; 17° from the vertical
8. 14 lb.; 22° and 38°.
9. 22½ mi. per hr.; N 44° E
10. 155 mi. per hr.; $\angle AOR$ = 10½°

EXERCISE 8-5, page 260

1. 20, 10; x = 8, y = 12   **2.** 36 ft.   **3.** 16½ ft.   **4.** 150 yd.   **5.** 840 ft.
6. 19 ft.   **7.** 5 in.   **8.** 9¼ in.   **9.** 22½ cm.

EXERCISE 8-6, page 265

1. Four times as great; 8 times as great
2. 33.1%   **3.** 18 in.   **4.** (a) 3:4; (b) 9:16   **5.** 20 cm.   **6.** (a) 2:1; (b) 4:1
7. Twice as great   **8.** 16:25   **9.** 137%, approx.   **10.** Four times as much

EXERCISE 8-7, page 274

1. (a) 0.3153   (b) 0.9380   (c) 2.2826
     (d) 1.2205   (e) 0.8027   (f) 0.2163
2. (a) 47°   (b) 14°   (c) 80°54'
     (d) 11°18'   (e) 3°26'   (f) 74°3'
3. 76.5 ft.   **4.** 369 ft.   **5.** 8.9 ft.   **6.** 1240 yd.

7. $\sphericalangle B = 23°51'$; $\sphericalangle A = 66°9'$; $AB = 10.4$ **8.** $25°38'$; $77°11'$; $77°11'$
9. 7,890 ft.   **10.** $BC = 59$ ft.; $AC = 72$ ft.

EXERCISE 8-8, page 280

1. Side $= 11.7$ in.; altitude $= 7.6$ in.   **2.** 23.1   **3.** $36°52'$
4. $\sphericalangle A = \sphericalangle B = 80°31'$; $\sphericalangle C = 18°58'$; $AC = BC = 24.3$ in.
5. $22°37'$ **6.** $r = 3.6$ in.; distance $= 10.6$ in.   **7.** 450 ft.   **8.** 31.2 sq. in.
9. $h = 9.0$ in.; side $= 9.8$ in.   **10.** $r = 5.8$ in.   **11.** 30,000 sq. ft.
12. 22.25 sq. in.

EXERCISE 8-9, page 285

1. N $10°17'$ W; 224 mi. per hr.   **2.** 416 ft. per min.
3. 177 mi. per hr. northward; 177 mi. per hr. westward
4. 50 lb.; $53°8'$ from the horizontal.
5. 4.8 in.   **6.** $r = 16.3$ in.; $118°4'$ **7.** 23.5 in.

EXERCISE 9-1, page 301

1. The positive integers and zero
2. t: $\{1, 2, 3, \cdots 7, 8, 9\}$; u: $\{0, 1, 2, \cdots 7, 8, 9\}$
3. $\{2, 7, 12, 17, 22, \cdots\}$; $\{0, 1, 2, 3, \cdots\}$; $2, 7, 12, 17, \cdots$
4. (a) $(5, 7)$ and $(7, 5)$ are simply ordered pairs of the same two natural numbers,
   with the order reversed in one case. (b) Whereas $(5, 7)$ means the ordered
   pair of natural numbers 5 and 7, the expression $\{5, 7\}$ means a set consisting
   of exactly two elements, viz. 5 and 7, irrespective of order.
5. 16, 64, 144
7. $\{\frac{1}{4}\%, \frac{1}{2}\%, \frac{3}{4}\%, 1\%, \cdots 5\frac{1}{2}\%, 5\frac{3}{4}\%, 6\%\}$; or,
   $\{0.0025, 0.005, 0.0075, 0.01, \cdots 0.055, 0.0575, 0.06\}$
8. (a) All x's < 5;
   (b) all x's $> +3$ and < -3;
   (c) all x's > 4;

   (d) $\left\{ \pm\frac{1}{3}, \pm\frac{3}{3}, \pm\frac{5}{3}, \pm\frac{7}{3}, \cdots \right\}$

   (e) $\left\{ \pm\frac{2}{3}, \pm\frac{4}{3}, \pm\frac{6}{3}, \pm\frac{8}{3}, \cdots \right\}$

   (f) all points on the number line to the left of point J
   (g) all points of segment JK, excluding the endpoints
   (h) all points on the number line except those of segment JK, including the
      endpoints
   (i) all points on the number line to the right of point K
   (j) all points on the number line

10. (a) $F(0) = -4$; $F(3) = 11$; $F(-5) = 11$
    (b) $f(1) = 4$; $f(-3) = -36$; $f(\frac{1}{2}) = 1\frac{5}{8}$; $f(0) = 0$
    (c) $f(1) = 10$; $f(2) = 100$; $f(0) = 1$; $f(-2) = 0.01$; $f(\frac{1}{2}) = \sqrt{10}$

11. Only (a) and (b) are functions; in (a), y: $\{1, 2, 3, 4\}$ and x: $\{4\}$; in (b), x: $\{2, 3, 4\}$
    and y: $\{2, 4, 3\}$

12. (b), (c), (d), (e), (j), (n), and (o)

14. (a) $F(1) = 2$; $F(0) = -1$; $F(-1) = -2$; $F(3) = 14$; $F(k) = k^2 + 2k - 1$;

$$F\left(\frac{1}{2}\right) = \frac{1}{4}; F\left(\frac{1}{x}\right) = \frac{1}{x^2} + \frac{2}{x} - 1; \frac{1}{F(x)} = \frac{1}{x^2 + 2x - 1}$$

    (c) domain of x: all the real numbers
    range of y: all y's $\geqq -2$

EXERCISE 9-2, page 312

1. $y = 3$; $x = -2$ **2.** $y = 0$; $x = 0$
3. $(10 - 2):(4 - 2) = (22 - 10):(7 - 4)$, or $8:2 = 12:3$

EXERCISE 9-3, page 316

1. (a) 2.10 (b) 1.72 (c) 13.8 (d) 2.16 (e) 0.267 (f) 2.12 (g) 1.23 (h) 25.3
    (i) 1.29 (j) 8.067

EXERCISE 10-1, page 323

1. $21   **2.** The latter   **3.** $.43   **4.** 3%   **5.** $4\frac{1}{4}\%$ **6.** 6 mo.   **7.** $2400
8. (a) 90; 92 (b) 93; 95 (c) 74; 76 (d) 54; 53
9. $4.80   **10.** (a) $12; (b) $12.27; (c) $12.10   **11.** $400   **12.** $200
13. $1238.10   **14.** 17.39%   **15.** 9 mo.   **16.** $300   **17.** The former
19. 4.2%   **20.** 6.8%   **21.** $\frac{60}{360} \times \frac{6}{100} = .01$; etc.   **22.** $16\frac{2}{3}$ yr. (approx.)

EXERCISE 10-2, page 331

1. (a) $61.80 (b) $76.90 (c) $18.55 (d) $4.06
2. (a) $241.83   (b) $216.65   (c) $173.68
    (d) $156.31   (e) $1126.16   (f) $610.52
    (g) $328.49   (h) $528.46
3. $i = 0.0406$ **4.** $j = 0.0494$
5. (a) 14 yr.; (b) $17\frac{1}{2}$ yr.
6. 12.7 yr. (actually, 13 yr.; why?)
7. 17.6 yr.   **8.** 3.48%   **9.** Yes

EXERCISE 10-3, page 336

1. (a) \$266.70   (b) \$780.01   (c) \$444.25
(d) \$67.17   (e) \$181.19   (f) \$1254.59
2. \$4917.24   3. \$4882.16   4. \$46.44   5. \$937.66   6. \$36.38
7. \$908.11   8. \$1076.74   9. \$195.14
10. Very nearly, but not quite; \$2721.09 *versus* \$2723.25

EXERCISE 11-1, page 340

1. 48   2. 81   3. 36   4. 8   5. 16   6. 151,200   7. 120   8. 306
9. 9; 6   10. 56

EXERCISE 11-2, page 343

1. (a) 12,144; (b) 13,824   2. 720; 20,160   3. 64   4. 256   5. 15,120
6. 40,320   7. 720   8. 11   9. 30,240   10. 2520

EXERCISE 11-3, page 346

1. 924   2. 15   3. 56   4. 455   5. 1296   6. 36   7. 792
8. 270,725   9. (a) 1408   (b) 700   (c) 1008   10. 56   11. 36

EXERCISE 11-4, page 350

1. $\frac{1}{6}$; $\frac{1}{3}$ 2. $\frac{1}{2}$ 3. (a) $\frac{1}{3}$; (b) $\frac{2}{3}$ 4. (a) $\frac{1}{13}$ (b) $\frac{1}{52}$ (c) $\frac{5}{13}$ 5. $\frac{3}{8}$; $\frac{5}{8}$
6. 7 to 2   7. $\frac{5}{6}$; $\frac{1}{6}$ 8. $\frac{1}{4}$; 3   9. $\frac{1}{20}$ 10. $\frac{1}{200}$ 11. $\frac{3}{4}$
12. (a) $\frac{1}{2}$; (b) $\frac{1}{4}$ 13. $\frac{3}{5}$ 14. $\frac{1}{12}$ 15. $\frac{11}{4165}$ 16. $\frac{1}{7}$ 17. $\frac{1}{32}$
18. $\frac{5}{16}$ 19. $\frac{1}{5525}$ 20. $\frac{2}{15}$ 21. $\frac{1}{8}$; $\frac{1}{64}$ 22. $\frac{1}{7}$

EXERCISE 11-5, page 352

1. $\frac{1}{36}$ 2. $\frac{1}{4}$; $\frac{1}{4}$ 3. Yes; $\frac{1}{216}$ 4. $\frac{4}{99}$ 5. (a) $\frac{5}{18}$; (b) $\frac{1}{6}$ 6. $\frac{1}{2}$
7. (a) $\frac{1}{12}$; (b) $\frac{1}{6}$; (c) 1:5   9. $\frac{625}{1296}$ 10. $\frac{1}{36}$

EXERCISE 11-6, page 360

1. 949,171   2. 818,235   3. 0.960201   4. 958,098; 0.2%   5. 998; 99.8%
6. 382,865   7. 0.98673

8. $_5p_{25} = \dfrac{l_{30}}{l_{25}} = 0.98447$; $_{35}p_{25} = \dfrac{l_{60}}{l_{25}} = 0.72165$; $_{55}p_{25} = \dfrac{l_{80}}{l_{25}} = 0.19353$

9. $_2p_{60} = \dfrac{l_{62}}{l_{60}} = 0.94539$; $_5p_{60} = \dfrac{l_{65}}{l_{60}} = 0.85262$; $_{10}p_{60} = \dfrac{l_{70}}{l_{60}} = 0.67065$

10. $_2q_{40} = 1 - {_2p_{40}} = 1 - \dfrac{l_{42}}{l_{40}} = 0.01273;$

$_5q_{40} = 1 - {_5p_{40}} = 1 - \dfrac{l_{45}}{l_{40}} = 0.03485;$

$_{10}q_{40} = 1 - {_{10}p_{40}} = 1 - \dfrac{l_{50}}{l_{40}} = 0.08201$

13. $p_{35} = 0.99541;\ 50,000 \times p_{35} = 49,770$ **14.** 650

15. $_2q_{18} = 1 - {_2p_{18}} = 1 - \dfrac{l_{20}}{l_{18}} = 0.00466;\ 400,000 \times {_2q_{18}} = 1864$ **16.** $35,600

17. $_5q_{18} = 1 - {_5p_{18}} = 1 - \dfrac{l_{23}}{l_{18}} = 0.01214;\ 200,000 \times {_5q_{18}} = \$1,214,000$

18. $_{20}p_{25} = \dfrac{l_{45}}{l_{25}} = 0.9078,$ or 90.8%

INDEX